Fo...
Co...

G000116281

User Guide

The Purple Book

Fourth edition
2004

Forms of Contract

Lump Sum Contracts
The Red Book
Fourth edition
2001, ISBN 0 85295 443 3

Reimbursable Contracts
The Green Book
Third edition
2002, ISBN 0 85295 444 1

Target Cost Contracts
The Burgundy Book
First edition
2003, ISBN 0 85295 458 1

Subcontracts
The Yellow Book
Third edition
2003, ISBN 0 85295 445 X

Subcontract for Civil Engineering Works
The Brown Book
Second edition
2004, ISBN 0 85295 453 0

Minor Works
The Orange Book
Second edition
2003, ISBN 0 85295 452 2

The Author

David Wright left Oxford with a degree in law and went straight into industry. He began as PA to the Sales Director of a company that manufactured electrical equipment primarily for the automotive industry. Following this he spent four years as Legal Adviser to Ferranti Ltd, writing and negotiating contracts, licences and other agreements covering the whole range of the electrical and electronic and defence industries. He then spent ten years in the oil and chemical engineering industry as Assistant Manager and Manager of the Legal/Contracts Department of Petrocarbon Developments Ltd, a process contractor owned by Burmah Oil. He then became Commercial Director of Polibur Engineering Ltd, a Polish Government/ Burmah Oil joint venture company. Finally he spent some years in the mechanical engineering industry as European Group Legal Manager to the Wormald group, before becoming a consultant on matters of contract and commercial law. He lectures regularly and is the leading speaker on several courses in IChemE's Continuing Education Programme, as well as advising clients on contracts and related issues. David is also a Visiting Lecturer in law at Manchester University and UMIST and Visiting Fellow in European Business Law at Cranfield University. He is a member of IChemE's Contracts Working Party and Disputes Resolution Panel. He is also an arbitrator.

Forms of Contract

User Guide

The Purple Book
Fourth edition
2004

by David Wright

For use with the millennium editions
of the Forms

Red Book (fourth edition) - 2001   5th=2012 !!
Green Book (third edition)
Burgundy Book (first edition)
Yellow Book (third edition)
Brown Book (second edition)
Orange Book (second edition)

Published by
Institution of Chemical Engineers (IChemE)
Davis Building
165–189 Railway Terrace
Rugby
Warwickshire
CV21 3HQ, UK
IChemE is a Registered Charity

Copyright © 2004
Institution of Chemical Engineers

ISBN 0 85295 451 4

First edition 1994
Second edition 1996
Third edition 1999
Fourth edition 2004

Printed and bound by CPI Antony Rowe, Eastbourne

Introduction

This book is a Guide to the Forms of Contract published by IChemE. It is intended to help engineers who use the conditions, and we hope that it may be of use to others as well.

Of course engineers and the organisations they work for differ widely. Some work as purchasers, some as contractors—main contractors or subcontractors. Many will have been all three. Some design or build plants, some operate and maintain plants, and some modify plants. They do different work and in different industries. They operate different contracting methods and procedures. They run projects of many sizes and types, involving a wide range of disciplines, processes and equipment, and see contracts and contract conditions from all sides of the negotiating table. Each has his or her own background, experience, knowledge and needs.

What IChemE tries to do is to produce sets of contract conditions which can be used as a basis for contracts in the process industries and which are fair to both sides. What I have tried to do is to explain the way in which those conditions are *intended* to work, and to do so in a way that will be of some use to most engineers who find themselves working with them.

I hope that I have succeeded.

However the many mistakes are entirely *my own*.

Historical note

In 1964 the Institution of Chemical Engineers (IChemE) appointed a committee to review the question of contract conditions for process plants. This led to the publication in 1968 of the first edition of the *Model Form of Conditions of Contract for Process Plant suitable for Lump Sum Contracts* (now commonly known as the Red Book). Encouraged by its rapidly increasing use IChemE set up a further committee to prepare an equivalent set for use with reimbursable contracts. The result was the *Model Form of Conditions of Contract for Process Plant suitable for Reimbursable Contracts* (the Green Book), published in 1976.

Since then the conditions have been revised on a regular basis. A second edition of the Red Book was published in 1981 followed by a third edition in 1995 and a fourth edition in 2001. A second edition of the Green Book was published in 1992, followed by a third edition in 2002.

Increasing use of the Forms has also led to the publication of additional sets of conditions—the Yellow Book *Subcontract* in 1992, the Orange Book *Minor Works Contract* in 1998, the Brown Book *Subcontract for Civil Engineering Works* in 2000, and the Burgundy Book *Target Cost Contract* in 2003.

Requests from users of the Forms led to publication of the first edition of the Purple Book in 1994. The aim of the book is to provide additional guidance on the intent and provisions of the Forms for users and potential users. This fourth edition covers the millennium editions of the Forms.

Contents

Introductory notes

1

1.1 The preliminaries

1.1.1 Rules, risks and relationships

Contracts bridge interfaces—between purchaser, contractor and subcontractor; between project requirement and external provider; between project management and the law.

The purpose of every project is to get something done—to get from here to there. When this requires skills, equipment and resources from outside the organisation, we have to use a contract to obtain them. The IChemE contracts are about 'process contracts', contracts to build or modify plants or equipment which will produce a product. They will always be significant in investment terms, and they will always involve the purchaser and contractor in a series of complex interfaces that have to be managed by the project managers on both sides if the contract is to be successful.

Many years ago we would have said that contracts of this kind were only to be found within the traditional petro-chemical industries. Automation has changed that. Now process contracts can be found in almost every manufacturing industry.

The purpose of any contract is to describe the obligations of the parties and then to set out the framework within which they will carry out those obligations. What the contract does is to define (at least some of) the *rules* as to how the parties will deal with each other, the *risks* that each will be responsible for, and the legal/contractual *relationship* that will exist between them during the project. The conditions do not define the technical relationship between the parties, although they do have things to say about it. Nor do the conditions define the commercial relationship between the parties, of which the legal/contractual relationship is only a part.

1.1.2 The IChemE Forms of Contract

This guide deals with the millennium editions of the IChemE Forms. These are:

- Main contract conditions under which the 'Contractor' will be responsible for designing, supplying and bringing into operation a 'Plant' for the 'Purchaser' on the basis of a priced contract, the Red Book, a reimbursable contract, the Green Book, or a target cost contract, the Burgundy Book.
- Subcontract conditions for the supply and installation of major subcontract packages, the Yellow Book, and civil engineering work, the Brown Book.
- Small projects, including plant modification, the Orange Book.

1.1.3 'Standard' and 'model' conditions

We use standard and model conditions of contract because they give us three basic advantages:

- They provide a known and predictable basis for contracts. Therefore it is easier to assess the technical and commercial problems involved. This then makes it easier to calculate and evaluate costs, risks and prices, etc.
- They save time, both in writing and in negotiating the contract. This preserves negotiating goodwill.
- As project/contract management teams become more experienced in operating under the conditions mistakes may be avoided and projects should run more smoothly.

However they also give us certain problems as well, which must always be kept in mind:

- They are designed around a *standard* commercial situation and set up a *standard* relationship. If an individual contract is different to that standard there must always be a risk that the contract conditions will be in conflict with the needs of the project.
- Because every contract is placed on the same basis we can forget that every contract is different, and needs to be considered separately.
- If we are not careful we can make the same mistake over and over again.

1.1.4 Model conditions versus standard (in-house) conditions

Every organisation works to standard conditions of contract for at least part of the time. It will have its own 'standard trading' sets of conditions, sale, purchase, maintenance and so on, in small print on the reverse of its sale and purchase order stationery, and it will try to use these conditions for most of its normal business.

Standard conditions are, of course, invariably biased in favour of the organisation that has produced them, though sometimes more so than others. The law recognises this. Therefore if a dispute arises involving a set of *standard* conditions the courts will generally interpret the conditions *against* the interests of the company that has put those conditions into the contract, unless the wording of the contract is very clear. In addition they will require proof that the conditions are 'reasonable', see below.

Where *model* conditions are involved the legal position is different. The law accepts that a set of conditions which has been drawn up and agreed by both sides of an industry represent a fair basis upon which companies within that industry are prepared to do business with one another. Therefore the courts will not interpret the conditions against the interests of whichever of the parties has put them forward.

In addition the courts will also treat *model* conditions as 'reasonable'. The Unfair Contract Terms Act (1977) prevents the exclusion or limitation of liability by any party to a contract unless it is reasonable to do so. Model conditions are not normally questioned in this way except in highly unusual circumstances, although *changes* to the model conditions, for example in 'Special Conditions' might be questioned.

This is especially true in the case of model conditions used in commercial, as opposed to 'consumer', contracts, where the parties anyway tend to treat clauses excluding or limiting the liability of either of the parties concerned as being more concerned with allocating responsibility for risk than with avoiding liability. Often, for example, what matters most in the commercial world is that one of the parties will obtain appropriate insurance cover. In such a case the question of legal liability is of merely secondary importance.

1.1.5 Contracts and law

The IChemE conditions are written with English law primarily in mind, though they are readily convertible to other legal systems. No competent contract specialist should have many problems in making the necessary changes to adjust any of the conditions to another legal system.

No-one can deal with contracts or with projects without at some point coming into contact with the law. Any major contract or project will be affected by the requirements of the law in many ways. Planning law, health and safety law, employment law, environmental protection law, land law—all these and many others may apply and need to be allowed for. The approach to contract law should be the same, and the aim of every project manager is to ensure that no legal problems arise, and that if they do he has carried out his project in accordance with the rules.

This book is not about contract law, but we must say something about the law of contract in order to put the conditions into their proper context.

Law is organised on a national basis and every country has its own law. Therefore many areas of law tend to differ widely from country to country. The obvious examples are tax law and administrative law. The law on subjects like work permits/visas or site safety or environmental protection will often be quite different from one country to another. Some of the widest divergences come in the field of social/criminal law. Bigamy is a crime in the UK, but not in Islamic countries for instance.

However, because the needs of commerce are the same the world over, almost all countries have laws governing *commercial* contracts that are similar in practice, though they may be different in theory. Where national systems of contract law tend to differ from each other is in their theoretical legal principles, administrative practices, and questions of national policy and interest.

Law protects the private individual against unfair exploitation by the commercial organisation. His rights as an employee will be protected and also his rights as a consumer. The organisation has no such protection. The law sees it as competent and professional. Therefore it does not need protection. It is free to make its own contracts and it must live with its own mistakes. This means that every company is free to drive a hard bargain with others if it is powerful enough or astute enough to do so, even if that hard bargain is damaging to the other party. The first rule of commercial contracts is, 'If you don't like the terms don't take the contract'.

In general terms each national system of law only prohibits or imposes requirements upon commercial contracts where the 'national interest' is involved. For instance English law lays down rules to prohibit or control commercial contracts that impose unreasonable restraints on trading freedom within the United Kingdom. German and French law lay down comparable, but not identical, rules for German or French contracts. EU law adds to national law within the European Union by prohibiting the unreasonable use of monopoly power and the distortion of trade within the Community. And so on.

A large part of the law of contract is about what may be called the procedural aspects of the contract. The law sets out rules dealing with:

- capacity—who can make contracts, and limitations on the ability of certain classes of people to make contracts;
- what is required for a contract, consideration, intention, legality of purpose, and certainty of terms;
- how a contract may be created;
- how a contract may be ended;
- how legal disputes concerning contracts are to be conducted;
- how damages for breach should be calculated.

The law of contract is actually not much concerned with making rules about the terms that may be included, or not included, in a contract. There are actually surprisingly few such rules, and most refer to consumer rather than commercial contracts. In the commercial world the parties are largely free to write their own contract terms so long as they comply with the various national interest rules.

What is far more important is the way in which the law goes about deciding what the words used in a contract mean if there is a dispute.

Most contracts are carried out reasonably successfully, and the parties sort out any problems that arise by discussion between themselves, without too much emphasis being put upon precisely what the contract actually says. Sometimes however a more serious dispute arises which will involve litigation or arbitration. It is then that the *precise* meaning of the actual words used in the contract will become an issue.

All systems of law operate on the same general principle. Where there is a written contract document it is presumed to be a complete and precise statement of exactly what terms the parties have agreed—no more and no less. What the lawyer always asks himself is, 'What did each of the parties *actually* promise to do—and has he done it?'

He will then answer that question by reading the contract. (Of course he will sometimes talk to the engineers as well, but the written words will always matter most.)

When a lawyer does this he concentrates on the precise meaning of the words and language used. The problem for engineers is that they are not trained to use, nor are they used to using, words or language *precisely* in a legal context. Most of us concentrate upon being clearly understood when we *talk* rather than being precise when we *write*. We therefore concentrate upon the skills needed to get our message across verbally, body language, tone of voice, etc. We do not concentrate at all on using only the written word.

As a result when we have to use only the written word we make mistakes. We get the grammar wrong, so that our sentences do not mean what they are intended to mean. We use words without thinking about what they really mean, or what their different meanings are.

Some words can have several, very different but equally valid, meanings. We use jargon. We use colloquial language. (For instance the word 'bit' means one thing to a computer programmer, something entirely different to a drilling engineer, something different again to a locksmith or a show-jumper or jockey, and they are all entirely different to what the word means to the rest of us. When we say 'Please wipe your feet' what we really mean, in precise terms is 'Please wipe your shoes—or boots or sandals'.)

In effect a contract states very exactly what the parties have agreed, using language very precisely. The project manager has to live within these precise rules/statements. Disputes concerning contracts often turn upon whether engineers have actually understood what their contracts mean (when interpreted in accordance with their *precise* meaning, or meanings, by the lawyers). Every project manager sometimes needs to know what the words of his contracts mean if he is to stay within the rules. Every project manager should have a good dictionary on his bookshelves, and he should use it regularly, and have advice from a contract/words specialist available when needed, if at all possible.

1.1.6 What contracts do

Every contract performs four distinct, but overlapping, functions:

- It defines the *normal performance* required from each party to the contract, together with ways in which that normal performance may be varied within the framework of the contract. (For instance it defines the work the contractor must do and the price the purchaser must pay. It will then include a variation clause or clauses allowing minor changes without the need to re-negotiate the entire contract.)
- It defines the share of technical, commercial and economic *risks* between the parties, design risk, price risk, delivery risk, etc.
- It defines contract *rules and procedures*. It acts as the rulebook for running the contract—and a professional should always know the rules.
- It identifies some, and hopefully most, of the more predictable *problems* that may arise during the contract and prescribes machinery and procedures for dealing with them if they do arise.

Model conditions are involved with all four of these, but especially the second, third and fourth. This is not surprising. Model conditions are about working relationships.

1.1.7 Model conditions

No set of model conditions of contract exists in isolation. Every set is written around a particular type of commercial/contract situation. It describes the various necessary stages that will be present in that type of situation. It allocates the risks, commercial technical and economic, between the parties to the contract in a way that makes sense within that situation in that industry, and provides appropriate solutions to the more predictable problems that may arise during the contract.

Different types of contract require different conditions of contract because the work is different, the problems are different, and even more important the risks are different.

To understand any set of model conditions, and therefore to be able to manipulate and make the best use of them in practice, you need to understand the following:

- The *basic commercial/contract situation* that the set is principally designed to cover. We call this the contract *scenario*.
- How *flexible* the conditions are, and therefore how easily and how far they can be adapted to cover other commercial/contract situations.
- The *commercial attitude* of the conditions. Do they favour one side as against the other, and if so how? Do they try to hold some sort of balance between the two? Do they treat the parties as having an equal degree of skill, or do they treat one party as having a lower degree of skill than the other?
- How much *freedom* they give the parties to run the contract in their own particular way.

1.2 General introduction

1.2.1 Contract complexity

Contracts lay down rules to control the relationship between the parties. The greater the number of interfaces between the parties, the more complex the relationship, and the more complex the rules need to become. In addition, if the plant is complex, then so is the contract Specification, and then the design process— and as a result the testing/proving procedures become more elaborate as well. The result is that the contract conditions have to expand to accommodate this and they become more complex still. If the Contractor has to construct this complex plant on the Purchaser's site then the project is really complex. It involves a whole series of interfaces between the parties at every stage of the contract—design, manufacture, construction, training, operating and testing— which all have to be controlled by the contract. It is then that we get projects, contracts and Specifications that are among the most demanding and complicated that there are.

1.2.2 The process industry

This is the background to the IChemE conditions. They are in many ways the most sophisticated of all the many sets of model conditions available within the UK. They originate from the chemical and process engineering industry. Strictly speaking it is not one industry but many—oil, pharmaceuticals, bulk chemicals, brewing, food, plastics and so on. They are very different, but they are all concerned with the operation of high-value, complex, processing/manufacturing plants.

The common elements of the conditions are:

- Firstly, the main contract Books are 'turnkey' contract conditions. The Contractor is responsible for the design, construction and testing of a complete operating plant and must therefore do whatever is necessary to carry out the whole of the project, from start to finish. The Yellow Book does so as well. The Brown Book and the Orange Book of course take a different approach.
- Secondly, they are truly multi-disciplinary, in that they are intended for complex projects, and require the Contractor to provide or obtain whatever engineering skills are necessary to carry out all aspects of the project.
- Thirdly, they are 'result-based'. The industry is mainly concerned not with a plant as such, but with a plant as a means to provide a product. Therefore the industry uses contracts which concentrate upon whether the plant will make the right product, rather than simply upon what that plant will be. They are concerned with the problems of ensuring that the Contractor will prove that the Plant will perform as required by the Contract. If the Plant cannot perform, for reasons that are the responsibility of the Contractor, then the Contractor will be in breach of the Contract.

This means that there are substantial differences between the IChemE Forms of Contract and other model conditions available.

Broadly speaking all the various building and civil engineering industry conditions, the RIBA/JCT and ICE/ECC conditions are 'work-based' conditions. They aim to ensure that the Contractor will carry out 'Works' in accordance with a design required by the Purchaser (or an Engineer or Architect acting on the Purchaser's behalf). They are mainly concerned with the problems of monitoring the way that the work is carried out, in the context of a complicated civil engineering construction operation on site.

The IEE/IMechE conditions, especially the MF1 conditions, are 'result-based' and therefore much nearer in approach to the IChemE conditions, but are equipment-related rather than plant-related.

1.2.3 The IChemE Forms of Contract

This guide covers the following editions of the IChemE conditions:

- the fourth edition, published in October 2001, of the conditions for lump sum contracts, the Red Book;
- the third edition, published in October 2002, of the conditions for reimbursable contracts, the Green Book;

- the first edition, published in December 2003, of the conditions for target cost contracts, the Burgundy Book;
- the third edition, published in September 2003, of the 'back-to-back' sub-contract, for use with either the Red, Green or Burgundy Book contracts, the Yellow Book;
- the second edition, published in April 2004, of the subcontract for civil engineering works, also for use with either the Red, Green or Burgundy book contracts, the Brown Book;
- the second edition, published in October 2003, of the contract for minor works, the Orange Book.

The Red, Green and Burgundy Books are all designed to suit contracts where the following contract scenario applies. The Contractor is responsible for the:

- design;
- manufacture and procurement from Subcontractors;
- delivery to site;
- construction/erection/assembly/installation, together with all necessary ancillary site operations;
- construction, taking over and performance tests; and,
- mechanical and performance guarantees

for a sizeable process plant, comprising a variety of different machines and equipment together with their metering and control systems and all necessary construction and other work, all assembled into one or more integrated production units. A process plant is a plant which converts one or more raw materials into a product, continuously or on a batch basis, using chemical, physical, mechanical, biological or other means to do so.

Typically the project will require:

- a considerable amount of design work by the Contractor, followed by a substantial amount of design co-ordination between the Contractor and Purchaser;
- the placing, co-ordination and control by the Contractor of a number of Subcontracts of different types and sizes;
- a considerable amount of work on the site preparing for and erecting equipment;
- substantial inspection and testing activity;
- high-quality project management, from both the Purchaser and the Contractor;
- a wide range of engineering skills and disciplines—process, electrical, mechanical, chemical, structural, civil, etc.

For comments on the contract scenarios of the subcontract and minor works forms, see the relevant sections below.

1.2.4 Flexibility

The three main contract forms are designed for contracts for the design and construction of plants and are not really suitable therefore for small contracts or for the procurement/installation of individual items of equipment. The Orange Book is much more suitable for these types of contract. Also they are not intended for civil engineering or construction work alone, although the Green Book has been used for civil engineering projects being carried out on a collaborative basis with considerable success.

With those qualifications, and bearing in mind that these are complex sets of conditions so that care is needed in drawing up special conditions to modify them, the Red, Green and Burgundy Books can be adapted to cover a very wide range of contracts. The Green Book is particularly flexible, and can be adapted to fit a wide range of commercial situations ranging from totally reimbursable to fixed-fee and guaranteed maximum price contracts.

1.2.5 Commercial attitude

All the IChemE conditions aim to promote a high degree of co-operation between Purchaser and Contractor. They are also reasonably fair to both parties. However 'fairness' must mean very different things in different contracts.

In the Red Book the conditions have to contend with the underlying adversarial element present in the fixed-price 'arms-length' contract. Here fairness means that the Purchaser/Project Manager is given the information and powers necessary to check on the progress being made by the Contractor, and to exercise control over his project. The Contractor is left in control of his own work, and the Project Manager may not interfere with that work, although he may make changes to it. The form gives the Project Manager a wide range of options to choose from when initiating and pricing those changes. Then clauses are included providing for co-operation in several areas, and for a full range of dispute resolution options. The position under the Yellow and Brown Books is very similar.

In the Green Book, for a reimbursable contract, the whole aim is towards a collaborative rather than adversarial approach. In return for payment for his work on a reimbursable basis (which should ensure that the competent Contractor will not make a loss on the contract) the Project Manager receives a high level of access to the Contractor's personnel and information and much greater control, if he wishes to exercise it, over the day-to-day running of the contract.

In the Burgundy Book, for a Target Cost contract, the aim is towards a collaborative rather than adversarial approach, as with the Green Book. However both parties are reminded that once a Target Cost has been agreed then any subsequent changes made by the Purchaser must be reflected in changes to Target Cost.

In the Orange Book, the task of the conditions is much easier. Most small projects can only be carried out on a collaborative basis anyway. The form therefore allows for whatever price/payment arrangements and scope of work the parties may agree, and sets out a framework around which the parties can put their contracts together.

1.2.6 The Conditions

The Conditions are made up of clauses that deal with a whole range of contract topics. There will be clauses to deal with contract procedures, clauses that describe the different stages of the contract (design, manufacture, procurement, site preparation, construction, testing), clauses that deal with project management personnel and powers, changes, claims, disputes and many more.

All these different clauses are spread through each of the Books. Any guide that simply goes through the conditions in numerical order will simply confuse rather than help. Therefore this guide divides each Book into groups of related clauses, summarises what they lay down, and then comments upon the more important provisions of the actual clauses.

Of course it is quite wrong to divide a set of contract conditions into separate groups, because in practice many clauses interact with almost everything else in the contract. (For instance the payment clauses in the contract will be affected by almost everything that happens.) Nevertheless, for the sake of clarity, it is necessary to do so. We have also dealt with each Book in a separate chapter. Inevitably this produces a degree of duplication, especially since the current editions of the three main contract Books have adopted a consistent clause numbering system, but it does minimise the need for cross-referencing between the different chapters.

Each Book is printed and distributed by IChemE in the form of a book containing the Model Conditions, together with Introductory Notes, and Guide Notes to the preparation of Contract Schedules and Special Conditions. The Introductory and Guide Notes give a considerable amount of advice as to how a process plant contract should be put together, and the considerations that the parties should bear in mind when doing so. This book does not in any way replace these Notes—it is a guide to the Model Conditions, the way they are intended to operate, and what they offer to each of the parties.

It assumes two things, however—that the conditions are being used without any Special Conditions which change the meaning of any clause, and that they are being used with the Schedules listed in the conditions.

1.3 Project management and contract strategy

Contract strategy and contract management are both parts of project management. Contract strategy is the selection of the contract numbers, type and content, including conditions of contract, that are appropriate to meet the needs of the project, and the selection of the correct style of management of the resulting contract(s). Contract management then includes, among other subjects, the proper use of those contract conditions once in place. Most of this book is intended to give the engineer information about the second of these two subjects, however something must also be said about the strategy of larger projects.

1.3.1 Strategy considerations

The main considerations when choosing between the Red, Green and Burgundy Books are as follows:

(1) The basic decision on contract conditions will generally be made by the Purchaser. He controls the funding for the project and begins the process. He should be 'pro-active'. Initially he has to decide three things:

- what is the aim of the project;
- what he will do for himself, and therefore what he will actually need to obtain from a Contractor (or contractors); and
- what strategy to use (one Contractor, two or more, what type of contract(s) etc.).

(2) Ideally the work of the Project Manager should begin several months before the initial enquiry is circulated to possible contractors. His function at this stage is to assist in deciding what form of contract is best suited to meet the needs of the Purchaser, and then in drawing up the enquiry document. Then as discussions take place concerning the bids submitted by possible contractors he has to ensure that the final contract to emerge is adequate to meet those needs and aims.

(3) The contract will vary according to a number of factors. A contract for a small skid-mounted plant has very different needs to one for a large plant that has to be built on site. A plant using well-established technology is different to a plant based on new technology. A contract with a very tight time-scale is different to one where the time-scale is more forgiving. A plant where product quality or process flexibility is the absolute priority is different to one where project cost is the priority. A contract where both the Purchaser and the Contractor are expert in the process is different to a contract where one party has much more expertise than the other. And so on.

(4) *The project should always decide the strategy* and form of contract to be used, rather than the reverse. Shoe-horning a project into an inappropriate strategy or set of contract conditions on the grounds that 'this is the way we always do it' will always result in the project being modified to fit the strategy or conditions, sometimes with disastrous consequences in time and cost.

(5) The choice of contract conditions by the Purchaser depends upon a number of other factors in addition to the needs of the project. The main factors are:

- The amount and level of project management man-hours and skills available to the Purchaser at the start and for the duration of the project. A project team with low-level skills or inadequate manning levels is likely to lose control and make mistakes in running a complex or sophisticated contract, especially if employing an unaccustomed strategy or using an unfamiliar set of conditions.
- The man-hours and skills required by the contract conditions. Different types of contract demand different management skills. Don't pick a contract that you cannot manage.
- Contract knowledge. There is always a learning curve in using new or unfamiliar contract words, and project managers often work better using conditions that they know well.
- The level of information available to the Purchaser at the enquiry stage. To obtain *satisfactory* fixed/firm prices the Purchaser has to be able to write a detailed enquiry specification, which requires a considerable level of technical information concerning the plant, the site and so on.

- Project time-scales, both to place the contract and then to carry it out. Price-based contracts take considerable time and effort to set up and time to carry out, whereas reimbursable or Target Cost contracts may be quicker though more costly.
- What matters most to the Purchaser. If low initial project cost is the predominant factor then the fixed-price contract resulting from a genuinely competitive tender procedure may be the best option, followed by a Target Cost and then a reimbursable contract. If other considerations are more predominant, such as time-scale, quality, 'whole-life cost' or plant design then a fixed-price option may not be the best choice.
- Availability of possible contractors and processes. The fixed/firm-price competitive process requires genuine competition between contractors to be effective.
- Risk levels and policy. Asking the Contractor to take unrealistic levels of risk may produce simply an unrealistic price or a Contractor who will deliberately manage his way out of the risk the moment he is given any opportunity to do so.
- Finally every contract needs conditions which fit the nature of the proposed relationship, and which have a contract scenario that is similar to that of the project.

The scenarios of the three main contract Forms are as follows.

1.3.2 The Red Book contract scenario

The scenario is that of a contract that is largely price-based (though, of course, the contract may include some items of work priced on a day-rate or other basis). The price may be either fixed or subject to adjustment in accordance with a cost/price escalation formula.

If the Contractor is to agree to a fixed price he must be able to assess all the commercial and technical risks and requirements to be imposed upon him by the contract so that he can allow for them in his price. This means that at the enquiry stage the Purchaser will need to define as exactly as possible what he requires the plant to produce, the site on which it is to be constructed and all his other technical requirements. He will also usually include much more detail. The Contractor must then be given time to prepare a fully-priced tender/ offer against those requirements. Therefore the contract will usually be placed after lengthy enquiry preparation and tendering periods, followed by a tender assessment and negotiating period.

This means that the Book is mainly suitable for contracts that are:

- of medium size;
- of short to medium duration;
- where the plant specification/design is clear at or before contract;
- not likely to be subject to any significant degree of change;
- where the Contractor can identify and price adequately for the various risks involved.

The contract will then be run as an 'arms-length' contract. The Project Manager will have the right to manage the Contractor but not the right to interfere in the Contractor's design of the Plant or his running of the contract, unless it can be shown that the Contractor is failing to carry out the contract properly.

From the Contractor's point of view the contract will be comparatively high-risk and high-profit.

1.3.3 The Green Book scenario

The Green Book scenario is completely different. The Purchaser is buying from the Contractor a team of qualified and skilled personnel to assist him in carrying out a project for the construction of a plant. Most, if not all, of the work carried out by the Contractor's personnel will be reimbursable, and the Contractor will be paid for their work by the Purchaser on a day-rate or time/cost basis. The Contractor will then be reimbursed for the cost of purchasing subcontracted work and equipment.

As a result the Contractor is much more certain of making a profit upon the contract. This should have three consequences:

- As the contract is comparatively low-risk it should also be comparatively low-profit for the Contractor.
- From the Purchaser's viewpoint the contract will be comparatively high-risk in two different respects. The cost to the Purchaser of a reimbursable contract is less certain than the cost of a price-based contract, and the overall cost may well be higher. The Purchaser will also be expected to provide a higher level of project management and to carry more risk than he would under a price-based contract, because the Contractor cannot price for risk in a reimbursable situation in the same way that he can under a fixed-price contract.
- the intention is that the contract will not be 'arms-length', but that the Contractor will collaborate with the Purchaser through the Project Manager. The Project Manager is therefore given much more power in the Green Book than in the Red to obtain information about and to control the day-to-day operations of the Contractor, including much greater control of the subcontracting process.

The Green Book is suitable for a much wider range of sizes and types of contract, and particularly suited for projects including a high degree of uncertainty at the time of contract, whether in design, time-scale or risk. It is also much more flexible than the fixed-price conditions. As a result it can be used for small-scale 'development' contracts, and also for contracts where fixed-price bidding is not a realistic option, either because of tightness or length of time-scale or because of design/specification or price/cost uncertainty. It can also be modified to include fixed fees or prices for different parts of the work, or to include a guaranteed maximum price. As a result it is suitable for alliance or joint venture/consortia relationship contracts.

The Green Book is also particularly suitable for the following:

- Where the result to be achieved is reasonably clear, but the work necessary to achieve that result is not. A typical example is where the Contractor has the task of debottlenecking or modernising an existing plant, and the Contractor cannot evaluate the true extent of the work that may be required until he can break into the plant and find out just what is there.

- Where the process to be employed is clear, but the end result that can be achieved or the work necessary to achieve a result is uncertain. A typical example of this is where the Contractor has the task of developing a process from, say, laboratory stage to pilot plant or full scale production.
- Where the Purchaser wishes to pool his own in-house skills with those of the Contractor in a joint development exercise. The Purchaser will perhaps have process knowledge but will wish to obtain the benefit of the Contractor's engineering, procurement or project skills.
- Where a reimbursable contract is used to shorten the time-scale of the project, by adopting a fast-track procedure. The procedures for placing a fixed-price contract with a Contractor for a complex plant inevitably take a considerable amount of time. Placing a reimbursable contract on the other hand can be far quicker—all the Purchaser needs to do is to specify roughly what he wants done and therefore what resources the Contractor must be prepared to provide. He still needs to satisfy himself that the Contractor can provide those resources at acceptable rates, but this need only take a matter of weeks. The result is that the Contractor can be given the go-ahead in a mere fraction of the time necessary to place a fixed-price contract. In addition the Project Manager's powers to manage the Contractor can then be used to fast-track the actual work under the contract, by using procedures for early ordering, parallel working etc.

As a final point it should always be remembered that the differences, in project management terms, between a fixed/firm-price contract and a reimbursable contract may be summarised under five different headings:

- *Relationship*: In the fixed/firm-price contract, even when highly co-operative, the relationship must always be 'arms-length', and potentially adversarial especially if problems or a large number of variations arise. In the reimbursable contract the relationship should be much more collaborative and this requires a very different style of project management on both sides. In particular it requires more project management time from the Purchaser.
- *Discipline*: The fixed/firm price contract imposes discipline upon the parties. The Purchaser must prepare a detailed specification of his requirements to enable the Contractor to submit a detailed bid. When the contract is made it will give the Contractor a Specification to be met, and a price and (usually) a fixed time-scale within which to comply. Any failure to comply is automatically penalised by the terms of the contract. The pure reimbursable contract imposes far less discipline on the Contractor, in that, even if he has a Specification to meet and perhaps also a time-scale within which to do so, he has no price restraint on him. Indeed the more man-hours he spends in carrying out the contract, the higher the profit he makes. Therefore, if there is to be discipline on the Contractor, it will not come from within the basic contract conditions. Usually a professional Contractor will need no discipline when working for a professional Purchaser. But if there is to be discipline, it will need to be imposed

by the Purchaser or Project Manager in such forms as detailed contract reporting procedures or arrangements to control and monitor the Contractor's work.

- *Incentive*: The fixed/firm-price contract gives the Contractor two incentives. The first is to run the contract efficiently, because this reduces cost and increases profit. The second is to 'design down to the Specification', because this does exactly the same. Therefore the fixed/firm-price contract must always be based upon an adequate Specification. The reimbursable contract on the other hand gives the Contractor no incentive to under-design—it almost gives him the incentive to over-design, which is actually an advantage in the context of a collaborative design exercise. What the reimbursable contract should however do is to give the Purchaser the incentive to ensure that proper project management techniques are applied to ensure that the Contractor performs efficiently—not always as easy as it sounds in a collaborative relationship.
- *Risk*: The fixed/firm-price contract automatically imposes a considerable degree of money risk on the Contractor and will usually impose a high level of other risk on him as well. However the Contractor is able to price for risk, in the form of contingency amounts built into his price. Under the reimbursable contract, on the other hand, it is very difficult for the Contractor to include any substantial risk contingencies in his rates. Payments to Sub-contractors are reimbursed at cost, and his own personnel are paid for on a low-profit day-rate basis. Therefore the Contractor can carry only a low level of financial liability, and the Purchaser has to carry a much higher proportion of the project risks.
- *Change*: The great weakness of the fixed/firm-price contract, from the Purchaser's point of view, is that it sets up a rigid contract structure, and copes very badly with anything more than the minimum degree of change during the life of the contract. This makes the tasks of the Project Manager and Contractor much more demanding if a substantial degree of change becomes necessary. The reimbursable contract, by its very nature, copes much better and is therefore inherently more suitable where significant change can be foreseen. However that change will still need to be managed.

1.3.4 The Burgundy Book scenario

The Burgundy Book scenario is different again. At first glance it looks to be simply an amalgamation of the Red and Green Book scenarios. The Contract will go through a 'Green Book' development stage when the Contractor and Purchaser work together in a reimbursable relationship to complete the detailed design of the plant. Then they will agree a Target Cost for the procurement of the equipment and the work necessary to construct the plant on site and bring it into full operation. Once the Target Cost has been agreed then the Contract moves much closer to the Red Book. The Contractor will now work to the Target Cost. The Target Cost will be coupled to a bonus/penalty (often called 'pain share/ gain share') arrangement to share any under or overspend achieved by the Contractor in carrying out the rest of the Contract.

As a result the Purchaser will get the benefits of a reimbursable contract—a collaborative relationship during design and a reasonable degree of collaboration during the procurement/construction phase. He also gets the benefit of a Contractor with a strong incentive to keep procurement and construction costs to the minimum.

The Contractor will get the benefits of a reimbursable relationship in that the plant design will have been agreed in detail by the Purchaser, and the Target Cost will be agreed in a rather less adversarial atmosphere than that of a fixed-price negotiation. He also has the possibility of receiving a bonus if he can achieve a saving against the agreed Target Cost.

Of course this is perfectly correct. However the Target Cost contract is different because it involves a change in the project management relationship during the Contract. On agreement of the Target Cost the relationship will usually become more arms-length and adversarial, whatever the conditions say. Managing this transition is not easy for either party. In particular the management of change, especially preferential change, and its effects on Target Cost can cause real problems.

1.4 Disputes and dispute resolution

The process industries are used to complex contracts, often with quite a lot at stake. For both sides, the difference between success and failure can be very important. That is the bad news.

The good news is that most project managers in the process industries are professionals who are experienced in managing complex work and complicated contracts. They will usually understand each other. They might not agree with each other all the time, but they will understand each other. That is a big advantage when trying to resolve disagreement.

Disagreement is a fact of every contract. Every professional worth his salt has his own opinions which will differ from those of others from time to time. When those professionals are project managers who are expected, naturally enough, to look after the interests of their own companies, then disagreements are inevitable. Furthermore a healthy level of disagreement is no bad thing in a contract, because it ensures that the important issues get discussed between the parties when they need to be discussed.

Disagreement is not a problem. The problem is the disagreement that is not settled quickly, but develops into a *dispute*. Dispute is a serious problem. It affects personal relationships, making project management more difficult. It distracts attention from the project. It is demanding in time, money and resources. If it becomes a legal dispute it brings the engineer into conflict with the lawyer and the lawyer will always win—and it destroys commercial relationships.

Therefore all model conditions have to concern themselves with the possibility of disputes and provide appropriate methods for resolving them should they arise. The IChemE conditions are lucky in that the level of dispute in contracts using them continues to be extremely low. Nevertheless they have to include all the clauses that are necessary and, as you will see, this means that there are four clauses dealing with different procedures for settling disputes in most of the Books.

At first glance four clauses and four different procedures looks like serious over-kill. However there are three good reasons for doing this:

- If the parties to the dispute are at daggers drawn with each other then the only route to settle that dispute will be legal. If however the parties are more ready to compromise then non-confrontational resolution becomes a possibility, and for that reason the conditions allow for mediation where possible.
- Disputes in any large-project industry can come in all shapes and sizes, from the multi-million pound argument about accusations of major contract breach down to the minor quarrel about the amount of time or cost to be awarded to the Contractor as a result of a contract variation. Legal dispute procedures, litigation (law courts) and arbitration are costly and suited to settling arguments about complex legal/commercial issues. They are not suited to dealing with complex factual/technological disagreement. Therefore the forms provide for arbitration to solve legal/commercial dispute, and for expert determination to solve factual/technological differences.
- We also have to allow for a recent change in law, providing for adjudication in contracts for construction work.

1.4.1 Summary

Negotiation is always going to produce the best chance of a satisfactory solution to any dispute. It is quick and avoids the bruising encounters that come with arbitration, litigation or adjudication. The cost to both sides is very much less, and the money that does not have to go in legal fees can then go towards funding the settlement. Above all it saves on man-hours—the endless sessions spent talking to lawyers, drawing up statements, trawling through files, etc—that can be the bane of any project manager's life for months or even years after the end of the project. Resolving disputes by the *formal* avenues of arbitration or adjudication should only be considered as a last resort if other means fail.

Mediation is preferable to arbitration. It is again much faster (and therefore much less costly) and less adversarial, though, like negotiation, it does demand from both parties the willingness to admit their own errors. As a result it will not usually be successful if either of the two sides have become so entrenched in their position that they have lost the ability to make concessions.

Arbitration is a better route than litigation for solving serious disputes. An arbitrator with appropriate skills and experience must always have a greater chance of understanding the complex engineering or process questions that are likely to arise than a court, quite apart from the greater confidentiality ensured by arbitration. Even in the case of a dispute centring on commercial issues an arbitrator is more likely to understand the way in which a complex process contract would be managed and administered. For these reasons IChemE has always adopted a policy of appointing arbitrators (and experts and adjudicators) with an appropriate technical or commercial background than from within the legal professions. It has also adopted the policy of leaving arbitrators etc to be named after the dispute has arisen, rather than being named in the contract. This is because it is considered best to pick an arbitrator who is suited to the demands of the dispute that has actually occurred.

The Expert is to be used to decide, not disputes, so much as differences of opinion concerning questions of fact which arise between the parties as the contract proceeds. His main function will probably be to resolve disagreement between the Project Manager and the Contractor concerning the cost or time effects of variations made by the Project Manager. He is there to prevent a disagreement dragging on until it sours contractual relations and damages the whole project, by settling a problem in weeks or months rather than the years that arbitration or litigation would take.

Finally, of course we have adjudication. As we have already said, it is hoped that the use of adjudication would be restricted to smaller and less complex claims. (Interestingly this does actually seem to be the case to date.)

1.4.2 Adjudication under the Housing Grants, Construction and Regeneration Act 1996

Adjudication springs from problems within the UK civil engineering and building industries during the 1970s and 1980s. We are all aware of the 'claims culture' that arose within the industry at that time, and which still exists today.

One of the consequences of the claims culture was that disputes regularly went to litigation or highly legalistic arbitration, therefore taking years to settle. Quite apart from the cost involved, this resulted in enormous delays in settling minor claims, with consequent delays in payments. The results were damaging to the industry, particularly to smaller subcontractors whose payments were often delayed until main contract claims were settled.

Adjudication was adopted in the Housing Grants Act as a solution to cut this gordian knot. It gives the claimant, who will normally be a contractor, and probably a small supplier or subcontractor, a quick (and therefore cheap and rough and ready) method of solving disputes with the other side, whether that other side be a main or higher-tier contractor or an end-client. The Act provides that *any* dispute under a contract within the UK that includes 'construction operations' can be referred to an adjudicator who must ascertain the facts of the dispute and then give a ruling on the matter within a basic period of 28 days. That ruling will then bind the parties unless reversed by arbitration or litigation. It therefore provides a fast-track route to an interim ruling on any claim, and therefore will get that claim roughly settled and payment made without the need to go through an expensive or long-drawn-out litigation or arbitration process. These can be so prohibitively expensive for a small claimant that the small company simply might be unable to contemplate taking that route to recover its debt.

Adjudication can be a tremendous boon to claimants in small contracts, enabling them to get quick settlements of minor or even quite substantial disputes (within the context of a small contract) because such disputes are usually based upon comparatively straightforward facts and contractual issues.

The definition of 'construction operations' in the Act is, however, sufficiently wide to include many contracts that have little or nothing to do with the civil engineering or building industries. The definition will certainly extend to most main contracts and all civil engineering subcontracts in the process industries. This means that the right to adjudication in the event of a dispute will then be imposed on top of the normal dispute resolution methods provided in those contracts. The probability is that the right will apply in almost all UK Red, Green and Burgundy contracts, and also in most Yellow and all Brown contracts, and in any Orange contracts which include any 'construction operations'.

(Very briefly 'construction operations' is defined in the Act as work within the UK on buildings and structures, works at or below ground level, such as walls, pipelines, railways, reservoirs, etc., the installation of equipment in buildings or structures, and site preparation work such as foundations, earthmoving, etc. However construction operations do not include among others *the mere supply of equipment or work involving plant/machinery/supporting steelwork not inside a building* on sites where the main activity is water/effluent treatment or the production, storage, or processing of chemicals, pharmaceuticals, oil, gas, steel or food products.)

The main guidelines of adjudication are now clear. It works well in small disputes in the building and civil engineering industries, and is being strongly supported by the courts. However adjudication in large disputes, say under a large main contract in a process environment, is much less likely to work properly.

The problem is simply that a large dispute, perhaps at main contract level in a process industry project, is not simple. The facts will be complex. The dispute will involve massive quantities of documentation that all has to be read. There will be a lot of conflicting evidence to be resolved. There will be several issues to be decided. These are not difficult problems but they do take time to resolve, and time is something that an adjudicator does not have. The requirements of the Act in practice only allow an adjudicator some four weeks at most, after allowing time for the preliminaries, to gather and then assess his information and produce his ruling. This could be almost impossibly short. The parties, and especially the defendant, may only have a few days to compile their submissions to the adjudicator. The adjudicator will then have not very much longer than that to reach his decision, particularly where he has other demands upon his time, and most good adjudicators are busy people. The result is that the adjudication exercise can become simply a lottery, which just makes things worse.

At subcontract level and minor works level adjudication becomes much more feasible.

As a result of the Act, however, the IChemE has been compelled to include clauses allowing for adjudication in all its conditions. It is also authorised to nominate adjudicators.

1.4.3 Major projects

The whole point of the dispute resolution strategy in any contract and in any form is always to minimise the negative impact of a dispute on the project, by the use of appropriate procedures. There is one more procedure that might be mentioned.

This is the 'Dispute Resolution Board', which is increasingly used in contracts for major projects. The Board will consist of perhaps two senior managers from both the Purchaser and Main Contractor, with perhaps an independent Chairman with legal and dispute resolution skills. The Board will be set up at the start of the contract and will remain in being until its completion. It will meet at regular intervals, perhaps every three months or six months, to discuss and resolve any disputes that have arisen within the project since the previous meeting. Usually its decisions will be stated by the contract to be mandatory.

There are several very useful principles embodied in this strategy. First of all there is the principle of negotiation under the chairmanship of a qualified independent person. Secondly, as the Board lives with the project all the way through, its members become experienced and knowledgeable about it. Therefore their decisions automatically become well informed. Thirdly, as they meet at regular intervals it becomes normal practice to refer disputes to them as soon as those disputes become difficult, which avoids excessive and abrasive argument between the project management teams on either side. Certainly dispute resolution boards seem to work well.

1.5 Liability law—delays and defects

1.5.1 Lateness law

The risk

Liability for late delivery of equipment or completion of work is a serious risk area for the Contractor:

- Every Contractor is late most of the time. Most delays are only small, but some delays will always be more substantial.
- It is impossible for the Contractor to predict at the date of contract:
  - how late he will be;
  - why he will be late—his own fault, force majeure or delay by the Purchaser; and
  - what effect any late delivery will have upon the Purchaser (this is dependent on factors of which the Contractor has no control or knowledge.)

There is, however, no doubt that *if* the Contractor does not take proper steps to set some limit to his potential liability for lateness and *if* he is seriously late, or his lateness causes serious losses to the Purchaser, he may be liable to major damages.

The law

Under UK law there are three, and only three, possible situations in regard to the time promise in a contract:

- time 'of the essence';
- estimated delivery date;
- liquidated damages.

'Time of the essence'

The law has always accepted that the time promise is a major term of the commercial contract. Therefore a promise to complete by a fixed date or within a fixed period is a serious promise, and the breach of that promise is a serious breach of contract. As a result where in a commercial contract there is a fixed date stated for delivery or the completion of Work, then that date is an essential term, or in legal language 'of the essence', of the contract. It is not necessary for the contract actually to state that time is of the essence of the contract, although many sets of conditions of purchase contain phrases such as 'time of the essence', 'delivery dates are of fundamental importance', etc. The mere fact that a fixed date or period is stated is sufficient.

If, therefore, a Contractor takes a contract to supply equipment or complete the erection or commissioning of equipment on site by a stated date or within a fixed period, in the absence of any qualification of that statement the date or period will be 'of the essence of the contract'. The meaning of 'of the essence of the contract' is that if the Contractor is late, even if only by one day, the Purchaser may, if he wishes:

- *both* claim damages for breach of contract;
- *and* in addition, in some circumstances, treat the contract as cancelled and refuse to accept delivery (or reject) the equipment (though this would be unusual in a process contract).

The damages that the Purchaser can claim in such a situation will be all the losses that he can *prove* that he has suffered and which the Contractor should reasonably have foreseen as being a possible loss at the time the contract was signed. This might be because the Contractor should have been expected to foresee them as a normal risk or because the Purchaser had told the Contractor, before the date of the contract, that that particular loss would be suffered if he should be late.

Clearly this is very serious for the Contractor. The purpose of a process plant is to produce revenue/profit for the Purchaser, so the damages that the Contractor might have to pay could easily be out of all proportion to any allowance he can make in his price.

Estimated delivery/completion date

Where there is no date for delivery or completion stated in the contract, then the law requires that the Contractor's obligations must be completed within a *reasonable* time. That will depend upon the circumstances. Equally, where a contract sets a date for delivery or completion, but then states that the date is either approximate or an estimate, then the Contractor has to carry out his obligations within a reasonable time of that date. If the Contractor fails to deliver or complete within that reasonable time, then the Purchaser can claim against the Contractor on the same basis as if the Contractor had failed to meet a fixed delivery date in a time of the essence situation.

There is no specific definition of what is 'a reasonable time'. In practice, other things being equal, it will usually depend primarily on the length of the delivery/completion period. As an educated guess, anything within 5–10% of the original period would generally be regarded as reasonable.

Problems

These two basic legal possibilities present problems for both Purchaser and Contractor. For the Contractor the problems are obvious. Firstly there is no right to an extension of the delivery or completion period if he is delayed for reasons which are beyond his control. Secondly if he is late he may know that he will be liable for damages, but he will have no way of knowing how large those damages might be. It is risk of this type which is always the most difficult to deal with on a realistic basis.

For the Purchaser there are also serious problems though they are not so obvious. Firstly he is only able to claim damages where he is able to *prove* the losses he has actually suffered. In practice this is often harder than it may seem, simply because the courts will not accept weak claims. Secondly whatever benefit the recovery of damages gives the Purchaser it totally fails to ensure that he obtains the plant which he wants as quickly as possible.

In most cases what the Purchaser really needs is to achieve the earliest possible delivery of his equipment even if that equipment is a little late. What he does not want to do is to get involved in litigation, risk losing his contract completely and then to have to go through the whole business of buying the equipment all over again from another Contractor.

Therefore the Purchaser needs a device which will impel a Contractor fairly firmly towards minimising lateness rather than a device which he can use only to reduce a late Contractor into mincemeat.

Liquidated damages and force majeure clauses

The device adopted in capital equipment contracts for ensuring that the Contractor is pushed towards minimising lateness in delivery or completion and that the Purchaser can claim damages without actually having to prove too much in the way of losses is that of the liquidated damages clause. Liquidated damages may be defined as 'a sum agreed between the parties as a genuine pre-estimate of the damage which would be caused to one party by a breach of contract by the other party', the breach in this case being the lateness in delivery by the Contractor.

In fact this definition is a little thin around the edges as it was decided long ago that the pre-estimate need not be a true or accurate one as long as it is one which the parties have actually agreed and it bears at least some relationship to reality. The liquidated damages agreed in most contracts bear little relation to either the potential maximum or minimum damage that might actually be suffered by the Purchaser in the event of serious lateness by the Contractor.

Liquidated damages clauses are a very good example of the 'bargain' element in contracts. Once two commercial organisations have agreed their liquidated damages the law will not usually ask whether the bargain is fair—it will simply enforce it.

1.5.2 Defects, site accidents, insurance and exclusions

The risk

Claims arising out of the supply of defective equipment or negligent work are a major risk because:

- Human error makes it inevitable that defective equipment will be delivered to customers from time to time, and that accidents will take place on site.
- Most defects or accidents will only cause a brief stoppage or minor damage, but there is always the risk of a major claim because:
  - defective equipment or site negligence could cause major damage;
  - even minor damage can cause substantial loss if it stops a plant from making product for a significant period.

It is impossible to predict when and where there may be an accident or how serious the consequences of that accident might be. But a serious accident is possible in every contract if the wrong thing happens at the wrong moment.

The legal principles

What follows is a brief explanation of UK law. The law in other countries is different, *but not so very different.*

There are three different types of liability under which a Contractor can be liable to pay damages to a Purchaser or others for defects in the plant or accidental damage due to negligent work while on site:

- *Liability under contract*: For having supplied equipment which fails to meet its Specification or for being in breach of conditions or warranties under the contract.
- *Liability in tort*: For causing damage or injury to another person, (primarily through negligence).
- *Liability under statute*: There are various statutes that can make the Contractor liable for defective work or accidental damage, such as the Occupier's Liability Act (the obligation to make one's premises safe for visitors) or the Employer's Liability Act (responsibility for employee insurance against industrial injuries). There may also be liability for the breach of secondary legislation, such as the Construction (Design and Management) Regulations.

Contractual liability for defects

Contract law about defects developed during the 1800s, and was then codified in the Sale of Goods Act (1893), and now the Sale of Goods Act (1979). The Supply of Goods and Services Act (1982) then extended sale law to contracts to construct plants. (Technically equipment incorporated into a process plant is not 'sold' to the Purchaser by the Contractor. It becomes the Purchaser's property when it 'vests' in him or is installed on his site). Finally the Sale and Supply of Goods Act (1994) has amended the Sale of Goods Act by substituting 'satisfactory' quality for 'merchantable' quality in Section 14.

The Acts lay down principles that apply to all contracts.

Specifications

Where goods are sold 'by description', it is an implied condition of the contract that the goods must comply with that description (except that minor failures to comply will be of no account). Obviously the Specification of the plant that goes into every contract is simply a description of that plant. Therefore the first rule has to be that the plant must always comply with the Specification. If it does not, however wonderful it may be, the Purchaser can claim damages for breach of contract from the Contractor and may be able to cancel the contract entirely if he wishes to do so.

Defects/quality liability

Sale of Goods Act 1979, Section 14, as amended states:

'Where the seller sells goods in the course of a business, there is an implied condition that the goods supplied under the contract are of *satisfactory quality*, except that there is no such condition:

(a) as regards defects specifically drawn to the buyer's attention before the contract is made; or

(b) if the buyer examines the goods before the contract is made, as regards defects which that examination ought to reveal'.

'Where the seller sells goods in the course of a business and the buyer expressly or by implication makes known. . . . any particular purpose for which the goods are being bought, there is an implied condition that the goods supplied under the contract are *reasonably fit for that purpose* . . . . except where the circumstances show that the buyer does not rely, or that it is unreasonable for him to rely, on the skill or judgement of the seller . . . .'

Note especially:

- there are two separate conditions, firstly of 'satisfactory quality', and secondly of 'reasonable fitness for purpose';
- normal contract procedures in the commercial world are such that the Purchaser will *almost always* make known to the Contractor the purpose for which he is buying the equipment;
- every product that the normal company sells or installs is sold/installed in the course of business;
- the Contractor is liable both for his own equipment and items that he buys in from Subcontractors;
- both these conditions will only be implied into a contract where not excluded by the terms of the contract.

Obviously there are detailed rules concerning exactly what the limits of reasonable fitness for purpose are, and for the definition of 'satisfactory quality'. For our purposes there is no doubt that virtually all contracts will be squarely within the terms of the Acts.

The remedies open to the Purchaser for breach of implied conditions are to claim damages for the breach, or to reject the equipment *and* claim damages for breach. The damages that the Purchaser is entitled to claim are not limited in any way. He can claim compensation for *all* 'direct' (as opposed to 'consequential or indirect') loss and damage that the Contractor could or should reasonably have foreseen would result from his breach of contract, however great that loss and damage may be. (In practice the Purchaser will often lose the right to reject the equipment by the time he actually claims—but could still claim the damages.)

There is one other point to remember. The liability of the Contractor is only to provide equipment that complies with the requirements of the Acts at the time at which it is sold or installed. To claim damages the Purchaser has to be able to show that the equipment was defective at the time it was supplied or installed by the Contractor. If he is unable to show that a defect was present in the equipment at that time or that it developed very soon after that time then he has no claim.

Liability in tort

'Tort' simply means a civil wrong. Negligence, libel, trespassing and assault are all torts.

Liability in contract is liability of one party to another under a contract between them. In other words, in the commercial situation, the Purchaser is normally the only person who can claim damages from the Contractor in contract. Under the law of tort the position is different. The wrongdoer is liable to anyone he injures.

The tort that concerns us is negligence. The principles of the law of negligence are as follows.

The duty to take care

If any person/company can foresee that his actions could cause damage or injury to another if done negligently or recklessly then he owes a duty to that person to take reasonable care not to cause him that injury or damage by his actions. Early definitions of this duty were phrased in terms of the biblical concept of a duty to one's 'neighbour'. In recent cases the Courts have defined the duty to take care in terms of 'proximity', but without any practical difference in concept. The principle is best explained by giving examples:

- When I drive my car along a road I can foresee that if I drive negligently I may cause an accident involving damage or injury to another road user. If therefore I drive negligently and I do cause just such an accident as a result, and another road user suffers damage or injury, then I am in breach of my duty of care to that other road user who may therefore claim damages from me.
- If I am working on scaffolding and people are passing underneath, I can foresee that if I let a hammer fall it may cause damage or injury to a passer-by who is struck by it. If therefore I do let a hammer drop by failing to take reasonable care and it hits a passer-by then I am in breach of my duty to that passer-by.

The basis of liability

If a person owes another a duty of care and then causes damage or injury to that person in a way which is in breach of his duty of care, then he is liable to compensate that person for *all* loss, damage or injury of any type that he could reasonably foresee as being likely to be caused to that person by his negligence, *however great* the extent (and cost) of the actual loss, damage or injury caused.

Everything is based on *foresight*—what consequences a person can (or as a reasonable person should) reasonably foresee as a result of his actions. We are liable to people who we ought to foresee as likely to be damaged or injured for the damage or injury that we ought to foresee that we might cause.

The law does allow the parties to a contract to agree that as between them the right to claim in tort may be excluded, but only by a clear statement to that effect.

Damages and problems

For the Contractor the results of this are as follows:

- He carries unlimited liability under both the law of contract and of tort, and could face enormous claims.
- A claim under the law of contract would be on a different theoretical basis to a claim under tort. (In contract for supplying equipment that is not in accordance with the contract—in tort for negligently causing damage). In practice, in most cases the claim could be brought against him either in contract or in tort.
- Both kinds of liability can be limited or excluded but only by clear wording in the contract.

For the Contractor the legal liability/risk for defective equipment or plant is potentially very serious. He runs a constant risk of a catastrophic consequential loss claim. Obviously sometimes the risk may be only theoretical, but in most contracts it is not too hard to imagine how the wrong failure at the wrong moment could cause a major accident or loss.

For the Purchaser the situation is also far from satisfactory, though the reasons are rather less obvious. These reasons are:

- All that the law of contract says is that equipment must be in good condition when sold (and now for a limited period thereafter). It does not allow the Purchaser any after-sales service, and in addition the Purchaser's rights to claim damages from the Contractor for equipment which fails are often of little *practical* use. In most cases what the Purchaser really needs if equipment breaks down is to have it put back into working order again as quickly as possible. He does not want to waste time and money going to court to claim damages.
- To be able to claim damages in the event of a major loss he has to be able to prove:
  - damage (although this will not be too difficult);
  - that the defect in the equipment which caused the damage was present in the equipment at the time it was sold or installed, and was not caused by his own misuse of the equipment. Even allowing for arguments based on 'latent' defects this can often be extraordinarily difficult, especially after the equipment has been in operation for a few months.
- The only way money can be guaranteed to be available to cover a major loss is through insurance. Every Purchaser will always therefore want to ensure that adequate insurance cover is available. However:

- small suppliers will only have limited insurance cover;
- large contractors will have more insurance cover, but even the largest contractor may well not have enough cover to deal with a major loss.
- Processing an insurance claim takes a great deal of time, and the time taken increases dramatically if the claim is either large or complicated.
- Even a simple claim against a single company will take up to a year or more to settle. A complex claim against two or more suppliers with a large amount of money at stake can easily take several years to settle. No Purchaser wants to wait that long.

Also when the Purchaser buys equipment he buys an asset. It is easy for the Purchaser to take out his own insurance cover on his own assets *to the total value of those assets* against all risks of loss or damage. Indeed the Purchaser *must have* that cover anyway to protect himself against the risk of his own employees causing a major loss. This insurance cover is *certain* from the Purchaser's point of view, and *considerably cheaper* than insurance cover provided by his suppliers, and *infinitely quicker* to produce money in a claim situation. Therefore as a matter of sheer business practicality Purchasers will always have their own insurance cover on the equipment they buy.

Therefore, although Purchasers are sometimes far from enthusiastic about a situation in which they agree to release a Contractor from potential liability, there are fairly strong practical reasons, particularly when a Purchaser is purchasing complex plant or plant which will operate in a fairly high-risk area for the Purchaser to do so, in return for:

- a free after-sales service for the guarantee period;
- no problems in proving the causes of defects;
- no need to rely on uncertain insurance cover.

The result is the typical 'Defects Liability' clause, under which the Contractor's consequential liability is limited or excluded in return for a defects repair service during a guarantee period. The contract will then provide for appropriate insurance cover, either separate or joint, to deal with the risk of loss.

Liability for site accidents

Accidents on site caused by the negligence of the Contractor's personnel while carrying out construction, commissioning or guarantee repair work will cause damage and loss to the Purchaser even more surely than defects in the plant.

The difference between liability for site accidents, in legal terms, is that defects liability can be established either under contract or in negligence (and in practice is more easily established in contract than in negligence), whereas site accident liability is almost always dealt with under negligence law. From the viewpoint of the parties involved, however, the insurance argument and considerations are precisely the same—that in practice the risk of a major incident is best insured either by the Purchaser, or by the parties jointly.

Therefore the risk of major accidents and damage on site is dealt with in many model sets of conditions of contract in almost the same way, in that the Contractor is relieved of the unlimited liability he would otherwise carry for accidents caused by his personnel. However not all his liability is excluded, since he is expected to deal with the consequences of small to medium-sized claims, and therefore to accept liability up to a reasonable limit. What therefore you usually find instead of exclusion clauses are clauses *limiting* the Contractor's liability to a fixed maximum amount, usually per incident, or that the risk is dealt with by joint insurance coverage.

the pre-delivery tests and pre-installation tests which will be carried out on any critical items of equipment, plus probably a general provision that all equipment will be subject to normal pre-delivery tests before being accepted for delivery to the Site. Clause 22 is a standard procedural clause, similar to the pre-delivery inspection clauses found in other sets of model conditions.

The Clause also allows the Project Manager to nominate inspectors who will exercise his functions under the Clause, if he wishes.

Principles

Clause 22.1 gives the Project Manager, and any inspector nominated by the Project Manager under Clause 22.7, access to the premises of the Contractor and also those of his Subcontractors. (The Contractor must take Clause 22 into account when preparing his Subcontracts.) The Clause gives the Project Manager the right both to observe tests and to inspect equipment in the course of manufacture and other work such as calibration. The Clause does not make any specific provision for the right to reject any equipment found to be defective by the Project Manager during any inspection, leaving the Project Manager and Contract Manager to settle the matter by discussion. It would, of course, be extremely unusual for the Contract Manager to refuse to take note of any reasonable objections raised by the Project Manager during any inspection. Indeed the Contractor could well be in breach of Clauses 2.4 and 3.2 (and 3.8) of the Conditions in doing so.

Clause 22.2 sets out the basic obligation of the Contractor to carry out tests.

Procedure

Clauses 22.3 and 22.5–6 set out the procedure for giving notification of readiness for test and the testing of equipment. The Clauses are reasonably self-explanatory. Note that the Clause does not deal with the costs of carrying out or witnessing any repeat tests. The Conditions assume that each party would bear its own costs.

Additional tests

A process contract will cover many different types and items of equipment, many of which may not have been identified at the time of Contract. It is impossible for the Contract to set out in detail what pre-delivery tests are to be carried out on every single item. Therefore Clause 22.4 allows the Project Manager to require any item of equipment to be given any pre-delivery tests that the Project Manager wishes, in addition to the tests specified in the Contract.

The Project Manager must notify the Contractor of any additional tests in adequate time to allow the Contractor to arrange for the tests. With respect to the equipment manufactured by the Contractor himself this could mean at almost any time up to delivery itself; if however a test would involve the use of scarce test-bed facilities, notice would in practice need to be given much earlier. With respect to equipment manufactured by a Subcontractor the problem is much more difficult because the Contractor would almost certainly be charged extra for *any* test not written into his purchase order. This would then lead to a claim by the Contractor for a Variation to the Contract. Therefore the Project Manager should, as far as possible, be prepared to indicate any tests that he might require at the time of procurement by the Contractor, so that the Contractor can make adequate provision when ordering.

As regards the cost of additional tests, Clause 22.4 provides that tests that are normal practice should not be charged for. Other tests may be charged for, as stated in the Clause. Of course the question will always arise of exactly what is 'normal practice', but few serious problems arise.

2.2.7 Site activities

Any engineer looking at the Conditions for the first time will wonder why they have so little to say about the construction of the Plant, especially compared, for example, to the ICE or RIBA model conditions. All that the Conditions do is to specify in outline the facilities that the Contractor is to provide and then to lay down general rules about the way that he is to organise the Site and his work-force. In fact the Site activities clauses occupy only two to three pages in the Conditions, compared with two pages on insurance/responsibility for Site damage, three pages on Variations, or over four pages on Site tests,

The reasons are simple:

- as the Contract is on a firm-price basis the Contractor must, to some extent at least, be left to run the project his way;
- the terms of the Contract relating to administrative detail and work quality and supervision can be safely left to the Schedules and Specification;
- as the Conditions are for use by professionals they concentrate upon the essentials—the testing procedures to demonstrate that the Plant will produce what the Contract requires it to produce—rather than the control of the construction process.

Since all the Clauses that deal with Site activities are concerned with setting out general rules, they are reasonably straightforward.

Availability and access
CLAUSE 23

In general terms this Clause speaks for itself.

Clause 23.1 deals with the date for access to the Site. It lists the possible options open to the parties for fixing the date in order of precedence. The Conditions do not make any specific provision for the consequences of delay by the Purchaser in making the Site available to the Contractor. Simple failure to provide access would of course be breach of the Purchaser's obligations, allowing the Contractor to claim costs, plus time. The Purchaser does have other options such as suspending the Contract under Clause 42, and/or allowing the Contractor to deal with delay under Clause 14.2(d), or, if justified, claiming force majeure.

Clause 23.2 then provides for the access route to the Site, stating that it is the responsibility of the Purchaser to provide an adequate access route to the Site boundary from a convenient point on a public road. Clauses 23.2 and 23.3

then make the Contractor responsible for the suitability of the route up to that convenient point. There are two problems with the suitability of any route—the weight of traffic or individual loads that it must carry, and its ability to take unusually wide, long and high loads. Should any Plant require the bringing to Site of 'extraordinary traffic' this would obviously need special consideration, and probably a Special Condition.

Clauses 23.4 and 23.7 are straightforward and need no comment.

Control and access
Clauses 23.5–6 are self-explanatory. The Contractor has possession of the Site under Clause 23.1 and therefore control of it. Under Clause 23.6 he can and must exclude from it any third party who does not have specific authorisation from the Purchaser and anyone who has no need to to be there, and under Clause 23.5 he can *and must* also refuse access to other contractors where their work would unreasonably impede his own. Of course this will often be of great importance to the Contractor. He has a large and complex construction/erection job to do, and the presence of others on the Site will almost inevitably impede his work at some time or another. Apart from that he must allow reasonable access to the Site to the Purchaser and other contractors. The consequences of Clauses 23.5–6 are that the Contractor will need to set up facilities for controlling access to the Site.

CLAUSE 24
Clauses 24.1, 24.2 and 24.4 need no comment.

One comment upon Clause 24.3 is necessary. It provides that the Contractor may not move anything on to the Site in advance of the Approved Programme without the consent of the Project Manager. This is because the Purchaser may need to prepare the Site or access route and arrange for permission for the Contractor's traffic to use the route from the owner of the land. The Purchaser will almost certainly use the Approved Programme as guidance as to when the Site and access route must be ready for the Contractor.

Construction
CLAUSE 3.3
The Clause is straightforward and needs no comment.

CLAUSES 26
This Clause is of major importance, but needs very little comment. The principles are straightforward and will be well known to all Contractors and Purchasers.

CLAUSES 26.1–4
These Clauses combine with Schedules 4 and 5 to set up a Site regime in line with best practice. It will be obvious from the wording of Clause 26.1 that the Clauses are drafted to comply with UK law—but there are no significant differences between UK law and law throughout the rest of the European Union, and probably very few between European law and law in the rest of the world. Therefore the Clauses would need modification in any Contract where the Plant

was to be constructed on a Site outside the UK, but they provide a good framework to begin from. In particular the references to UK legislation in Clause 26.1 would need amending. Note especially the requirements of Clauses 26.3 and 26.4(c).

CLAUSE 26.5

This Clause requires the Contractor to accept responsibility for pollution and hazardous material, and all consequential costs, arising from the Works, subject however to a number of limits, as follows:

- where pollution occurs as the inevitable result of the Works;
- where pollution occurs as the inevitable result of instructions by the Project Manager or Purchaser;
- where the pollution was already in existence at the Site but could not have been foreseen; or,
- where the sheer extent of the pollution was more than could reasonably have been foreseen.

The effect of the Clause is to underline the need for both parties to plan for the risks of pollution and hazardous materials that might arise during the Contract, and to carry appropriate insurance cover.

CLAUSE 27

This Clause deals with the subject of the resources needed to construct, erect and test the Plant, apart from the Site management team called for by Clause 12. The principle is very simply that the Contractor is to provide everything required to carry out the Work on the Site unless it is specifically stated in the Contract that a particular item is to be provided by the Purchaser. There is no mention of any right for the Contractor to use any power supplies or lifting gear or other facilities of the Purchaser on the Site.

Clause 27.1 is simply a clear statement of the general principle. The Contractor will provide all the materials at the Site as stated in the Contract together with all resources such as labour, construction equipment and services necessary to carry out the Works, other than those which the Purchaser is to provide.

Clauses 27.2 and 27.3 are a straightforward list of the main support services that the Contractor is expected to provide for the construction operation. In effect the Contractor is being asked by these Clauses to ensure that the Site can operate as a complete, safe, self-contained unit without needing any support from the Purchaser.

Clause 27.4 needs no comment.

Clause 27.5 requires the Contractor to be able to produce certification for his construction equipment, such as safety inspection certificates for cranes and slings, whenever requested.

Clause 27.6 requires the Contractor to make the necessary arrangements to ensure that no construction equipment will be removed from Site until no longer needed. In particular this may require special arrangements to be made with the suppliers of equipment under hire, so that the hiring agreements can be transferred from the Contractor to the Purchaser in case of the Contractor's receivership or liquidation.

Employment conditions

Clause 28 is really not so much a clause as an outline statement of a number of agreements in principle that may need to be covered at greater length in Special Conditions.

CLAUSE 28

Clause 28.1 requires the Contractor to provide, and to require his Subcontractors to provide, reasonable pay and conditions for personnel working on the Site. Clause 28.3 then adds to this by stating that where the Site on which the Contractor is working is covered by a general agreement on working conditions the Contractor will conform to that agreement. (On very large construction sites, or sites where a number of different contractors are working, general agreements are sometimes used to minimise disputes over problems such as differential pay rates, poaching of labour, job demarcation, etc. A general agreement will provide for common or co-ordinated recruitment of labour, generally similar pay structures for all contractors, co-ordinated safety procedures, common policies for personnel matters, etc.)

Then Clause 28.2 requires the Contractor to keep the Project Manager/ Purchaser advised of any potential or actual industrial relations problems on the Site.

Clause 28.4 allows the removal of *any person* from the Site (compare Clause 12.5) for unsafe conduct, incompetence or serious misconduct of any other kind, at the cost of the Contractor.

Clause 28.5 is self-explanatory.

Site clearance

CLAUSES 34.1–2

These Clauses are standard and need no comment.

2.2.8 Vesting

CLAUSE 25 and CLAUSES 34.3–5

In one sense it is illogical to deal with these Clauses at this point, because they are more concerned with the problem of the possible liquidation of the Contractor than the delivery of equipment to Site. They provide a standard 'vesting'/ 'devesting' procedure. Its purpose is, so far as possible, to try to minimise the disruption to the project in the event of the financial collapse of the Contractor.

Essentially a vesting procedure seeks to minimise the problems that might be caused by a seller's financial disaster. It can do no more than that. If a company goes into liquidation, control of all the assets of the company will pass to a liquidator who has a duty to convert the company's assets into money for distribution to creditors. He will therefore sell those assets, including any work in progress, to the highest bidder. The purpose of a vesting clause is to transfer ownership of equipment from a seller to a buyer, while it is still work in progress. If then the seller gets into financial difficulties and is put into liquidation (or receivership) the buyer would have the right to take possession of the equipment, as it is his property, and remove it from the seller's premises. Then any necessary work can be carried out by another manufacturer and the equipment put into use. Of course the liquidator would have the right to recover reasonable payment from the buyer for any work done by the seller, but would not have any other legal power to delay the project.

Clause 25.1 provides that where the Purchaser is due to make phased payments for equipment under the Contract, and does actually make such a payment, then the ownership of the equipment will transfer to the Purchaser. The Clause applies to all equipment, both manufactured by the Contractor and by Subcontractors, therefore this Clause needs to be taken into account in Sub-contracts by the Contractor. (By 'phased payments' we mean any advance, stage, or progress payments.) Clause 25.3 is self-explanatory.

If the Contract does not include for phased payment then ownership will transfer on delivery to the Site (not on installation/erection).

Clause 25.2 deals with marking/storage considerations. If a vesting clause is to work properly it must allow the Purchaser to be able to identify precisely which items have become his property, otherwise a liquidator would quite properly refuse to release them.

Clauses 34.3–4 then deal with the situation that arises when items are no longer needed for the project or need to be removed so that they can be replaced or reworked. They are reasonably self-explanatory. Finally Clause 34.5 deals with the question of surplus materials that are to be left on Site.

2.3 Completion and testing

The Clauses to be covered in this section are those listed under the heading 'Tests' in Figure 1 (see page 31).

2.3.1 General approach

The completion and testing phase is the most critical part of any process Contract both for the Contractor and the Purchaser.

For the Contractor it is the crunch, the culmination of everything that he has been trying to achieve, and it happens so late in the Contract that there is very little time to put things right if they go wrong.

For the Purchaser the position is much the same. If the Plant passes its tests then he has to accept it, even if it is not really what he wants, and if it fails then his project is potentially a disaster.

Consequently there is a change of emphasis as the test period approaches. In the design and manufacturing periods the question is always 'does the Plant (or Works or Materials) meet the Specification?' At the testing stage that question changes to 'will it pass the tests?' The tests become the definitive requirement of the Contract in place of the Specification.

The Conditions assume that the Contract will contain or result in an agreed test or tests which will be a fair examination of whether or not the Plant does comply with the Contract. It is critical to both Contractor and Purchaser to ensure that this is so. If the tests are too stringent or lax the result will be unfair to one or the other. The issue is of particular importance because of the scope of testing provided by the Conditions.

2.3.2 Defining the tests

Every Contract Specification has to deal with three separate aspects of the equipment or Plant that it describes. These are *physical* dimensions and characteristics, *quality* of finish or manufacture, and *performance*.

When a Specification deals with something very simple, such as a knife or fork, the Specification will be very simple. It concentrates on the physical nature and quality of the item being described. It will not mention performance at all. When the buyer wishes to check whether the item meets the Specification the test that he will carry out will be equally simple. He will merely inspect the item to check that it is made from the proper materials to the proper dimensions, the quality of finish, and that there are no obvious defects.

When a Specification deals with something slightly more complex, such as a bicycle, the Specification/tests will cover more ground. In addition to physical characteristics and quality, the Specification will now also deal with performance required, and the buyer's checks will include a running test to ensure that the wheels go round and the brakes work.

Go to something more complicated such as a machine tool, and the Specification will change again. It will concentrate less on detailed physical description, though it will still deal with the physical characteristics that are required. Instead it will deal more with reliability, quality and performance. Also the running test will now concentrate on the ability of the machine to produce the product. (If a performance test is a test to demonstrate whether anything performs in accordance with the requirements of the Contract, then a running test is a performance test for a machine.)

Once the Specification has to deal with a Plant, it will include only the minimal amount of physical description. It will put far more emphasis upon the general characteristics, quality and performance required. Also the running tests on the Plant will change. Because a Plant comprises a large number of separate items of equipment which must operate as a single integrated unit there will now need to be tests to show that each item of equipment works and then tests to show that integration has been achieved. This is difficult to do properly without putting the Plant into operation, and a series of tests now need to be carried out.

2.3.3 The tests in context

The testing Clauses are part of a series of design/approval/testing stages that accompany or are allowed for by the Conditions.

The very first stages take place pre-contract. There may be a formal pre-qualification stage. Negotiations for the Contract will certainly include discussions on the Contractor's ability to design and construct the Plant, together with the design of Plant that he will supply. The Purchaser will wish to be sure that the Contractor can do the job. He will check that the Contractor understands what it is that is required, and that he can and will construct a Plant that is at least approximately what the Purchaser wants it to be.

These negotiations will also need to settle a number of specific contractual questions. These are:

- the wording of the Specification;
- the description of the Works (Schedule 1);
- the description of the various items and services to be provided by the Purchaser in accordance with Clause 4 and Schedules 2 and 3, both to assist the Contractor in the design/construction of the Plant, and also during the test stages;
- detailed descriptions, so far as can be achieved at this early stage of the project, of the various inspection and testing procedures to be carried out before delivery and at each test stage, comprising:
  - pre-delivery tests under Clause 22.2 (Schedule 13);
  - construction completion tests (Schedule 14);
  - take-over procedures and take-over tests (Schedule 15);
  - performance tests (Schedule 16).

The next two stages are then those of Documentation approval and pre-delivery inspection under Clauses 21 and 22, when the Project Manager is given the opportunity to query the Contractor's detailed designs, and when the Materials are inspected and tested.

Then come three test stages following construction of the Plant—construction completion, take-over tests and performance tests. (The Conditions state that performance tests are optional, but this is an option that the Purchaser will almost always use unless his process is secret.) The purpose of these stages is to demonstrate progressively the fitness of the Plant to meet the requirements of the Contract.

The construction completion procedures demonstrate that the construction of the Plant has been completed and that it is in a good and safe condition for commissioning.

The take-over test demonstrates that the Plant is in operating condition and can be run on a production basis. As the Plant can now run the Purchaser is getting benefit from it, therefore the risk in the Plant will transfer from the Contractor to him and the Defects Liability Period will commence.

The performance test demonstrates that the Plant is capable of meeting the output/quality guarantees given by the Contractor in the Contract, once the Plant has been run up to full operating condition and any final adjustments or modifications have been made by the Contractor.

2.3.4 Test specifications

The tests become the definitive requirement in the Contract. It is always entirely a question for the parties to agree upon what the tests are to be, though of course in practice one party will tend to impose its own ideas upon the other. There is no such thing as a standard test. Therefore it is impossible to set out any precise rules for defining any test under the conditions.

Tests will also vary depending on precisely when they are carried out. This is a question to be decided by the Purchaser. Practice varies considerably. In some industries, such as the water treatment or food industry, it is normal practice for the Contractor to carry out the take-over test on a Plant that is effectively in full normal production. In other industries, such as the pharmaceutical industry, the Purchaser might not use the Plant until after the Contractor has withdrawn from the Site. Nevertheless there are a number of general suggestions that can be made.

2.3.5 Construction completion tests

The purpose of the Construction Completion Certificate procedure is to demonstrate that the Plant is complete and in good condition. It also needs to show that the Plant is in a *safe* condition, because no process material can be allowed into the Plant if there is danger of leakage or accident.

Therefore following the issue of any draft Construction Completion Certificate by the Contractor, the Project Manager should conduct a complete inspection of the relevant parts of the Plant to check, so far as he has not done so already, that:

- those parts have been completely constructed;
- nothing is in poor or damaged condition;
- the parts have been correctly constructed (for instance non-return valves operate in the correct direction);
- there is no internal obstruction or dirt left inside them;
- all work is of the correct quality.

Next the Project Manager will wish the Contractor to demonstrate that the various items of equipment are in working order, that valves open and close, etc. Finally the Contractor may be required to carry out appropriate tests to demonstrate mechanical integrity, perhaps pressure tests or leak tests using water or air rather than the process fluids, and perhaps tests to demonstrate that the control and safety systems and equipment are in operational order.

The specific requirements for this programme of inspections, demonstrations and tests should be included in Schedule 14.

2.3.6 Take-over tests

The take-over tests are important for both sides. The Purchaser will usually want to get the Plant into operation as soon as it is in working order, because delay in bringing the Plant on stream can have a serious effect on the economics of the project by delaying and then extending the pay-back period for the Plant. However he will not want to take over a Plant which is not capable of being put into production, and the Project Manager will not want to release the Contractor from his obligations until the Plant is in operating condition.

The Contractor will obviously want the Plant to be taken over as soon as he has put it into operating order. The Take-Over Certificate will almost certainly trigger a payment and also transfers responsibility for the Plant to the Purchaser, starts the guarantee period running, and gets the Contractor off a major Contract hook. However once the Plant has been taken over, the Contractor will lose control over it and will still be responsible if it fails the performance test. Therefore the Contractor will not want to carry out a take-over test until the Plant is generally fit for the performance test.

The take-over procedures in Schedule 15 will normally do two things. First the Contractor will be required to demonstrate that all the various parts of the Plant, electrical and mechanical equipment, control systems, etc are in proper order. Then the Contractor will be required to carry out a running test on the Plant, either using process materials or using a non-process material such as water, to demonstrate that the Plant is capable of normal operation.

2.3.7 Performance tests

The performance test is a test to prove that the Plant is capable of manufacturing the products for which it is designed under all normal operating conditions foreseen by the Contract.

That is the theory. In practice of course no Purchaser can expect this. The Plant is still at the teething stage, in need of fine tuning, and being run by operators who are not yet used to its little ways, and perhaps not yet fully experienced in the process or the equipment. Most companies would expect the production from any Plant to be measurably higher after a year or two of normal operation than at the time when the Plant is first put into production.

Also no test can really reproduce all normal operating conditions.

Therefore every performance test (and take-over test) has to be something of a compromise. It has to be for a comparatively short operating period, and probably the Plant will only make a limited selection of the possible product range, or operate under a part of the full range of operating conditions. But it has to be a test from which the parties can make deductions about the capability of the Plant to make the full range of products over its normal operating life.

Again there are a number of general principles:

- The test should not be unreasonably long. Obviously it needs to be long enough to enable proper measurement of performance and to give some indication of equipment and process reliability. However a test that goes on for too long proves very little and risks being interrupted by something that has nothing to do with the Plant at all, when the whole thing has to start all over again at the Purchaser's cost.
- The test must be selective. The Purchaser can never expect any test to cover the whole of the Plant's product range.
- There has to be a limit to the number of parameters that the parties seek to measure during the test.
- The test should be run using the Plant's own controls and instrumentation. It is seldom practicable to try to install supplementary instrumentation to measure additional parameters during the test.
- Finally the most important. Unless you can design a test that will measure something accurately there is no point in asking for it to be guaranteed.

2.3.8 Performance guarantees and liquidated damages

The main reason why any performance test must be selective is that the test is used to do two entirely distinct things. First it is used to determine whether the

Plant operates in accordance with the Contract. Secondly it is used to measure the degree of any shortfall in the performance of the Plant.

Should there be a major shortfall, the Plant will fail the test and must be modified or adjusted before being re-submitted.

Should there be only a minor shortfall in performance however the Plant may be accepted by the Purchaser, subject to the payment by the Contractor of liquidated ('agreed' in legal jargon) damages. Liquidated damages may be fixed for a number of different parameters, such as production quantity, degree of impurities, wastage of raw materials, usage of power or chemicals, etc. The problem for the Purchaser is that the more complex the test he uses, or the more parameters he tries to measure for liquidated damages, the more tempting it becomes for the Contractor to set the Plant up to minimise his exposure to damages rather than to make the product.

There is no standard way of setting up a liquidated damages structure, but again there are some general principles:

- unless a parameter can be measured accurately it should not carry liquidated damages;
- unless a parameter has *real* significance in process *and* economic terms it should not carry liquidated damages;
- always allow a measuring tolerance—no instrument outside a laboratory ever measures with complete accuracy;
- one, or perhaps two, parameters may be treated as mandatory, with no shortfall allowed (except for a measurement tolerance);
- one, two, or perhaps three at most, other parameters may then be subject to liquidated damages;

If it is the intention of the Purchaser to include provision for liquidated damages in the Contract then Schedules 16 and Schedule 17 should be completed. In other words, the performance test and liquidated damages should be defined in the Contract and not left to be agreed later.

The Conditions set out a practicable testing scheme. Clearly no two projects and no two Plants will ever be the same and therefore the Clauses will often be modified or supplemented by the parties.

The scheme is as follows. The Contractor issues a draft Construction Completion Certificate under Clause 32 when the Plant, or any part of the Plant, is fully erected. That work is then inspected. Once the Plant has been fully constructed, take-over procedures are carried out under Clause 33 including any take-over tests specified in the Contract. On successful completion of the take-over procedures, a Take-Over Certificate is issued by the Project Manager and the Plant then passes over to the Purchaser and the guarantee period commences. When the Purchaser (or perhaps in practice both parties) is ready, performance tests are then carried out during the early part of the guarantee period under Clause 35, and an Acceptance Certificate is issued once those performance tests have been properly completed.

2.3.9 The testing procedure

Construction
CLAUSE 32

This Clause requires few comments. Clauses 32.1–4 set out a procedure for the approval by the Project Manager of a series of Construction Completion Certificates as the work of constructing the Plant is carried out. Clause 32.5 deals with the certification procedure for tying back the completion of construction to the Contract dates set out in Schedule 11, if appropriate. Finally Clause 32.6 suggests that any dispute concerning certification should be decided by an Expert.

Clause 32.1 establishes that the Plant may be treated as a single construction exercise, or as a number of separate exercises. This allows for two possibilities that can often happen in practice, that the various sections of the Works might be carried out at different times, or that they might be treated as entirely separate exercises. For instance preliminary civil engineering work to prepare the Site might be carried out by a different workforce well before the erection of the Plant begins. The erection of a tank farm might be carried out over the same time-scale as the main Plant, but by a separate workforce.

Clause 32.2 then sets out a further basic principle, that approval of construction can, and probably will, be carried out on a piecemeal basis, rather than as a single all-embracing exercise.

The procedure is initiated by the Contractor who may issue a Construction Completion Certificate for all the Plant (or a section of the Plant if Clause 32.1 applies), or any 'appropriate part' of the Plant, when he considers that it is 'substantially' complete. An appropriate part of the Plant will be any area or part that can reasonably be inspected and tested as a unit. Something is 'substantially' complete when it is sufficiently complete to be capable of use for its intended purpose, though not necessarily absolutely complete.

In the Certificate the Contractor will define the part of the Plant being offered for inspection and tests and will set out his programme for the tests. The Project Manager is allowed a week's grace to make whatever preparations are necessary before the inspection/test period begins, unless he is prepared to respond more quickly.

Clause 32.4 then provides that if the part fails on inspection and test the Project Manager must identify the shortcomings that he has found so that the Contractor knows precisely what to correct before re-submitting the part.

Clause 32.3 then deals with the proper form to be used by the Project Manager when accepting that construction of any part of the Plant is complete and also reminds him of the whole purpose of the construction completion exercise. He is to endorse the Construction Completion Certificate with the statement that the part is complete and *safe for the taking-over work to commence*, and then return the Certificate to the Contractor. When returning the Certificate he may also attach a snagging list—a list of minor items, that do not affect the safety of the Plant or taking-over procedures, that need correction.

Certification of Completion of Construction

Under Clause 32.5, if completion of construction is of contractual significance—that is if it is referred to in Schedule 11 to the Contract—the Project Manager is required to issue a certificate when construction of the entire Plant or a section is complete.

Taking over
CLAUSE 33

Clause 33.1 allows for the Plant to be taken over in sections where stated in the Contract. Sectional taking-over is, to some extent at least, always an advantage to the Contractor, because it enables him to concentrate his resources on each part of the Plant in turn, rather than having to bring the entire project up to taking over simultaneously. It gives the Contractor the added benefit perhaps of obtaining some payments earlier than might otherwise be the case, and also getting part of the Plant through its Defects Liability Period earlier.

Of course sectional taking over also benefits the Purchaser, simply because the sooner he can put some part of the Plant into production the sooner he can obtain a return on his investment. This consideration is the key to the approach any Purchaser should take towards sectional taking over. Ideally, though in practice it may not always be the case, where a contract allows sectional taking over, each section should produce something that the Purchaser can *use*.

The basic procedure

The basic procedure for taking over is set out in Clauses 33.2–4, and 33.6–7.

Following the completion of construction, the Plant is prepared by the Contractor for taking over. When he is satisfied that the Plant is ready, he gives notice to the Project Manager under Clause 33.2 and the procedures specified in Schedule 15 are carried out, including any taking over tests (that is, running tests) specified.

If the Contract does not include a Schedule 15 then the Project Manager can still introduce take-over tests and procedures by using the Variation procedure. It is, however, questionable whether it is advisable to use this route.

When successful procedures (and tests) have been carried out a Take-Over Certificate is issued by the Project Manager under Clause 33.7. The Plant is now taken over by the Purchaser and the Defects Liability Period commences. From this point the Contractor is no longer responsible for the care, maintenance or operation of the Plant, but will be responsible for correcting any defects or damage under Clause 37.

Although the Clauses are logical and clear in what they say they need to be operated carefully by the parties.

Clause 33.4 sets out the basic principle that the Contractor meets the cost of providing everything necessary for the take-over tests except where the Purchaser has agreed to supply it. This raises the question of how the Contractor should price for carrying out tests. Essentially the more complex the test the greater the chance that the test will fail because of some fault in equipment that was not or could not be detected until the test was carried out, however careful the Contractor has been. The Contractor will probably wish to allow proportionately more in his price for carrying out the more complex take-over tests than for simple inspections.

Clause 33.2 simply permits the Contractor to give the Project Manager reasonable notice of when the Contractor intends to commence the take-over procedures, provided that the Contractor cannot do so until after the approval by the Project Manager under Clause 32.2 that construction has been completed. Clause 33.3 then entitles the Project Manager to observe the procedure, and obliges the Contractor to ensure that it is possible for him to do so. In the somewhat unlikely event that the Project Manager fails to attend the procedures Clause 33.6 allows the Contractor to proceed without him.

If the Plant passes the take-over procedures and tests then under Clause 33.7 the Project Manager must issue a Take-Over Certificate to the Contractor, although the Project Manager does not have to issue the Certificate until after the Contractor has dealt with the construction completion snagging list. The Project Manager cannot however withhold the Take-Over Certificate for minor defects that emerge during taking over. These are to be dealt with by another snagging list, which must then be dealt with promptly by the Contractor under Clause 33.8.

The Plant then passes from the Contractor to the Purchaser.

Failure of a test
Clause 33.5 provides the usual procedure to require the Contractor to repeat whatever take-over tests the Project Manager considers reasonable, if the Plant fails the tests.

Issue of a Take-Over Certificate in other circumstances
Clause 33 then provides, in Clauses 33.9 and 33.10, two possible ways in which the take-over tests may be postponed or shelved, one by agreement and the other by default.

Under Clause 33.9 the Project Manager may, with the Contractor's consent, issue a Take-Over Certificate without the Plant having completed the take-over procedures. The Certificate may be issued even if the Plant has actually failed procedures. This allows the Purchaser a route to bring the Plant into operation if he is in serious need of it, without waiting for taking over to run its course. The only condition is that this can only be done with the Contractor's consent, which cannot of course be unreasonably refused. The Contractor's consent is required because the Contractor must be satisfied that the Plant is in proper condition for future take-over procedures and tests, and probably also for performance tests, and that the Purchaser is able to run it *safely* before he allows it to be put into operation. The Contractor will then remain liable to carry out the remaining take-over procedures during the Defects Liability Period, if requested to do so, but any extra costs will be borne by the Purchaser (Clause 33.11).

Clause 33.10 provides the usual protection for a Contractor who is prevented from carrying out any take-over procedure, by allowing him to bypass that procedure and claim his Take-Over Certificate. However the Clause contains two safeguards for the Purchaser. First the Contractor is only permitted to bypass those procedures that he is actually prevented from carrying out, and where the Contractor is acting reasonably in claiming the Certificate. (It might be unreasonable to claim the Take-Over Certificate if the Purchaser had delayed the commencement of the test by one day—it might be very reasonable if the start of the test was delayed for several days or weeks.) Any other procedures must be completed. Secondly the Purchaser can require the Contractor to carry out the remaining procedures during the Defects Liability Period as under Clause 33.9. In other words delay by the Purchaser in providing facilities for the tests does not mean that the Contractor can avoid the need to carry out the tests altogether, only that they may be postponed.

The final safeguard is added by Clause 33.12, which permits the revocation of any Take-Over Certificate which has Acceptance Certificate status (see below) in the event that any deferred take-over test fails.

Finally Clause 33.11 deals with the question of the extra costs of any testing procedures which have been deferred under Clauses 33.9 and 33.10.

Performance tests

The performance test/Acceptance Certificate stage is covered by Clauses 35 and 36. Clause 35 deals with the tests themselves and Clause 36 deals with the issue of the Acceptance Certificate, confirming that the Plant is accepted by the Purchaser as complying with the requirements of the Contract.

CLAUSE 35

Under Clause 35.1 performance tests are, in theory anyway, optional. The Clause only applies if the Contract calls for performance tests. In practice the performance test is one of the main benefits of these Conditions for the Purchaser.

Clause 35.2 allows performance tests to be specified in Schedule 16, or to be agreed during the Contract. In theory both methods offer equal advantage to both sides. (Before Contract the Purchaser has more negotiating power to demand whatever tests he thinks appropriate. After Contract he learns more about the Plant and the process, so that he can negotiate with greater knowledge.) In practice most Purchasers prefer to include details of the performance tests in Schedule 16.

Procedure

The basic procedure is set out in Clauses 35.3–6 and Clause 35.8–9. The procedure is intended to ensure that the performance tests are carried out as quickly as possible after the Plant has been taken over, so that the Plant can then be put into normal operation.

Under Clause 33.7 the Purchaser is required, when the Plant is taken over to *start up* the Plant and *prepare* it for performance tests, and then *carry out* the performance tests. (Clause 35.9 follows on from this by requiring the Purchaser not to cause unreasonable delay to performance tests.) Clause 35.4 then requires the Purchaser to carry out the performance tests as soon as practicable after the Plant or section has been taken over. (Possible sectional performance tests are covered by Clause 35.2, and the same considerations apply as for sectional take-over tests.)

In practice the Purchaser will obviously exercise some control over the timing of the performance tests. This is important because the Purchaser has to provide all the resources necessary for the test. The actual procedure for initiating a test is that the Purchaser must give notice under Clause 35.5, which must then be acknowledged and accepted by the Contractor.

Strictly speaking the Contractor will not be entitled to make any further adjustments to the Plant between take-over and the commencement of the performance test. In practice his Site personnel will almost inevitably advise either the Project Manager or the Purchaser of anything that they consider needs doing before the performance tests begin.

The reasoning behind these Clauses is straightforward. The Contractor has demonstrated that he has constructed the Plant and put it through its preliminary tests (construction completion and take-over). It is now the responsibility of the Purchaser to complete the testing sequence and to do so with reasonable speed so that an Acceptance Certificate may be issued and the Contractor may be paid whatever sum is due to him.

The test will then be run in accordance with Clause 35.4. Note the words in the last sentence of Clause 35.4 that the test will be run 'as far as practicable' in accordance with the Contract. This is reality—no Plant is ever run precisely in accordance with the Contract or Specification.

During the test the performance of the Plant will be monitored and recorded by both sides acting together. Then, once the test is complete, the results will be jointly evaluated by both sides. The reasons for joint evaluation are so that:

- The parties can reach an agreed interpretation of what the results of the test actually show. In some processes the simple output figures will not tell the whole story.
- The parties can agree measurement tolerances and allowances.
- The parties can agree any necessary adjustments to the test results. No test ever runs totally smoothly, and minor hitches in operation seldom justify the trouble, time and expense of repeating the whole test.

Problems

Clause 35.6 deals with the question of whether or not a test that is failing to achieve its required parameters may be terminated. Of course it may be terminated if the Contractor and Project Manager agree that it should. Unless they agree then the test may not be terminated unless there is risk of damage or injury, or it is unacceptable to either party (for good reason) to allow it to continue. The reason for this is that the results of even a complete failure are of importance, because they enable the Contractor to analyse what is wrong and to plan corrective action.

Clause 35.9 allows the Contractor only a limited period after taking over within which to achieve a successful performance test. Obviously there is a conflict here. The Purchaser has overall control of the tests, since he has to provide resources and trained operators, and give notice of any test. However if a test fails and has to be repeated, especially if it needs to be repeated more than once, it will be the Contractor who will be eager to move as quickly as possible.

The answer to this conflict lies in Clause 35.4, that tests must always be carried out as quickly as possible.

The problem is also covered by Clauses 35.10–11. Clause 35.10 allows the Project Manager to defer the work of carrying out modifications to the Plant if the Purchaser is not willing to take the Plant out of production during the test period allowed by the Contract. Any extra costs caused to the Contractor by the deferment will then be met by the Purchaser under Clause 35.11. Any deferment beyond the end of the Defects Liability Period brings the Contractor's obligations to an end.

Where the results of any test falls short of the requirements of the Contract, but are within the limits of the performance liquidated damages specified in Schedule 17, the Contractor has a choice (Clause 35.9). He can either pay the appropriate liquidated damages, or seek to modify or adjust the Plant to improve performance and then repeat the test, provided that this can be done within the Contract period. If he decides to pay liquidated damages then under Clause 35.9 the Plant has to be accepted by the Project Manager and an Acceptance Certificate issued.

If the results of the tests are outside the limits of Schedule 17, or the Contractor chooses to carry out further work on the Plant, then Clause 35.7 will apply. The Contractor has to decide what further work to carry out and must, if the Project Manager requests, inform the Project Manager of what he intends to do and get his approval before doing it. The Contractor must then be allowed reasonable opportunity to carry out the adjustments or modifications before the Plant is put back into operation and the test repeated. In the meantime the Purchaser is entitled to operate the Plant.

If the Plant fails the performance tests then Clause 35.9 allows the Purchaser to reject the Plant, or to accept it on whatever terms are agreed between the parties or fixed by an Expert.

Clauses 35.12–15 then deal with the question of what happens if the Purchaser, or events outside the Contractor's control, prevent the Contractor from successfully completing a performance test within the Contract period. Essentially if that happens the Project Manager must issue an Acceptance Certificate, so that the Contractor can be paid, but the Contractor will remain liable to carry out the tests when possible during the Defects Liability Period. The extra costs to the Contractor of delayed tests will be met by the Purchaser. The Project Manager can require the Contractor to provide security for any payments or liquidated damages that might be involved before issuing the Acceptance Certificate so that, if the Plant fails when the test is finally carried out, the Purchaser can recover the payment from the Contractor.

2.3.10 Acceptance Certificate

CLAUSE 36

The Acceptance Certificate is the last stage of the approval/testing process. In one sense it is purely a formality because it follows and is governed directly by the performance test. But it is a very important formality because it will virtually always be a payment document. It also acts as conclusive evidence that the

Plant is accepted by the Purchaser as complying with the requirements of the Contract.

If there are no performance tests required by the Contract then the Take-Over Certificate will double as the Acceptance Certificate.

The Acceptance Certificate must be issued by the Project Manager as soon as the Contractor has complied with the terms of Clause 35. Like all other Certificates up to this point it may contain a snagging list to be corrected by the Contractor in the usual way.

2.4 Variations, changes and claims

The Clauses to be covered in this section are those listed under the heading 'Claims & Variations' in Figure 1 (see page 31).

2.4.1 General approach

These Clauses cover two areas, first the procedure for dealing with Variations to the Contract and secondly the procedure for dealing with claims under the Contract. Remember that the Conditions use the Variation Order procedure to do two different things. It is used to order a change to the Works by the Project Manager. It is also used to record and formalise *other changes* to the Contract, see for example Clause 14.1.

Change is the most likely area for project management problems. At least one in three project managers will say that change management is the most difficult problem they face.

This is unavoidable. Change is a function of the complexity (not size) and duration of the project. A simple contract, however large, that takes merely a few days or weeks to carry out is unlikely to be subject to any changes. A complex contract that takes a few years to carry out is likely to be subject to a whole range of different types of change. Some changes may be outside the parties' control, such as a change in legislation, or the loss of a particular feedstock for the Plant. Others will be partly or wholly within control, such as a change to product range to meet market requirements, or a modification to the Plant to improve its performance.

Change is a problem because:

- The relationship between Project Manager and Contractor alters when a change is ordered. When a fixed-price Contract is placed, the Contractor has to compete. When a Variation is ordered he is a monopoly supplier. The result is that the Project Manager suffers loss of control of the situation.
- A Variation is never cost-effective. When a Contractor takes on a fixed-price Contract he will plan the Contract in the most efficient way that he can. This reduces cost and therefore maximises his profit. The Variation always disrupts the Contractor's plan and causes an increase to the overall cost, over and above the cost of the Variation itself. In addition the cost of work carried out as a Variation will always be higher than that of the same work included in the original Contract, as it will be done or bought in piecemeal rather than wholesale or on the basis of urgency rather than planning.

- A Variation is always hard to price accurately.
- The Project Manager will always have difficulty in assessing the Contractor's charges for the extra work. Even where work is being carried out on Site and can be monitored by the Project Manager, accurate assessment can be difficult. When much of the work has to be carried out off-Site (process design, equipment modification or manufacture, etc.), adequate monitoring is almost impossible.
- Changes in a fixed-price Contract always create potential conflict. If the Contractor has to carry out additional work this will increase his costs of carrying out the Contract and extend the time he needs to complete his work. If the Contractor does not obtain an increase in price his profit will suffer. If he does not obtain an extension to the Contract period he risks being penalised for being late, and again his profit would suffer. Therefore commercial pressure forces the Contractor to *demand* additional time and money. The Project Manager on the other hand must defend the interests of the Purchaser against excessive changes in cost or project time-scale however much he knows that the Purchaser must meet the costs of the disruption he has caused to the Contractor.
- The process plant is always especially vulnerable to change. Because a process plant is designed to operate as an integrated unit changes to any part can affect other parts of the plant as well.

The Conditions assume that some change is virtually inevitable. They give the Project Manager a range of options to use in initiating Variations and controlling the pricing of those Variations. They also assume that the Project Manager is sufficiently process-skilled to be able to manage the Contractor and negotiate Contract amendments. In case problems arise which cannot be solved quickly by the parties they allow for the use of an Expert as the preferred option to resolve the matter.

For ease of reference the Clauses covered in this section can be divided into the following groups:

- changes in legislation (Clauses 7.3–4);
- Site problems (Clause 6.3);
- Variations:
  - definition and limits to the Project Manager's powers (Clauses 16.1 and 16.7);
  - initiation by the Project Manager (Clauses 16.1–3, 16.5–6, 33.13 and 37.3–4);
  - feasibility studies (Clause 16.4);
  - Contractor's proposals (Clauses 3.5 and 17);
  - valuation (Clauses 19.1–4);
  - claims and disputes (Clauses 4.3, 16.8–9, 18 and 19.5);
- claims for extensions of time.

2.4.2 Changes in legislation

CLAUSES 7.3–4

Clause 7.3 allows the Contractor to claim what is in effect a Variation (although Clauses 16–19 will only apply to a limited extent) to cover any increases in cost as a result of legislation which is passed or comes into force after the Contractor has committed himself to his fixed price.

The date on which the Contractor will commit himself to that price will be the date stated in the Agreement as the date of the Contractor's 'tender' for the Contract. Obviously this may cause practical problems. Legislation may be on the stocks at the date of Contract, but not yet actually enacted or in force. The Contractor may submit more than one tender, or the Contract as signed may be for a Plant which is different to that which the Contractor tendered. If negotiations for the Contract are protracted, the Contractor may be asked to extend the validity of his tender—often for a considerable period.

There may also be some doubt as to what actually would constitute a 'tender'. A tender (as opposed to an 'offer') certainly implies a written document. It does not however necessarily mean a comprehensive offer document. A simple letter confirming that the Contractor stands by a price for the project/Contract on agreed terms could be sufficient. In general terms the date of the Contractor's tender would normally be the date of the latest comprehensive written tender/confirmation/revalidation.

The Clause then states that if, after the date of the tender, any new primary or secondary or delegated legislation is enacted or comes into force, with which the Contractor has to comply and which changes the cost of carrying out the Contract, the Contractor will be entitled to his extra costs, *but not profit.* (If the result is to *reduce* cost then the Contract Price would be similarly reduced.) The amount of the addition or reduction would be decided under the terms of Clause 19.

Note by the way that the Clause is not limited to legislation in one particular country. Therefore the Clause could apply if legislation in Japan, which made the export of a key item of equipment more costly, affected a UK contract.

Two further comments upon the Clause:

- Clause 7.3 does not lay down any particular procedure for deciding the actual amount payable to the Contractor. Therefore the correct procedure would simply be for the Contractor to give notice and submit a claim in writing to the Project Manager in accordance with Clause 18, and for an appropriate adjustment then to be agreed between the parties or decided by arbitration. *By agreement* the problem could instead go to the Expert.
- As well as additional cost the Contractor would also be entitled to claim an extension of time under Clause 14.2(a), if appropriate.

The effect of Clause 7.4 is to exclude all tax and related charges from Clause 7.3. They remain with the Contractor. If therefore the Contract was likely to be affected by any exceptional tax it would need to be dealt with by a Special Condition.

2.4.3 Site problems

Unforeseen ground conditions will always be a problem in Contracts involving site construction work. The higher the ratio of civil/building work to structural/process/electrical/mechanical work, the worse the potential problem. Within the chemical or oil industries the problem is small because the ratio is often low. In other process industries the position may well be different.

CLAUSE 6.3
The Contractor needs to conduct certain Site investigations in order to prepare his price. The extent of those investigations is limited. He is expected to take account of:

- the information actually in his possession concerning the Site, including all information provided by the Purchaser—see comments on Clause 6.2 on page 36;
- information available from a visual inspection of the Site;
- information resulting from reasonable enquiries prompted by that visual inspection;
- information in the public domain, such as geological maps of the area.

The phrase 'visual inspection of the Site' means precisely what it says. All that the Contractor is required to do is to look at what is visible on the Site at and above ground level and then draw reasonable conclusions and ask whatever reasonable questions are prompted by that inspection. He is not expected to conduct pre-contract surveys of the Site.

If then at any time during the Works, usually but not necessarily during the Site construction period, the Contractor comes up against unforeseeable problems on the Site, other than weather (though of course truly exceptional weather or the *result* of weather, such as flooding, could qualify) which cause extra cost then the Contractor will be entitled to claim his additional costs, plus a reasonable profit. Of course unforeseeable conditions would usually be ground-related, though the Clause will also cover other Site problems, such as a pollution problem caused by other premises in the vicinity.

The Clause lays down a precise procedure that the Contractor must follow in making his claim, and also lays down a strict time limit for any claim. Provided that the claim is made in accordance with the Clause, the Contractor is entitled to his extra costs, etc. The remedial work would usually be carried out on an open-book basis under Clause 19.5.

2.4.4 Variations

Definition of a Variation and the limits to the Project Manager's powers
CLAUSE 16.1
The first principle laid down by Clause 16.1 is that only the Project Manager, or a Project Manager's Representative specifically authorised by the Project Manager under Clause 11.5, can initiate a Variation.

Secondly Clause 16.1 defines a Variation. Clarifications will not constitute a Variation, nor will an instruction to carry out work already covered by the Contract. However any change, even minor, to the Specification or work to be carried out by the Contractor will constitute a Variation. Also any changes to methods of working, which are not simply to rectify unsafe methods being used or proposed by the Contractor, will be Variations.

Therefore *any* order or instruction by the Project Manager to the Contractor to make any material change, whether an amendment, increase or omission, will constitute a Variation Order. In particular any instruction that is in conflict with the Contract, and especially in conflict with Schedule 1 or the Specification must be deemed to be a material change and therefore to be a Variation. (Clause 33.13 makes the same point with regard to Variation work following taking over.)

Under Clause 5.1 a Variation can only be ordered in writing. Therefore Clause 16.1 allows the Contractor to insist that the Project Manager issues formal written Variation Orders to cover any material changes instructed by him.

CLAUSE 16.7

This Clause deals with the limits to the Project Manager's power to order Variations by allowing the Contractor to object to Variations in certain circumstances. It is unacceptable for the Project Manager to have the right to use Variations to change a Contract by more than is reasonable, since this could place excessive strain on the Contractor's organisation and his ability to plan the Contract properly. Therefore Clause 16.7 allows the Contractor to object to any Variation once the cumulative effect of Variations is to increase or reduce the Contract Price by more than 25% (or 5% post-take-over). In effect once this percentage change in Contract Price is reached the Contractor is able to pick and choose which Variations he wishes to carry out. (Of course if the Contractor is happy to carry out Variations above the 25% limit then there is nothing to prevent him doing so.)

In addition Clause 16.7 allows the Contractor to refuse to comply with any Variation when it would have the effect of requiring the Contractor to infringe the terms of any agreement with a third party, such as its process licence, or any third-party patent or other intellectual property right.

Finally Clause 16.7 allows the Contractor to refuse to comply with any Variation which would have the effect of pushing the Contractor into areas where he lacks the appropriate technology or expertise, unless the Project Manager agrees that a suitable nominated Subcontractor may be brought in (when Clause 10.7 would protect the Contractor against claims).

The Clause then sets out the proper procedure for objections to Variations by the Contractor. Essentially the Clause requires the Contractor to set out his objections in writing by at the latest two weeks after any order and even before the order if possible.

Initiation of Variations by the Project Manager

Normally the Purchaser would consult the Contractor in advance about the way in which the Contract may need to be amended to take account of a Variation (Clause 16.5).

The principles followed by the Conditions are then straightforward. They are that Variations to a complex process plant may well be complex in themselves. Therefore the Purchaser may need assistance from the Contractor in deciding whether a particular Variation is feasible (Clause 16.4 below). The Contractor may notify the Project Manager of any problems likely to be caused by a Variation (Clause 16.6).

Even more important, perhaps, is the principle set out in Clause 16.2 that the Project Manager must decide clearly what changes to the Plant he wants before the Contractor can be expected to begin work.

CLAUSE 37.3
This Clause deals with a further power of the Project Manager, to require the Contractor to repair defects in equipment supplied by the Purchaser or damage caused by the Purchaser in the Plant or equipment as a part of the defects repair service by the Contractor, but paid for as a Variation. It covers defects that arise both during the construction period and the guarantee period.

Feasibility studies
Any process plant is best known to its designer, and the designer of the Plant is the Contractor. Therefore the Conditions give the Project Manager the right to call upon the Contractor's expertise to investigate potential Variations. The Purchaser, however, must pay a reasonable price for the service.

CLAUSE 16.4
If required by the Project Manager the Contractor will draft or collaborate with the Project Manager in drafting the technical content for a possible Variation Order. The Contractor will also provide a statement on the Contract implications in line with Clause 16.5. In return, the Contractor is entitled to be paid his costs of carrying out the study plus a reasonable profit.

Contractor's proposals for Variations
CLAUSES 3.5
Clause 3.5 is very much a 'teamwork' clause. It requires the Contractor to make the Project Manager aware of any possible improvements/modifications to the Plant, Works or methods of operation which would either eliminate defects or hazards, or which could benefit the Purchaser. If appropriate the Contractor will then take action under Clause 17.

CLAUSES 17.1–2
Clause 17.1 then recognises a situation that may often arise in a process context—that the Contractor may find himself in a position to recommend an improvement in equipment or process to the Purchaser. (Of course this Clause partly overlaps Clause 3.5.) If this should be the case the Contractor must put forward a proposal for the improvement to the Project Manager. The choice of whether the improvement is to be incorporated in the Plant is then for the Purchaser/Project Manager to make within the time-scale(s) provided in the Clause. In addition the Clause would also be used by the Contractor to put forward a proposal for any Variation to correct any error in the Plant which was the responsibility of the Contractor.

Clause 17.2 would then permit the Contractor to insist upon the right to carry out a Variation which he has proposed under Clause 17.1 where there were safety or operating implications, and if necessary to appeal the point to an Expert. The Variation would be free of charge to the Purchaser if the hazard or defect covered by the Variation were the responsibility of the Contractor, but otherwise, under Clause 17.3, would be at the Purchaser's expense in the normal way.

CLAUSE 17.3

This Clause then deals with another problem, where the Contractor has detected an error in the Contract. (This could of course be due either to an error by the Purchaser or the Contractor, but would be more likely to be used by the Contractor in the case of an error by the Purchaser.) It is straightforward and needs no comment.

Valuation of Variations

Many Variations will in practice be carried out on the basis of a fixed price agreed in advance between the parties. In a large and complex project this may not always be possible. Therefore the Conditions provide alternative options for use by the Project Manager, and also lay down basic rules designed to ensure fair play between the parties. Either side can insist upon a price change in the event of a Variation. The price change must allow the Contractor a profit (unless the Contractor has requested a change because of his own errors), but the Contractor must open his books to the Project Manager.

The Project Manager may agree a price for the Variation in advance, at any time during the work or after work has been completed.

CLAUSE 19.1

Where the cost of the Contract to the Contractor is changed by a Variation either party can require an adjustment to the Contract Price. Any such adjustment must be a *reasonable amount,* which includes a *Profit* for the Contractor whenever it is reasonable to do so (see Clause 11 of the Agreement). (Of course where a price is agreed between the two parties it would be automatically assumed that such is the case.)

CLAUSES 19.2–4

Clause 19.3 requires the Contractor, if requested to do so by the Project Manager, to provide an estimate of the cost to the Purchaser of carrying out the Variation, at the latest within four weeks after the date of the Variation Order. The estimate would be based upon Schedule 18 or any other reasonable basis, but would not necessarily be a full quotation for the work.

Clauses 19.2 and 19.4 then allow the Project Manager to agree the adjustment to the Contract Price with the Contractor at any time before, during or after the completion of the Works, which gives the Project Manager the maximum flexibility in handling changes. Once an adjustment has been agreed there can be no further argument.

See also Clause 39.3 (page 97 below).

2.4.5 Claims and disputes

Disputes over the effects of any claim or Variation upon the Contract, price, delay, Specification etc., will always be a severe problem in large contracts. What often happens is that the parties leave resolution of the problem until the end of the Contract, often because the project management teams on either side are just too busy to handle the extra work involved while the Contract is still live. This causes difficulties for both sides. Claim/Variation problems are best settled at the time they occur. This is what the Conditions aim to do.

Giving notice
CLAUSES 16.6 and 18.1/3

All Variation Orders should, and usually do, deal directly with the cost/price of the Variation, either stating the agreed price for the extra work, or stating how it is to be priced. If there is no agreed price the Variation Order should also state any particular additional cost records to be kept by the Contractor (Clause 18.1). The entitlement to a modification to the Contract Price is automatic however, and the Contractor does not need to give any formal notice of his right/claim to extra payment. (A 'claim' is simply an assertion of a contractual right.)

However the Contractor does need to give notice in accordance with Clause 16.6, as already mentioned above, if any Variation Order would give him a problem in complying with the terms of the Contract.

When dealing with a claim, however, for example in respect of unexpected conditions on the Site or a breach by the Purchaser of his obligations under Clause 4.2, the Contractor does have to give notice under Clause 18.1. Notice must be given as soon as possible and in any event within a week of the cause of the claim becoming known to him. *If the Contractor does not give this notice, and then complies with Clause 18 the Contractor loses any right to claim additional payment in respect of that event.*

Keeping records
CLAUSES 4.3, 16.9 and 18.1

Clause 16.9 provides an 'open-book' approach to pricing Variations, a device that is often used in the pricing of complex additional work. The Clause requires the Contractor to preserve his records of the cost of carrying out all work on any Variation for which no price has yet been agreed and to allow the Project Manager to inspect those records (as an aid to fair price negotiations). In addition the Project Manager may also require the Contractor to keep special records if he thinks it necessary.

Then Clause 18.1 lays down the same principle for all other claims. Contemporary records must be kept/preserved of the work done and costs incurred, in accordance if necessary with any instructions of the Project Manager and open to his inspection.

Clearly both these Clauses require the Contractor to be careful to keep accurate cost records for all work in respect of Variations and in respect of other claims, or he may run the risk of not receiving adequate payment for the extra work.

Then Clause 4.3 imposes the selfsame obligations upon the Purchaser. If he intends to make any counter-claims against the Contractor he must maintain accurate cost records also—or the counter-claim will fail.

Content of claim
CLAUSES 18.2 and 19.5

The Conditions do not include any specific requirement for the submission of a formal claim made by the Contractor in respect of the cost of a Variation.

Clause 16.9 simply provides that the Contractor must keep records, open to the Project Manager, and then leaves it to the parties to settle the problem in due course. Clause 19.5 then says that any claim actually made in respect of a Variation must be supported by notice in writing of the grounds for the claim and the facts upon which it is based.

In respect of claims however the Form has rather more to say. Clause 18.2 states that the Contractor must submit a formal claim together with any other details required, and in accordance with Clause 19.5, as soon as possible. The object is to give the Project Manager the information he needs to deal with the claim as early as possible. A late claim would be an invalid claim.

Clearly under Clause 19.5 the Contractor would be required to submit his cost records etc in support of the claim. If the Contractor has not kept cost records he cannot submit a proper claim.

(Note that Clauses 39.11–12 allow the Purchaser and Project Manager to audit the Contractor's cost records and make consequent adjustments to payments under the Contract if any errors/discrepancies are found, see section 2.7.)

Settlement of claims and Variations
CLAUSES 16.8, 18.2 and 19.6

Clause 16.8 provides simply that either side can call for the appointment of an Expert under Clause 47 to decide any dispute about the pricing of a Variation or the consequent changes to the Contract, Specification, guarantees, dates or programme. This type of dispute is usually about fact rather than law and an Expert can probably decide the question in weeks, rather than years, which avoids or reduces the risk of acrimonious arguments over disputed claims at termination of the Contract.

There is a slightly different procedure laid down in respect of claims. Under Clause 18.2 the Project Manager must consider the claim and give a formal response to it. Then Clause 19.6 makes the same provision as Clause 16.8.

Claims for extensions of time
In this section we have only mentioned in passing the question of the Contractor's rights to claim an extension to the Contract dates or period. Claims for an extension of time for a Variation will be discussed in more detail in section 2.5.

At this point it is only necessary to point out that the Contractor must always remember that if he wishes to claim an extension of time for any Variation, and in most cases this will be the case, then he must notify the Project Manager of his claim in accordance with Clause 14.2 *as soon as reasonably possible.*

2.5 Delays and lateness

2.5.1 Lateness law
See section 1.5.

2.5.2 The Conditions

The Clauses to be covered in this section are those listed under the heading 'Delay' in Figure 1 (see page 31).

For ease of reference the Clauses can be divided into the following groups:

- suspension (Clause 41);
- extensions of time (Clause 14);
- liquidated damages (Clause 15 (& Schedule 12)).

2.5.3 Suspension

In one sense Clause 41 is closely allied to the Variation procedures discussed in section 2.4. There is always the risk in a Contract with a long time-scale that some unexpected but serious (either actually serious or potentially serious) problem will be found. Perhaps the Contractor may be found to have committed a serious error that has put the success of the Contract into question. Perhaps a change in market conditions means that the Purchaser needs time to consider whether the Plant should be modified to manufacture a different product. Perhaps a serious problem has arisen on Site. Perhaps the Plant may need modification to handle different raw materials. When that happens it may sometimes be advantageous to the Purchaser to, so to speak, stop the clock for a short time while he considers how best to tackle the problem. The suspension clause allows him to do just that.

Of course one can never stop the clock, or more accurately one can stop the clock only to some extent, in the sense of asking the Contractor to suspend work, but one cannot stop the Contractor's costs increasing. Therefore the Clause should only be used when *really* necessary, because there will always be a cost to the Purchaser, unless the suspension is because of a serious error by the Contractor.

From the Contractor's point of view also the Clause is a difficult one. His problem is different. He must keep his Contract team and his Subcontractors idle but ready to recommence work if and when requested to do so, and probably in a situation of considerable uncertainty. He may be able to employ *some* resources on other contracts, but will not be able to transfer major resources to other contracts in case they need to be transferred back again.

Neither party can therefore allow a suspension of the Contract to last indefinitely.

CLAUSE 41

Clause 41.1 needs no comment. It is a simple enabling clause allowing the Project Manager to suspend the Works, subject to any safety implications.

Clause 41.2 deals with the consequences of a Suspension Order. Where the Suspension Order is due to breach/error by the Contractor, the Contractor must bear the consequences. Otherwise the Contractor is entitled to extra time, which should be claimed in writing as soon as practicable in accordance with Clause 14.1, and also to his extra costs resulting from the suspension. He is given up to fourteen days to give notice that he intends to claim cost.

Clause 42.3 then allows the Contractor to require the Project Manager to decide whether or not the Contract is to be resumed if suspension continues for three months, so avoiding indefinite suspension, and Clause 41.4 deals with the programme implications of a suspension/resumption.

Disputes on cost and time should go to the Expert.

2.5.4 Extension of time

There are two groups of reasons which allow an extension of the Contract dates or periods. There is 'force majeure', which permits both the Contractor and the Purchaser to claim an extension of time if they are delayed by causes beyond their reasonable control. Then there are other delays that entitle the Contractor to a reasonable extension of time.

CLAUSE 14.2

The term 'force majeure' is regularly used commercially as meaning events generally beyond a party's control. The Conditions define the term as events which are beyond a party's control and which affect that party's ability to perform the Contract to time. The Clause then lists a number of circumstances that are within the definition and some others that are not.

There will always be some difficulty in defining, in the abstract, all the possible circumstances that could be considered to come within this definition of force majeure. In purely contractual terms the problem is one of exactly how the Clause should be interpreted. Would it, for instance, include terrorist activity—near the Site or near a route to the Site—which was making people reluctant to stay on the Site?

The answer is, of course, that nobody does know what the abstract answer is, but that the abstract answer is unimportant. Like all 'force majeure' clauses Clause 14.2 is not intended to define the parties' rights with legal precision. All it does is to lay down the basic principle, which is that if some fairly serious event or chain of events causes delay to either party then that party should have a defence against claims by the other party arising out of the delay. It is up to the parties to the Contract, or an arbitrator, to reach a common-sense and fair decision between them about any actual circumstances that may arise.

CLAUSES 14.1 and 14.3–6

Clause 14.1 sets out the procedure for claiming an extension of time and also deals with the rights of the Contractor to claim an extension to the Contract in a range of situations, including force majeure, but mainly situations which arise out of the natural interplay between the parties in a complex long-term Contract.

The Clause lists the different circumstances that allow an extension of time:

- Clause 14.2(a)—Clause 6.3 deals with the consequences of problems on the Site. The Contractor is also entitled to claim his costs plus profit under Clause 6.3.
- Clause 14.2(b)—the parties would need to use Clause 16 to amend the Contract and Clauses 16 and 19 to amend the Contract Price.

- Clause 14.2(c)—Clause 41.2 would also allow the Contractor his costs of Suspension.
- Clause 14.2(d)—breach of the Contract by the Purchaser covers a range of Clauses, such as a failure to do work or provide information (Clause 4), or lateness in providing access to the Site (Clause 23). See also Clause 14.4.
- Clause 14.2(e)—see Clause 10.7. The Contractor would also receive an indemnity against extra costs, but must be able to demonstrate proper management by him of the nominated Subcontractor.

The procedure is that the party (Contractor or Purchaser as the case may be) claiming extra time should give notice of the delay to the Project Manager under Clause 14.1 'forthwith' (as soon as is practicably possible) after delay has actually occurred. The Contractor should then follow this with a further notice of the extension of time caused and therefore claimed. The Project Manager must then investigate the impact of the delay upon the Contract, and grant a reasonable extension by means of a Variation Order. (In other words the extension granted by the Project Manager may be for a shorter or longer period than the actual duration of the situation causing the claim.)

Clauses 14.3–5 are reasonably self-explanatory and need no comment.

Finally Clause 14.6 allows either party to bring the Contract to an end if force majeure circumstances, claimed or not, cause the Works to be completely or substantially stopped for a *continuous* four-month period. In that case the Purchaser would be required to pay the Contractor his costs/profit up to termination. (Note that there is a difference between Clause 14.6 and Clause 41.3. Under Clause 14.6 *either* party can terminate after 120 days stoppage. Under Clause 41.3, after 90 days stoppage, the Contractor can ask the Project Manager to make a decision in a further 28 days whether to terminate or recommence work.)

2.5.5 Liquidated damages

Clause 15 then deals with the question of delay by the Contractor in carrying out the Contract. In commercial terms the Clause is of enormous importance because it provides that delay by the Contractor is to be recompensed by liquidated damages. Little comment is necessary here, however. Clause 15.1 simply allows the parties to decide and negotiate their liquidated damages, as Schedule 12 to the Contract.

Clause 15.2 sets out a procedure to deal with one difficult point, where an excusable delay occurs after liquidated damages have become payable. It simply suspends damages until the excusable delay has ceased.

Clause 15.3 suggests the Expert as the proper route to settle disputes on time problems.

2.6 Defects, Site accidents, insurance and exclusions

2.6.1 The law

See section 1.5.

2.6.2 The Conditions

The Clauses to be covered in this section are those listed under the headings 'Defects/Final Certificate', 'Insurance etc' and 'Liability' in Figure 1 (see page 31).

For ease of reference the Clauses can be divided into the following groups:

- guarantees:
  - guarantee period (37.1–2 and 37.13);
  - normal defects procedure (Clauses 37.2–4);
  - extension of guarantee period (Clause 37.6 and 37.10);
  - repetition of tests (Clause 37.5);
  - repair by the Purchaser (Clauses 37.7–9);
  - access to Plant records (Clause 33.14);
  - access to Site (37.11);
- Final Certificate:
  - procedure (Clause 38.1);
  - purpose/effect (Clause 38.4);
  - time of issue (Clauses 38.1–3);
  - disputes (Clause 38.5);
- insurance:
  - responsibility for cover (Clauses 31.1–3);
  - administration (Clauses 31.1 and 31.4);
- Site work—accidents and responsibilities:
  - Contractor (Clauses 30.1–4);
  - limits of Contractor's liability (Clauses 30.3–4 and 30.7–8);
  - employee risk (Clauses 30.5–6);
- overall exclusions:
  - liability (Clauses 15, 37.12, 43 and 44).

2.6.3 Guarantees

Guarantee period

CLAUSES 37.1–2 and 37.13

The basic Defects Liability Period is set by Clause 37.2. It starts when work commences or Materials arrive at the Site and continues until one year after take-over. If a different period or periods is agreed, a Special Condition will be necessary to modify the Clause.

Clause 37.1 provides that where the Plant is taken over in sections, each section will have a separate Defects Liability Period.

Then Clause 37.13 provides for any items incorporated into the Plant which have only a limited life to be listed in Schedule 10 and then to have shorter Defects Liability Periods, as stated.

Normal defects procedure

The Clause enables the Purchaser to ensure that the Contractor repairs or replaces equipment that is found to be defective as a result of some error in design or manufacture, for which the Contractor is responsible, during the guarantee period. Clauses 37.2–3 do this, and they also cover two other situations as well, firstly that of a defect which comes to light before the guarantee period commences, and secondly that of a defect which is not due to the fault of the Contractor. There is a cross-relationship between these Clauses and the testing and Variation Clauses.

CLAUSES 37.2–3

The Project Manager may notify the Contractor in writing of a defect in work/Materials or failure of the Plant/section to conform to the requirements of the Contract. Therefore 'defect' has a very wide meaning. It includes a deterioration in the performance of the Plant as well as equipment breakdown or failure. Clause 37.3 then extends the meaning of 'defect' further by including defects which have been caused by the Purchaser or others, for instance by incorrect operation of the Plant.

The notice by the Project Manager must describe the defect and must be given quickly. The Project Manager is not entitled to delay notification because it might be more convenient to delay repair, since this could increase the cost of repair to the Contractor. If the Purchaser does delay then the Contractor is entitled to charge him with the increase in his repair costs.

The Contractor must then be given all necessary access to the Plant and must carry out whatever work is necessary to correct the defect. The Contractor has the right to decide what corrective action to take—whether to repair or replace a defective item for example—but must inform the Project Manager of what action he intends to take if the Project Manager asks him to do so and obtain his approval.

Clause 37.3 then deals with costs. Where the defect is the responsibility of the Contractor then the Contractor must carry out the necessary corrective action free of charge. Where the defect is not the responsibility of the Contractor (or if notice of the defect is delayed) then the corrective action must be priced in accordance with Clause 19 (See Clauses 33.13 and 16–19.)

Extension of guarantee period

Clearly if the Plant becomes defective the Purchaser suffers in two ways. He may lose part of his original guarantee protection because an item of equipment will have been changed or replaced. Also he may lose part of his guarantee period because the Plant will have been put out of action for a time. The Conditions deal with both of these problems.

CLAUSE 37.6

This Clause gives the Purchaser a new Defects Liability Period of one year upon any repair and on any item of equipment or work which is replaced, not merely re-adjusted, under Clauses 37.2–3. The Clause is fair—since repair/replacement implies a greater degree of failure than re-adjustment—but it will obviously influence the Contractor's thinking when faced with the decision how to make good any particular defect.

CLAUSE 37.10

This Clause then provides that any Defects Liability Period will be extended by the time that the Plant or relevant section has been put out of use due to a defect.

To a certain extent this remedies the possible shortcoming of Clause 37.6, in that it applies to delay due to re-adjustment, but it does raise one problem of its own. It only applies where the defect is sufficient to put the Plant/section out of use. In other words where the defect or corrective work by the Contractor does not actually stop the Plant operating/producing, but only *limits* or *restricts* its use then the Purchaser is not entitled to any extension, even though the restriction in output may be relatively serious.

Repetition of tests
It is normal to provide for the possible repetition of Contract tests on the Plant, in case serious defects show themselves during the guarantee period, to demonstrate that the corrective action taken by the Contractor is adequate to ensure that the Plant has been put back into proper order.

CLAUSE 37.5
The Project Manager may require the Contractor to repeat take-over tests to establish that defects have been properly corrected. The Clause refers only to take-over *tests*, however, not to take-over *procedures* or *performance tests*, and also allows the Project Manager only to require *appropriate* take-over tests. In other words, Clause 37.5 will apply only where the defect is of such a type that a take-over test is suitable to decide whether the defect has been properly corrected and the defect will normally have to be fairly serious to justify a repetition of a complete test. Clause 37.10 then allows an appropriate extension to the Defects Liability Period to allow for these tests.

Repair by the Purchaser
Clauses 37.7 and 37.9 provide the Purchaser with the usual remedy against the Contractor who fails to honour his defects obligations. He can carry out repairs for himself and then back-charge the costs to the Contractor. The Purchaser will often wish to retain some form of security against this possibility, usually in the form of a bond/bank guarantee or a cash retention. Clause 37.8 deals in the same way with urgent repairs.

CLAUSES 37.7–9
Where a repair is urgent the Purchaser can carry out repairs himself (Clause 37.8) without invalidating the guarantee, if the Contractor cannot or will not do so. Furthermore if the Contractor fails to correct *any* defect with reasonable speed, even a defect which has been caused by the Purchaser, Clause 37.7 permits the Purchaser to carry out the repair, provided that he must first give the Contractor fourteen days notice that he will do so. In both cases the Purchaser is then entitled to recover his costs of corrective action from the Contractor under Clause 37.9.

The Clauses pose two practical problems for the Purchaser. The first is how to assess whether the Contractor is moving with reasonable speed in carrying out corrective work. The second is that the Purchaser's ability to use the powers given to him by the Clauses may be limited by a lack of knowledge of the process or technology involved.

Access to plant records

A process plant is a highly complex unit. This means that it may not always be easy to diagnose the root cause of a process problem or defect. Therefore the Contractor must have access to the Plant and to all operating data. It may also be necessary to investigate the way in which equipment is performing to assist in diagnosis.

CLAUSE 33.14

Clause 33.14 lays down the general principles of the Contractor's right of access to the Plant and its associated operating records, and also sets out the procedure to be followed. The right is primarily there for use in case of defects problems, but is a general right of the Contractor and could be used at any time during the Defects Liability Period.

Access to Site

CLAUSE 37.11

If the Purchaser, for whatever reason, does not give access to the Contractor to carry out the necessary work to correct a defect, then the Contractor does not have to carry out that work. If the Purchaser simply *postpones* the correction work then the Contractor will carry out the work at the end of the postponement and will be entitled to the extra costs of the delay.

There are three problems. The first is the difference between refusing or not allowing access, and deferring access. This is all a matter of degree in one sense, but one test of refusal/deferment is whether or not, when access is denied, a date is set when access will be given (and is then given). The second is that delay in repairing a defect may simply mean that the defect becomes more serious and difficult to repair. The third is that repairing defects often involves equipment manufactured by Subcontractors, who are considerably less than enthusiastic about extending the guarantees on their equipment (under Clause 37.6) in these circumstances.

2.6.4 Final Certificate

Procedure

The procedure for issuing a Final Certificate is essentially the same as for any other certificate. It is to be issued by the Project Manager to both the Contractor and Purchaser. It should be issued when it is due without any need for application by the Contractor, unless a payment is also due.

CLAUSE 38.1

The Clause states the procedure in simple terms and needs no comment. The Clause does not require any application from the Contractor for the Certificate per se. Where take-over is by sections then a separate Certificate should be issued for each section.

Purpose and effect

The Conditions operate on the principle that the Contractor's obligations end once the Defects Liability Period or Periods have been completed. The purpose of the Final Certificate is therefore to confirm formally that the Contractor has carried out all his obligations, *and therefore* to bar the Purchaser from any actions against the Contractor for breach of the Contract once it has been issued. As a result the Project Manager must take great care in issuing the Final Certificate.

CLAUSE 38.4

The Final Certificate performs a number of functions:

- it brings to an end the Contractor's obligation to do any further work on the Plant or relevant section under the Contract, except for any 'insurance' repair work;
- it confirms that the Plant or section as constructed complies with the Contract;
- it confirms that the Contractor has properly performed his obligations during the Defects Liability Period;
- the Certificate (or, where take-over has been by sections, the *last* Certificate) will act as a formal legal document which the Contractor can use to prevent any litigation/arbitration by the Purchaser for breach of Contract, ('conclusive evidence . . . in any proceedings that the Contractor has completed the Works');

This last function actually raises a problem in the Clause. The Clause *requires* the Project Manager to issue the Certificate once the Defects Liability Period is complete. However the Clause does not formally permit the Project Manager to qualify a Certificate. Therefore there could be a problem where the Project Manager is required to issue a Final Certificate under a Contract which is the subject of a dispute. Effectively the Project Manager would have to issue a qualified Certificate.

Time of issue

The Clause provides that in principle a Final Certificate is to be issued by the Project Manager when the relevant guarantee period has been completed, but this is subject to a number of qualifications that are listed in the Clause.

CLAUSE 38.1

This Clause provides for the basic time of issue of the Certificate—when the defects liability has expired. It then allows the first qualification, that the Certificate may be delayed until all corrective action in respect of any defects being carried out by the Contractor under Clause 37 has been completed.

CLAUSE 38.2

This Clause then provides a further qualification. Where any equipment or work has been replaced or renewed under Clause 37.6 it is to be treated separately from the rest of the Plant or section, and separate Certificates issued as the different guarantee periods terminate.

CLAUSE 38.3

Clause 38.3 deals with the question of a delayed performance test by simply allowing the Project Manager to delay any Certificate until any matters relating to delayed tests have been resolved.

Disputes

Clause 38.5 states that any disputes about whether or not the Plant qualifies for the issue of a Final Certificate or not—that is about issues of technical fact—should go to an Expert rather than to arbitration.

2.6.5 Insurance

Responsibility for cover

The discussions in sections 1.4 and 1.5 have already emphasised the importance of avoiding legal disputes or at least minimising their impact upon the project as a whole. One of the most serious areas of risk is that of accidents and damage occurring during the construction of the Plant on the Site and while the Contractor is repairing defects.

There are a number of reasons why the risk is substantial in Contracts for process plants. Firstly, there is the sheer number of different companies that may be involved in Site work at any one time, the Contractor, the Purchaser, and any number of Subcontractors. Secondly there is the fact that all these different parties may be working in close physical proximity to each other. Thirdly there are the linked problems of double insurance, under-insurance and non-insurance.

The intention of Clause 31 is therefore to provide a framework within which the parties can organise a coherent insurance scheme for the project. The aim is to achieve adequate cover for the work and to avoid, wherever possible, the risk of cross-claims—disputes between different insurance companies as to which of them has to meet the costs of making good any damage. The problem is that when insurance companies argue, their clients become sucked into the dispute whether they want to or not.

CLAUSE 31.1

Clause 31.1 sets out the scheme as follows:

- the Contractor is to be responsible for arranging the principal project insurance package for the Works through insurers acceptable to both parties;
- the package is in the joint names of all parties involved, Purchaser, Project Manager, Contractor and Subcontractors, simply to eliminate cross-claims and consequent delay in settling a claim;
- the insurance cover is to be against all normal insurable risks;
- the period covered by the package will be primarily that of Site construction, but the package will also cover defects in the Plant and any work done by the Contractor or any Subcontractor during the Defects Liability Period;
- the package will include the main areas of construction risk, the Documentation, the Materials and Plant
- the insurance will be for full replacement cost, *unless* the Contract states differently (in which case the parties will need to make other arrangements for any risk in excess of the agreed amount).

Note that if under the terms of the Contract the Contractor has to remove any items of equipment belonging to the Purchaser from the Site, for example because they require refurnishment, then special insurance might need to be arranged.

CLAUSE 31.2

The second main area of cover is that of the Site, other than the Works and other property of the Purchaser adjacent to the Site. This is to be kept covered against all normal risk by the Purchaser, subject to the Contractor being liable for the first £5 million of any damage caused by him in any single accident. It is therefore very much the responsibility of the Purchaser to make certain that he has an adequate level of insurance cover for his other property on or in close proximity to the Site, particularly because of the indemnity given by him to the Contractor under Clause 30.7.

CLAUSE 31.3

The Contractor is responsible for providing adequate insurance cover against the risk of accidental damage etc, both to the Purchaser and also to third parties. He will need adequate cover against the risk of damage to third-party property, especially if the Site is adjacent to high-value plant or equipment not owned by the Purchaser or its affiliated companies. (This is often the case. Major process sites regularly house plants belonging to different groups of companies, quite apart from the possibility of damage to property on adjacent premises.)

The only major areas omitted from this package are that of the Contractor's construction equipment, tools, site facilities, etc, which the Contractor and his Subcontractors will be expected to hold covered anyway, and the risk of injury to the employees of the various parties (which is covered, within the UK at any rate, by compulsory Employer's Liability insurance).

Administration

The administration of the insurance package is straightforward. The Contractor, who has set up the package, is responsible for paying the necessary premiums, which will of course be included in the Contract Price. Clause 31.1 then provides for the management of claims by the Contractor on behalf of all parties. But the decision on settlement of any claim must be with the agreement of the Purchaser. Any payments made by the insurers will be to the Contractor who will then use the money to comply with his obligations under Clause 30.2–3.

CLAUSE 31.4

This Clause needs no comment.

2.6.6 Site work–accidents and responsibilities

Contractor

The Contractor has full responsibility for managing the Site during construction, and must repair any damage that may occur to the Works for any reason during that time. He is therefore responsible for meeting the costs of repair, subject to the limits stated in Clause 31.8, but will be assisted by payments received from the insurers under the Clause 31 insurance package.

CLAUSE 30.1
This is the basic 'responsibility/control' clause. It needs no comment.

CLAUSE 30.2
This Clause sets out the Contractor's obligations to repair or make good any accidental (and also deliberate—for example, theft or sabotage) loss or damage to the Plant and to Materials. Up to take-over the Contractor must repair and make good *all* loss and damage (Clause 31.2). After take-over the Contractor must repair/make good where Clause 37.2 is applied by the Project Manager.

CLAUSES 30.3–4
These Clauses confirm the principle laid down in Clause 30.1, that the Contractor is in control of the Site and therefore responsible for carrying out repairs to all accidents and damage. They then list certain categories of loss or damage that the Contractor will repair, but at the cost of the Purchaser:

- political instability, sonic and nuclear risks (which are in any event uninsurable commercially) are best dealt with by the Site owner;
- problems arising from the use of the Site by the Purchaser need no comment;
- damage caused by the fault/negligence of the Purchaser, or designs/information provided by the Purchaser, which would be breach of the terms of the Contract and need no comment (although it is worth pointing out that the Clause 31.1 insurance policy would probably indemnify/protect the Purchaser).

Limits of the Contractor's liability
The Conditions put a number of limits to the Contractor's liability for loss or damage on Site. These are all straightforward.

CLAUSE 30.7
(The Purchaser's property and premises).
This Clause is easy to deal with. In the insurance policy required to be maintained by the Contractor under Clause 31.3, the Contractor is required to insure against damage to the property of the Purchaser for an amount to be agreed between the parties. Clause 30.7 then limits the Contractor's liability for this damage to £5million, unless otherwise agreed. Effectively therefore what Clause 30.7 does is to limit the Contractor's liability for damage to the property of the Purchaser to the amount of insurance cover agreed between the parties pursuant to Clause 31.3.

However Clause 30.8 makes the Contractor liable for all *third-party* claims, even when made against the Purchaser because third parties suffering damage will usually find it easier to claim against client than contractor.

Employee risk
CLAUSES 30.5–6
These Clauses deal with the risk of injury to the employees of the different parties involved during work on the Site. They provide simply that each party will accept responsibility for its own employees. This is normal practice in view of statutory Employer's Liability Insurance, and avoids cross-claims.

2.6.7 Overall exclusions

Liability

Liability of one party to the other under a Contract, and the liability of either of the parties to any third party, is always a highly emotive and contentious area, but it is an area with which all model forms have to deal.

Clauses 15 and 43 of the Conditions have already been discussed.

CLAUSE 37.12

Clause 37.12 allows for the situation where the parties have agreed some overall limit to the Contractor's potential liability for the cost of repairing defects.

CLAUSE 44

The intention of Clause 44 is to put certain clear limits to the Contractor's liability.

Clause 44.1 excludes the Contractor's liability for various types of what may be called 'consequential' damage, together with damage caused because the Purchaser has imposed direct requirements upon the Contractor (subject to recovery under insurance).

Clause 44.2 then puts a general limit to the Contractor's liability. He is only to be liable for those damages allowed by the Conditions.

Perhaps, therefore, it is desirable to summarise the liability of both parties as set out by the Form:

- Performance of the Plant—if the Plant fails to pass its performance tests by a small amount, the Contractor will be liable to the Purchaser for breach of the Contract and his liability will be as agreed by the parties in Schedule 17 to the Contract. If the Plant fails to pass its performance tests by a significant amount, or fails to pass its take-over tests, the Contractor will be in breach of the Contract. (In each case the Contractor will certainly be liable for damages, and perhaps also to termination or cancellation of the Contract.)
- Third-party intellectual property—each party is liable to the other if it causes any infringement of any patent or other right owned by a third party, essentially to indemnify the other party against any claim.
- Delay—if the Purchaser delays the Contractor other than by reason of force majeure, the Purchaser is liable for the Contractor's extra costs. If the Contractor is late other than by force majeure or various other acceptable reasons, then the Contractor will be liable to the Purchaser, and his precise degree of liability will be set out in Schedule 12 to the Contract.
- Disruption—if the Purchaser disrupts the Contractor's work on Site by failing to supply work or information then the Purchaser will be liable to meet the Contractor's extra costs.
- Damage to property—damage to the Plant by either party during construction should be covered by joint insurance arranged under the Contract. The Contractor would then be expected to insure his own Site facilities and construction equipment. Damage to the Plant during the guarantee period by the Contractor would be covered by the joint insurance package. Damage by the Purchaser would be insured separately by the Purchaser. Damage to third-party owned property would be insured separately by the parties. If this insurance were inadequate then the parties would be liable for the excess.

2.7 Payments

The Clauses to be covered in this section are those listed under the heading 'Money' in Figure 1 (see page 31).

2.7.1 General approach

The general approach taken by the Conditions to Contract Price and payment terms is that the parties should be quite capable of agreeing for themselves what the Contract Price is to be and when and how the Contractor is to be paid.

Therefore the Clauses do not seek to deal with questions which relate to the make-up of the Contract Price, payment documentation, or the times/dates or instalments by which the Contract Price is to be paid to the Contractor. The Purchaser and Contractor are left to agree all these matters. The Conditions simply provide the appropriate locations for them to be inserted into the Contract. The Contract Price goes into the Agreement (Clause 4) and any prime cost or provisional amounts included in the Contract Price and payment terms, documentation go into Schedule 19.

Not all the Contractor's work need be at a fixed price. Very often the Contract will contain additional price information, such as rates payable for extra day-works that may be requested by the Project Manager during the Contract, agreed profit levels for extra work or Variations, etc. These should be included in Schedule 18.

What the conditions concentrate on is the procedure to be followed for the approval of the Contractor's invoices, and the periods within which the Project Manager and Purchaser might actually make any payment.

Provisional and prime cost sums
CLAUSE 40
This Clause allows for the inclusion of provisional sums and prime cost sums.

A provisional sum is a sum stated in the Contract that is available for use if the Project Manager decides that he wishes the Contractor to carry out certain additional work. Provisional sums are often allowed for in Contracts when the Purchaser or Project Manager realise at the start of the Contract that additional or ancillary work may be needed, but when it is impossible to decide precisely what may need to be done until the Contract is well advanced. Typical examples are optional items of equipment or 'site improvement' work, such as landscaping, fencing or paths. A provisional sum might also be used to cover more important items of work, which are known to be necessary but which cannot be accurately priced at the date of the Contract, such as building or foundation work.

A prime cost sum is an amount included in the Contract Price to be used for a specific purpose as instructed by the Project Manager. Prime cost sums are regularly used where the Purchaser/Project Manager may wish to nominate a Subcontractor.

CLAUSES 40.1–2
Clause 40.1 deals with the authorisation of work against provisional sums by the Project Manager. It needs no comment.

Clause 40.2 deals with prime cost items in the same way.

CLAUSE 40.3

This Clause deals with the price and payment implications in the customary way. Provisional and prime cost sums are both treated as an intrinsic part of the Contract Price. However, adjustments have to be made to take account of *actual* expenditure as the Contract proceeds, and the Final Certificate must allow for *actual expenditure* against any provisional sum, and the *actual price charged by any nominated Subcontractor plus the Contractor's supervision and management costs* against any prime cost sum.

VAT

CLAUSE 39.10

VAT, if applicable, will be paid as an addition to the Contract Price.

Payment by instalments

CLAUSE 39

Clause 39 lays down the principle that the Contract Price should be paid by instalments, on the basis agreed in Schedule 19 to the Contract. It then deals with the procedures for payment of the Contract Price and the time-scale for those procedures.

Clause 39 lays down one further principle, which is of major importance. It provides that interim assessments and payments must be made for any Variations or other additional work as the Contract proceeds. It is not permissible to leave settlement of claims until after the Contract has been completed.

Finally Clause 39 deals with one other matter, the Purchaser's right to audit the Contractor's cost records compiled pursuant to Clause 18.1.

CLAUSES 39.1–2

Clause 39.1 establishes that Schedule 19 should set out an agreed programme for the payment of instalments of the Contract Price.

Clause 39.2 then deals with the Contractor's entitlement to claim payment of instalments payable on a 'milestone' basis.

CLAUSE 39.3

This Clause deals with the timing of claims for payment by the Contractor. Claims are to be submitted on a monthly basis for whatever amounts are due at that time. These amounts might be for:

- milestones achieved by the Contractor;
- other payments due under Schedule 19; or
- any Variations or other claims where work has been carried out.

Procedure and time-scale

The procedure is that the Contractor should submit a 'statement', in effect a draft invoice, for each instalment as it falls due. The draft invoice should be based upon Schedule 19, take account of any extra work, and state what amount is actually being invoiced and how that figure is calculated, and be supported by all relevant supporting information (Clause 39.3).

The statement must be checked by the Project Manager within a tight time-scale. He must then issue a certificate to both parties for the instalment (Clause 39.4). The Project Manager has powers to disallow incorrect items in any invoice. (On any contract of any size the Project Manager will almost certainly need accounting/financial assistance).

The Contractor may then invoice the Purchaser for the amount certified by the Project Manager, and the Purchaser must then pay the invoice (Clause 39.5).

The permitted time-scale for payment is four weeks from submission of each statement, two weeks for certification by the Project Manager and two weeks for payment by the Purchaser.

CLAUSES 39.3–4

Clause 39.3 deals with the submission by the Contractor of his draft invoices. The Clause *requires* the Contractor to include an assessment of the price changes due to any Variations, etc., to the Contract in each draft invoice as work proceeds. Clause 39.4 then *requires* the Project Manager to certify a reasonable amount for those changes in each certificate.

There is a very serious purpose in requiring payment to be made for Variations and claims as the Contract proceeds. It is to at least try to avoid the build-up of unexpectedly high claims by the Contractor at the end of the Contract. The aim is to improve overall project cost control. If therefore the Contractor fails to include an assessment of the cost of modifications/Variations in any draft invoice, then the Project Manager should take action to remedy the situation.

CLAUSES 39.5–10

Clause 39.5 is the payment Clause. It needs no comment.

Clause 39.6 deals with late payment. The point that really demands comment is the level at which the Clause permits the Contractor to levy interest for late payment by the Purchaser. IChemE considers that the practice by Purchasers of making late/delayed payments to Contractors under fixed-price contracts to be very much against the interests of all parties and is therefore to be discouraged.

Clause 39.7 gives the Purchaser a right of set-off in respect of sums due from the Contractor to the Purchaser under the Contract. Note that the proper procedure is that the *Project Manager* must certify the full payment due from the Purchaser to the Contractor; then when the Contractor invoices for that amount the *Purchaser* may deduct amounts owing to him before making payment.

Clauses 39.8–10 are mostly concerned to give the Contractor powers to suspend, and perhaps even terminate, the Contract in the event that the Purchaser fails or refuses to pay any certified sum.

Right of audit
CLAUSES 39.11–12

These Clauses give the Purchaser/Project Manager the right to audit cost records kept by the Contractor, pursuant to Clause 18.1, and to make any consequent adjustments to payments in the event of error. The Clauses are straightforward and need no comment.

The Green Book

3

3.1 Procedural and general clauses

3.1.1 Reimbursable contracts

The Green Book is still the only set of model conditions specifically designed for *reimbursable* contracts for capital plant published within the UK. It has also been described by the International Bureau for Comparative Law in Switzerland as being the most fair and reasonable model set of reimbursable conditions that there is.

Being result-orientated rather than work-orientated the conditions, like the Red and Burgundy conditions, are more truly multi-disciplinary than other model conditions and are suitable for projects involving work in several different engineering disciplines, such as process/chemical engineering, civil/structural engineering, electrical/mechanical engineering etc.

This is a particular problem for the Project Manager in a Green Book contract, because using a reimbursable contract to the best advantage is a far more complex operation than using fixed-price conditions. The relationship between the Contractor and Purchaser is less well defined and controlling the overall cost of the project is considerably more difficult.

In a fixed-price contract the Purchaser does not need to monitor the Contractor's expenditure or use of financial resources. The risk and resources involved are, from the Purchaser's viewpoint, strictly limited to the agreed Contract Price. The only time when it ever becomes necessary for the Purchaser to consider the price/cost of doing work is when he has to agree the price to be paid to the Contractor as the result of a claim or Variation to the Contract.

Under a reimbursable contract however there is no automatic price control. The Contractor has a right to be reimbursed for his reasonable expenditure. Therefore if the Purchaser is to retain a proper degree of control over the overall project cost he can only do so by being prepared to make available the necessary resources in terms of properly qualified manpower to oversee and control the Contractor's work.

To use the Green Book conditions successfully as a Purchaser requires the willingness to put into the project adequate resources *both* to monitor *and* to control price/cost *and also* the various technical/design elements of the Contractor's work.

In addition a Green Book Contract requires a different approach, to some extent at least, from both the Project Manager and the Contract Manager. A fixed-price contract will always tend to generate an arms-length, and adversarial, relationship. In a reimbursable contract this arms-length relationship can and should be replaced by a closer, more collaborative and therefore more *complex* relationship which brings great benefits but is much more difficult to control. Managing a reimbursable contract demands more *and different* skills from the project management on both sides than a fixed-price contract.

The situation is that the Contractor is being employed by the Purchaser to make available a team of people with suitable engineering and project skills to carry out a project for the Purchaser. The Contractor's team will work almost as an extension to the Purchaser's own organisation and therefore may be subject to close control/manipulation (perhaps even on a day-to-day basis) by the Purchaser through his Project Manager. The flexibility, collaboration and control that the reimbursable contract gives the Purchaser are major benefits, counterbalancing its possible extra cost.

A further point to remember is that the Contractor is in effect paid to provide his personnel on a day-rate basis (containing only a comparatively low profit-factor) and therefore cannot include the normal contingencies that would be usual in a fixed-price contract. Therefore the Purchaser has to be ready to carry far more of the remedial costs of faulty work by the Contractor than would be the case under a fixed-price contract, even including the costs of run-of-the-mill mistakes, almost as if those mistakes had been made by his own personnel.

The net result is that if the relationship is to work successfully there has to be mutual confidence and professional trust between the parties. Inevitably the conditions tend to work best where the two project teams have overlapping or complementary skills and respect each other's ability.

3.1.2 The Agreement

On pages 5–6 the Green Book provides a form of Agreement for use in setting up the Contract. I would always recommend you to use this Agreement, or something very like it. Of course you may very well choose another contract form, such as a Purchase Order, but the Agreement is important. It is a reminder of the points that must be covered when setting up the Contract, and of the various additional documents that are necessary to complete it properly. It also sets out the shape that the Contract should take, so that its various parts will relate correctly to one another. The heading and preamble to the Agreement set the scene, and Clause 1 incorporates the Green Book conditions and lists the other Contract documents.

Clause 2 of the Agreement is self-explanatory, but states an important principle. Nothing counts that is not a part of the Contract.

Clauses 3–12 are straightforward and need little comment. Clauses 3 to 5 set out the extent of the Contractor's risk/liability. There could be considerable cost and other implications arising from the date fixed by Clause 7, as it sets a date from which certain things switch from the risk of the Contractor to that of the Purchaser. The point to be remembered here is that 'the date of the Contractor's tender' is a slightly artificial concept. The Contractor will often submit not one but two or more 'tenders' as the negotiations proceed towards a conclusion and the parties explore different technical or commercial possibilities. Often the Contractor's initial tender will have been submitted anything up to a year before the Contract is made. Therefore the date inserted in Clause 7 should be either the date of the Contractor's initial formal tender for the project or the date of a later tender by the Contractor that has been submitted after proper consideration of all the circumstances, as opposed to a simple price update or re-validation exercise.

The additional documents listed in Clause 1 are as follows.

The Specification

I said earlier that the Specification is the most important part of any price-based contract. This is not necessarily the case in a reimbursable contract. One reason why a reimbursable format may be used is because the Purchaser wishes to use the Contractor to help in writing the detailed specification for the Plant. But it will still be very important. Even if the Specification cannot define, it still needs to deal with:

- the Plant that is to be constructed;
- any other work which the Contractor is to carry out;
- the process requirements, performance, raw materials, products, operating and safety considerations and so on;
- the design standards and other requirements that the Plant must meet; and
- testing and inspection standards.

The Special Conditions

Although the form of Agreement adds the words '(if any)' to paragraph 1(b), it is virtually certain that every Contract will need to include Special Conditions to adapt the conditions to the particular needs and circumstances of the project.

The Schedules

The list of Schedules in the previous edition has been expanded, and pages 53–69 give guidance on compiling the Schedules with reference to the appropriate Guide Notes. This list of Schedules is not quite as formidable as it looks. Its purpose is to act as a reminder of the various issues to consider, and as a framework to organise the Contract contents so that the right information ends up in the correct pigeonhole.

First-time users of the Forms should find the Guide Notes invaluable in explaining how to go about the task of producing the Contract. Certainly no other Institution produces anything comparable to them.

3.1.3 The procedural clauses

The clauses to be covered in the remainder of this section are those described as Procedural and General Clauses in Figure 2 (see page 102). For ease of reference they can be split into the following groups:

- Contract interpretation (Clauses 1 and 2);
- responsibilities (Clauses 3.1–2, 3.4, 3.6, 3.8–9, 4.1–2, 4.4 and 7.1–2);
- intellectual property (Clauses 8 and 20);
- termination (Clauses 42 and 43);
- notice procedures (Clauses 2.6 and 5);
- disputes provisions (Clauses 45, 46, 47 and 48).

3.1.4 Contract interpretation

Clause 1 defines a number of words and expressions. 'Defined Terms' as they are called are used in every set of model conditions. They are verbal shorthand. Defined Terms always mean their *definition*, whenever and wherever they are used, that is anywhere in the Contract and also in any correspondence between the parties arising from the Contract. They help to ensure consistency between the different parts of the Contract and accuracy in correspondence during the Contract. Always be careful when using any Defined Term that you are clear as to precisely what it means, and then that you use it correctly. Then in Clause 2 a number of other points of interpretation are also laid down.

Definitions

CLAUSE 1

The definitions set out in Clause 1 are all reasonably straightforward but note the following points.

'Agreed Rate' defines the starting point for the calculation of interest payable on late payments under Clause 39.6. Essentially the viewpoint of the Conditions is that overdue payments should carry interest at a rate that is sufficiently high to make deliberate delay in payment unappealing. Remember, too, that there is legislation on the point *within the UK*, the Late Payment of Commercial Debts (Interest) Act (1998).

'Applications Software/Contractor's Software/Standard Software'. Note the three definitions of different categories of software referred to in Clause 8.

The definition of the 'Contract', and other definitions as well, refers to an 'Agreement'. See the earlier comments on the advisability of using the recommended form of Agreement set out on pages 5–6 of the Form.

(For comments on the significance of the 'Acceptance Certificate' see page 144.)

'Contract Manager' means the manager appointed by the Contractor to manage the project.

'Contractor's Equipment' is an expression used to describe everything that the Contractor may bring on to the Site to assist in the construction of the Plant (as distinct from items brought on to the Site for inclusion within the Plant). The

	START	SITE COMMENCEMENT	TAKING OVER	FINAL CERT.
Procedural & General Clauses	1 2 3.1–2 3.4 3.6 3.8–9 4.1–2 4.4 5 7.1–2 8 20 42 43 45 46 47 48			
		DESIGN / MANUFACTURE	SITE CONSTRUCTION / COMMISSIONING	DEFECTS REPAIR
Main Project Activity II		3.7 9 10 11 12 13 21 22 29	3.7 11 12 13 29	
Site Work			3.3 23 24 25 26 27 28 34	
Tests			32 33	35 36
Claims & Variations		3.5 4.5 7.3–4 16 17	3.5 4.5 6 7.3–4 16 17	37.3–4
Delay		14 15 41	14 15 41	
Defects/Final Certificate			37	33.13 37 38
Insurance etc		31	4.6 30 31	4.6 30 31
Liability		15	15 43 44	43 44
Money		3.7 18 19 39 40	3.7 18 19 39 40	3.7 18 19 39 40

Figure 2 The Green Book

expression is therefore very comprehensive, covering everything from a spanner to site huts or heavy lifting or construction equipment.

Note that 'Documentation' means *both* drawings *and* other technical documentation, such as data, calculations or diagrams and also non-technical documentation, as appropriate in the circumstances, both in hard copy and electronic
form.

'Plant', 'Works', and 'Materials'. The purpose of the Contract will be that the
Contractor will carry out Works including the provision of:

- services of various kinds (such as design, procurement, site supervision,
  testing);
- the supply of Materials;
- the construction, installation and erection work necessary to build the Plant
  on the Site from the Materials and any equipment or other items provided for
  that purpose by the Purchaser;
- the testing of the Plant.

'Materials' means everything that the Contractor supplies that is to be incorporated into the Plant and/or necessary for its operation. It includes such things as
equipment, piping, structural steelwork, control systems, computer programmes
(or at least the discs or chips containing the programmes) and civil engineering/
building materials. It may also cover such things as operational spare parts, lubricants, fuel, chemicals or catalysts.

The 'Works' will, together with any other work done and equipment provided
by the Purchaser, result in a process plant that can be put into operation by the
Purchaser.

The 'Project Manager' should always be known and identified, even if not
formally nominated, well before the Contract is made. He *can* be a firm or company, but should really be a person, as this gives the Contractor a clear point
of contact and decision-making.

'Subcontractor' means any and every company that carries out any work or
supplies any Materials or Contractor's Equipment to the Contractor.

'Site' means the area both where the Plant is to be built and any other areas
to be used by the Contractor for the purposes of construction. It may be either
the whole or only a part of the Purchaser's own site, and may also include other
areas to be used by the Contractor for the purposes of the Contract.

Note the difference between the Specification and the Description of Works,
which is set out in Schedule 1, together with a description of the Site. In
essence it is that the Specification is a statement of the technical requirements
for the Plant. The Description of Works is a statement of what input is required
from the Contractor (and therefore also from the Purchaser) towards achieving
that final result. The two fit together—and of course the description could be
anything from a statement that 'the Contractor shall do everything' downwards.

Interpretation
CLAUSE 2
Clause 2.1 provides for the Contract to be governed by English law, but of
course there would be no difference if another UK law were to apply. The Green

Book can easily be adapted to non-UK contracts and non-UK law—the changes that would be necessary present few problems to the professional draftsman and in most cases there would be little difference in meaning.

Clause 2.2 defines the order of priority that is to apply between the different parts of the Contract. Special Conditions, i.e. conditions specially written into the Contract, prevail over these Conditions. These Conditions then prevail over the Specification and the Specification over the Schedules. It is therefore important to minimise overlap between the Specification and Schedules.

The consequence is that changes to these conditions *must* be made by a Special Condition—*it is not enough to try to do so by writing possible changes into a Schedule or the Specification*.

What Clause 2.4 means is that before either party can refuse any approval or consent he must have a valid reason for doing so. The only reasons that will normally be valid are the intervention of force majeure, that the other has failed to comply with the relevant terms of the Contract or good engineering practice, or has overlooked something and is not therefore entitled to be given the approval or consent which he has requested.

3.1.5 Responsibilities

Basic principles
CLAUSES 3.1–2 and 3.4
Clauses 3.1–2 and 3.4 set out the Contractor's obligations in broad terms.

Clause 3.1 simply establishes the basic principle that the Works must be carried out in accordance with the Contract.

Clause 3.2 then says that all work must be carried out by the Contractor *both* safely and in accordance with good engineering practice, *and* to the reasonable satisfaction of the Project Manager. There is a big difference between a Contract based on a Specification which sets out in great detail exactly what the Contractor has to achieve (the Red Book) and a Contract which requires the Contractor to carry out his work to the satisfaction of the Project Manager (the Green). The Contract cannot do both. Either the Specification or the Project Manager must have the ultimate power to decide what the Contractor is to do. The Red Book, as a firm/fixed-price contract should, resolves this conflict in favour of the Specification. It provides that if the Specification sets out what is to be supplied then the Project Manager is not empowered to change that. In effect the Contractor can supply whatever he wants, provided only that it meets the Specification. The Green Book goes the other way—which is fair. After all, in a reimbursable contract, the Purchaser pays the bill.

CLAUSE 3.6
This Clause is obvious in meaning but important in principle. Essentially it allows the Purchaser the right to insist that the Contractor retains the necessary resources within the project, and also perhaps even to terminate for breach if the Contractor fails to do so, even if the Contractor is not actually in breach of the terms of the Contract in any other way. (In addition, by making a specific reference to *financial* resources, it links to Clause 43.1 which gives the

Purchaser a way of closing out the Contract if the Contractor is having financial problems that are sufficiently serious to affect his ability to carry on the project properly.) Quite apart from the obvious problems that can result from receivership or administration, effective procurement by a Contractor usually requires a reasonable degree of financial credibility.

CLAUSE 3.7
The first part of this Clause deals with an important function within a reimbursable contract—cost control and cost reporting. Of course the Clause can only lay down the basic principles.

CLAUSES 3.8–9
Clauses 3.8–9 need no explanation, but underline two important principles, the provision of training in the operation and maintenance of the Plant, and the establishment of an adequate quality assurance system by the Contractor. In addition Clause 3.8 makes provision for *validation* of the Plant by the Contractor. Broadly speaking validation comprises the provision of whatever documentation is necessary, as the project proceeds, to prove precisely:

- the design of the Plant;
- the Materials used in its construction;
- that the Plant has been constructed in accordance with the design; and
- the accuracy and repeatability of the process, and therefore of the products made by the Plant.

Validation is often an essential stage in product approval in industries such as pharmaceuticals.

CLAUSE 3.10
Finally this Clause simply clarifies designer liability under UK law.

3.1.6 Purchaser's obligations

CLAUSES 4.1–2 and 4.4
Clauses 4.1–2, supplemented by Schedule 2, is a simple description of the contribution to the project to be made by the Purchaser. The words need little comment. Nevertheless while the Clause is simple it deals with an area that is always likely to give rise to claims by the Contractor. The problem is that any failure to comply with the terms of Clause 4 (except where due to 'force majeure' under Clause 14.2) is a breach of contract, for which the Contractor is entitled to claim damages, i.e. the cost of any extra work caused to the Contractor (plus Profit), together with any extension of time needed by the Contractor under Clause 14.1(d). Therefore the supply of services and information by the Purchaser is one area where the Project Manager will always need to exert close control.

Clause 4.2 adopts a similar approach to Clause 3.2. Where there is an express description in the Contract of what is to be provided by the Purchaser then that is precisely what must be supplied—no more and no less—and other considerations do not apply. Where there is no express description ('express' meaning a description in clear technical terms) then the Clause lays down a number of general and obvious rules for the Purchaser. These are that the Purchaser must carry out his work in a proper way, reasonably quickly, and in a manner which will cause the Contractor no unreasonable time, quality, design or safety problems in carrying out the Contract.

Clause 4.1 refers to the supply of any or all designs or technical or other information to be supplied by the Purchaser under the Contract and does so in much the same terms that Clause 4.2 uses for the supply of Materials or Work. The Purchaser will be responsible for the information which he supplies to the Contractor in a number of ways:

- under Clause 8.4 he may be responsible if he has provided 'drawings or instructions' to the Contractor which result in an infringement of a third-party intellectual property right;
- then under Clauses 30.4(b) he may also be responsible if designs or information lead to an accident on Site, or are responsible for a failure of the Plant to meet its guaranteed performance.

Clause 4.1 lays down one very important principle. The only permissible route for the transfer of information to the Contractor is through the Project Manager. The consequence is that the Contractor should *only* act upon information provided by the Project Manager or authorised members of his staff.

3.1.7 Compliance with legislation

CLAUSES 7.1–2 and 7.4

The first sentence of Clause 7.1 reflects recent changes in safety law, and in particular the responsibilities imposed by law on both sides to the project. In all projects within the European Union, both parties will have obligations under legislation arising from Council Directive 92/57/EEC (in the UK the Construction (Design and Management) Regulations of 1994) in respect of the way the work on the Site is organised and carried out. The second part of Clause 7.1 refers both to planning permission and any permissions that may be needed from the owners of adjacent land, such as wayleaves or rights of way or permission to bring services to the Site. Outline planning permission is usually obtained by the Purchaser, but there will often be logical reasons for the Contractor to be involved in the application for detailed planning permission due to his process knowledge. In practice if the parties decide that the Contractor should apply or assist the Purchaser in any particular case, then it is a simple matter to amend the clause. Clause 7.2 is self-explanatory.

Clause 7.4 is straightforward, but is of very great importance, especially in any Contract with an export/import content.

3.1.8 Intellectual property

The Conditions deal with a number of issues relating to the use and protection of intellectual property by the parties. Clause 8 deals with four—the licensing and use of third-party processes used in the design and operation of the Plant; responsibility for third-party claims; the ownership and possible further use by the Purchaser of the Contractor's design information outside the Contract; and finally the ownership of and rights to use software. Clause 20 then deals with confidentiality.

CLAUSE 8

Clause 8.1 establishes the principles that apply where the design of the Plant uses any processes, know-how or software which are the property of a third party. The Purchaser (not the Contractor, as in the Red Book) will agree terms with the third party for the supply of the necessary design package and assistance. This will usually be done under the terms of a licence agreement that will allow the Contractor to use information to carry out the Works including testing and commissioning the Plant.

If the licence agreement is on the basis of a single 'all-in' lump sum fee then there will be no further fees payable by the Purchaser. Otherwise the Purchaser will then agree with the licensor any output or use-related royalties or fees required by the licensor and will accept responsibility for their payment.

In practice, of course, wherever a significant third party process is involved, it will normally be necessary for the Contractor and Purchaser to incorporate a whole series of Special Conditions into the Contract to deal with the issues involved and a series of discussions between the Purchaser, Contractor and process owner will probably be necessary to agree them before the Contract can be signed.

Clauses 8.2–4 are standard intellectual property infringement/liability clauses that require each of the parties to be responsible if the information and design input which it makes towards the Contract is claimed to infringe the rights of a third party. In other words each party carries the cost/risk of any dispute over infringement of patent or design rights etc. which he may cause.

Note, by the way, the general obligation of the Contractor under the last sentence of Clause 8.2. The purpose is clear—but it is uncertain for how long the Contractor's obligations under the Clause will last. The answer is not very long. Realistically no third party right can adversely affect the Purchaser's right to use or operate the Plant unless it pre-dates the design or construction phase of the Contract. The longest timescale of any intellectual property right is that of the patent which can take some three to four years to obtain/publish.

In case of any claim of infringement the third party claimant would almost certainly take action against the Purchaser as well as, or even instead of, the Contractor. The Purchaser will always be the more vulnerable of the two. He has invested heavily in a production plant that could in theory be rendered useless or prohibitively expensive to operate by a successful claim, and might not have the technical knowledge to defend the claim himself. This is the reason behind Clause 8.3 which sets out a procedure by which the Contractor will, in consultation with the Purchaser, take over the responsibility for dealing with any infringement claim made against the Purchaser which relates to the Contractor's design of the Plant. The Clause is intended to ensure three things:

- there must be no unreasonable delay by the Contractor in initiating action to deal with any dispute;
- the Contractor must deal with the claim as efficiently as possible; and

- the Contractor must keep the Purchaser informed of his policy and progress in dealing with the claim,

because the result of a successful claim would probably be to prevent the Purchaser from operating the Plant, or being able effectively to use or market products from the Plant, except at a very high price. If process information is provided by the Purchaser, of course, the Clause might need to be reversed.

CLAUSES 8.5–6

Clause 8.5 simply provides that the Contractor and Subcontractors retain copyright in the drawings and other documents which they supply, subject only to pre-existing rights—which could include any licensor or the Purchaser for instance. This is necessary to ensure that they retain ownership of their design information. It also ensures that they keep the right to take action if there is any attempt to use their designs which is not authorised by the Contract, either by the Purchaser or by any other person who has acquired copies from the Purchaser. Afterall the Contractor, who is in the business of building plants, has a much greater interest to protect than the Purchaser who is only concerned with operating one plant.

Clause 8.6 then gives the Purchaser two rights to use those drawings and documents. Firstly he is given the right to use them in the operation and maintenance of the Plant. Secondly he is given the further right, subject to the restrictions stated in the Clause, to use the drawings to debottleneck, enlarge or improve the Plant.

Two comments should be borne in mind here:

- This second right must always to some extent affect the willingness of the Contractor to hand over *detailed* drawings. It is also very much a compromise. The Contractor is reluctant to see information that may contain his valuable know-how being released by the Purchaser to other contractors or suppliers in order to buy equipment. The Purchaser wants to have freedom to modify or carry out work on his own Plant, and to use information that he has paid for in order to achieve that. It has to be said that the compromise can sometimes give rise to problems, although not insoluble problems;
- The clause will usually be deleted, or heavily modified, wherever a third party process licensor is involved.

CLAUSES 8.7–8

Clauses 8.7–8 deal with the ownership of or the copyright in computer software which forms part of the Materials, typically the programmes forming part of the Plant's control system. The basic law is that the copyright in computer software vests in the writer until transferred. Therefore, unless a Contract says otherwise, the copyright in the control programmes will normally remain the property of the Contractor (or his Subcontractor) and a Purchaser of that software would simply receive an implied licence to use it for the purposes for which it is purchased.

The Clauses modify this basic position as follows:

- the Purchaser obtains the *ownership* of all software written by the Contractor or Subcontractors *as a part of the Contract*, which usually includes the Plant's operating/control systems;

- the Purchaser gains a specific licence to use all necessary software for the lifetime of the Plant;
- the Purchaser receives the information and source codes that he needs to be able to modify and update the software.

CLAUSE 20

Little comment is necessary on this Clause. It requires both parties to respect *all* confidential information received from the other during the Contract, both technical and commercial.

The Contractor is allowed to use the Purchaser's confidential information only during the period of the Contract and for the purposes of carrying out his work. The Purchaser is permitted to use the Contractor's confidential information during the lifetime of the Plant but only for the purposes of operation and maintenance. Maintenance does *not* include 'repair', therefore the Purchaser would not be entitled to use information provided by the Contractor, or by Subcontractors, to have spare parts manufactured.

Note that Clause 20.2 specifically provides that the Purchaser may at any time require confidentiality undertakings from the Contractor's personnel, and also from Subcontractors if he wishes. There is no equivalent clause giving the Contractor the same rights in respect of the Purchaser's personnel. If this were to be required, say where a process licence was involved, it would need to be included by a Special Condition.

Photographs etc.

Clause 20.4 bans the use of cameras and imaging software by the Contractor without prior consent. This looks old-fashioned, especially since when properly used a camera is an invaluable means of recording a situation, and therefore a vital project management tool. There are two reasons for the Clause. The first is that photographs/images of the Purchaser's Site should not to be used for publicity without his consent. The second is that a photograph should not be taken of any secret process or equipment belonging to the Purchaser without his consent.

3.1.9 Termination

There are two completely separate termination clauses in the Form—Clause 42 which permits termination where there has been no breach by the Contractor, and Clause 43 which provides for termination by the Purchaser where there has been breach of Contract by the Contractor.

Termination 'for convenience'
CLAUSE 42

This Clause gives the Purchaser the right to terminate the Contract at any time before the Contract is completed; however this is at the Purchaser's expense. This will obviously be a very costly exercise and means that the Purchaser may have to pay the Contractor a considerable amount for something that is of very little use. Therefore this is really a solution of last resort which the Purchaser will only use when he has absolutely no practicable alternative but to end the Contract.

The Clause is long and complex in wording and procedure but little different in content from similar clauses appearing in other sets of model conditions. What the Clause does is to set out the basis and procedure for calculating and paying a reasonable termination payment to the Contractor. The termination settlement will cover the cost of all work done by the Contractor up to termination, plus that of closing down the Contract and dealing with any long-term commitments made by the Contractor for the Contract, plus profit on that work.

Termination for breach
CLAUSE 43

Clause 43.1 allows the Purchaser to terminate the Contract where the Contractor is in major financial difficulties (and see also Clause 3.6) on whatever terms will allow the Purchaser to get the best out of the disaster that has hit his Contractor. The Clause does this by allowing the Purchaser to terminate the Contract if he wishes, which means that the Purchaser can deal with an administrator or liquidator from a position of strength, supported perhaps by the terms of Clause 25 (see below).

Clause 43.2 then deals with the Purchaser's right to terminate the Contract in the case where a Contractor ceases to continue the proper performance of the Contract or is in 'material', i.e. rather more than insignificant, breach of Contract. The Clause then lays down the procedure to be followed. If after written notice by the Project Manager the Contractor fails to take reasonable action to correct the breach then the Purchaser can terminate the Contract, also by written notice.

Clauses 43.3–4 then make practical provision for the completion of the Works by the Purchaser in the event of termination and then closing down what may well be a substantial construction operation.

Then Clauses 43.5–11 deal with the consequential financial settlement that will take place after termination—deciding what the costs of termination and completion of the work are, and therefore how much is owed by one party to the other. The Clauses are complex but straightforward and need no explanation.

There are two comments that I would make:

- Although there is a clause like this in virtually every set of model conditions, it is a clause that will only be used in the most extreme cases. The risks and problems of changing horses in mid-stream are normally so great that termination of any Contract for breach is very much a solution of last resort. A process Contract tends to lock the Purchaser into the Contractor at least for most of the Contract period.
- The complex demands that a process Contract makes on both parties are such that, however skilled their project management, both the Purchaser and Contractor will regularly be in breach of their contractual obligations. Documentation will be incorrect or delivered late. Approvals will be delayed or wrongly refused. Incorrect information will be given. Equipment will be faulty. There will be mistakes and errors on both sides throughout the Contract. It is very rare for any party to a complex Contract to be blameless. Therefore termination by the Purchaser for breach of Contract can often be strongly contested by the Contractor.

110

3.1.10 Notice procedures

CLAUSE 2.6

This Clause deals with the correspondence/communications between the parties during the Contract. Everything that might be important must be in writing. Then the Clause defines 'writing'. Writing means a permanent record and the more common types of permanent record are listed in the Clause. Note the reference to 'secure e-mail'. Secure e-mail means an e-mail system that retains a permanent copy of the e-mail text originally transmitted, so that any subsequent alterations of that text can be identified. Note also that a drawing is writing.

CLAUSE 5

This Clause needs no comment. It is procedural and self-explanatory. But the Clause is vital as it lays down the basic rule for all formal documents that may need to be exchanged between the parties and the Project Manager. Disregard the rule at your peril.

Two comments should be made regarding the procedure set out in the Clause:

- The Clause simply states that *oral* communications must be confirmed in writing within seven days *by the issuing party* in order to become valid.
- Problems often arise with communications made during progress meetings (Clause 5.3) because it may not always be clear to the receiving party that a notice has actually been given to him. Therefore to avoid doubts the authorised minutes of the meeting should always be written in such a manner as to make it absolutely clear when a notice or instruction has been given by either side. Note that it is only properly approved minutes that have 'decision/instruction/notice' status.

3.1.11 Dispute provisions

(See also section 1.4)

The IChemE Forms have an unusually good record in the dispute area, with possibly the lowest rate of serious dispute of any of the major model forms. In nearly thirty years of existence the Green Book contract has never been the subject of litigation.

CLAUSE 45

Clause 45 is the essential preliminary clause. Clauses 45.1–2 and 45.5 set the scene by stating that both sides should try to avoid the escalation of problems into dispute. Clearly this is in one sense a pious hope, but it is always better to say it and hope, than to say nothing and expect the worst.

Clauses 45.3–4 set up a formal procedure to identify any dispute. The aim here is to ensure that neither side leaps into any dispute procedure without both parties realising that an identifiable issue has arisen which has assumed 'Dispute' status. This is actually of great practical importance in the case of adjudication. There is nothing worse for the adjudicator than to have to waste precious days trying to identify what the dispute is actually all about.

Then Clauses 45.6–7 offer the first alternative settlement routes, negotiation and mediation.

Adjudication
CLAUSE 46
This Clause simply makes provision for adjudication in accordance with the Housing Grants Act. Of course in doing so it assumes two things—that the Site is within the UK and that the Contract does include some element of 'construction operations'. If either of these is not the case then Clause 45 should really be deleted by a Special Condition.

The Expert
CLAUSE 47
This provides for the referral of certain disputes to an Expert. A number of Clauses in the Conditions allow disputed decisions by the Project Manager or claims by the Contractor to be referred to the Expert for independent assessment if the Contractor and Project Manager cannot agree upon the matter reasonably quickly. The parties may also agree to ask him to decide other questions as well. The device enables such points to be settled fast (often simply by submitting documents to the selected Expert for his decision) and cleanly without the need to struggle through a mediation or arbitration procedure which is not designed for settling that type of dispute.

Therefore the Expert is given the power to decide questions submitted to him by whatever procedure he thinks fair, and to demand from both parties whatever assistance he requires for that purpose. He can therefore deal with the matter in whatever way he feels to be conducive to a speedy but equitable decision and consistent with the rules of natural justice.

He is also given the right by Clause 47.3, for very practical reasons, to decide any ancillary contractual issues that relate to the dispute. He can also decide who pays his charges for deciding the dispute.

His decision will also be binding on the parties and is not open to appeal. The whole aim of the Clause is to provide a speedy method of solving essentially factual disputes. It does appear to be extremely effective and extremely fair.

The Clause allows the parties to agree upon their own Expert, and if they are unable to do so either party can require an Expert to be appointed by IChemE. If so asked, IChemE would appoint some person with the appropriate qualifications, knowledge and experience to decide the issue, possibly but not necessarily an engineer, and probably competent to act as an arbitrator.

Arbitration
CLAUSE 48
Properly handled by an arbitrator who knows his stuff (and it must be said by solicitors and barristers who understand the differences between arbitration and litigation—of whom there are fewer than might appear at first glance), an arbitration can be quicker than going to the courts, much more confidential, rather more informal and likely to produce a more accurate decision on technical issues. However it is no less complicated to carry out than litigation. Arbitration will also be less expensive than litigation, but do realise that any argument between the parties that has to be settled through formal methods, whether arbitration or the courts may be horribly expensive both in money and

man-hours. The legal profession makes a very expensive and often commercially unsatisfactory subcontractor.

3.2 Project/contract management

The Clauses to be covered in this section are those listed under the headings 'Main Project Activity' and 'Site Work' in Figure 2 (see page 102).

For ease of reference the Clauses can be divided into the following groups:

- management personnel (Clauses 11 and 12);
- management control/manipulation (Clause 11.2);
- programme and time management (Clause 13);
- drawings and approvals (Clause 21);
- subcontracting (Clauses 9 and 10);
- project meetings (Clauses 3.7 and 29);
- pre-delivery inspection (Clause 22);
- Site activities (Clauses 3.3, 23–28 and 34).

3.2.1 Management personnel

The Conditions provide the same management/control relationship as the Red Book Conditions, but with one critical difference—that the Project Manager is given much wider powers to control/manipulate the way in which the Contractor carries out his work.

The structure comprises a project manager appointed by each party and dealing with each other, both having full power to control the running of the Contract together with authority to act on behalf of the company which they represent. These two project managers, the Project Manager for the Purchaser and the Contract Manager for the Contractor, are responsible for the overall management of the Contract.

The Project Manager is then supported by one or more Representatives who may either be responsible for the day-to-day management of the Contract, or responsible for managing various aspects of the Contract, such as work on Site, or the process control system, for example.

In other words the Project Manager may run the project on the basis of a two-tier management structure, with a Representative carrying out all day-to-day management and the Project Manager simply making the major 'policy' decisions; or he may carry out day-to-day management himself using Representatives as his assistants, or indeed without any Representatives at all.

The Contract Manager is supported by a Site Manager who is responsible for the control of construction and testing work on the Site.

CLAUSE 11
This Clause deals with the Purchaser's project management personnel.

The Contract is to be managed by the Project Manager, who must be named in the Contract (Clause 9 of the Agreement). The Contract should also state his address and how he may be contacted. This is important because the Project Manager is going to have to be responsible for a complex operation. If he is named in the Contract then he should have helped to set the project up or at least be reasonably well acquainted with its details. Therefore he will be able to take informed decisions from the start. There is nothing more annoying or disruptive to the Contractor than having to deal with a Project Manager who does not understand the basics of the project.

The Project Manager may then appoint one or more Representatives. A large project may well require the appointment of several Representatives, and Representatives may be changed as the project advances from the design to construction and testing stages. Often a Representative will be located at the Site once construction begins, as the Purchaser's Site Manager.

Clause 11.4 gives Representatives the basic power to reject, and therefore also to approve, any work by the Contractor, together with the authority to receive copy-notices from the Contractor. Under Clause 11.5 the Project Manager can delegate powers to his Representatives. Obviously if a Representative is to act as the day-to-day project manager or Site Manager he will need some additional powers, to order Variations for instance. This is for the Project Manager to decide. The greater the powers delegated by the Project Manager, the lower the degree of direct control he has over the project.

The conditions allow for the Project Manager to be either an employee of the Purchaser (or a sister-company of the Purchaser) or someone independent of the Purchaser, such as a consulting engineer. If this is to be the case it is preferable for both the Purchaser and Contractor if an individual *person* is named as the Project Manager rather than an organisation (see the definition of Project Manager in Clause 1). The reason for this is that if an organisation is appointed as Project Manager there will always be doubt as to precisely by whom and how authority may be exercised. Quite apart from this, project management requires firm and consistent decision-making to drive the project, which is inherently more likely with an individual than a committee.

The Purchaser needs to have a Project Manager in place for the whole duration of the Contract. He has to issue the Final Certificate. The Purchaser may wish to name a different person as Project Manager once the Plant has passed its takeover and performance tests and passes into the control of a production department, but the Final Certificate process requires knowledge of the Contract history.

The Conditions stress the need for fair treatment of the Contractor by the Project Manager and the Purchaser during the Contract, and Clause 11 deals with two aspects of this, in Clause 11.1, and in Clauses 11.3 and 11.4.

Clause 11.1

Clause 11.1 sets out the conduct expected from the Project Manager in managing the Contract. In addition Clause 11.1 makes it clear that the Purchaser is legally responsible for any failure by the Project Manager to act properly. The Clause states the following:

- The opening lines give the Project Manager 'full authority' to act on behalf of the Purchaser. The words 'full authority' are a little uncertain in their meaning (could someone else also have authority, for instance?), but the wording of the Clause makes it quite clear that the Purchaser is bound by any decisions made by the Project Manager.

- Paragraphs (a), (b) and (c) then make it clear that the Purchaser takes full responsibility to the Contractor for any failure or neglect of duty by the Project Manager by giving the Contractor the right to claim direct against the Purchaser if the Project Manager fails to perform properly.
- Finally, under Paragraph (d), the Project Manager is required to act using professional judgement and with impartiality as between Purchaser and Contractor. Obviously in practice no Project Manager can ever be *totally* impartial. Every Project Manager is the prisoner of his or her background and experience. Nevertheless the Clause requires the Project Manager to avoid any *significant* degree of bias when making any decision that affects the technical or commercial interests of the Contractor. Any failure will be a breach of the Contract for which the Purchaser will be liable.

Clause 11.1 is a strong clause. The IChemE conditions go further than any other model conditions in spelling out the duty and obligations of the Project Manager.

Clauses 11.3–4

As is normal in any contract, Clause 11.3 permits the Purchaser to replace the Project Manager.

In the process industry the Purchaser will often be a member of a group of companies and may buy in project management services from another company within the same group. Therefore Clause 11.4 treats any Project Manager employed by any other company within the same group as being employed by the Purchaser. The Clause also deals with a problem that may arise as a result of a change of Project Manager during the Contract. Experience has shown that, in certain situations, a Project Manager who is not employed by the Purchaser may find it rather easier to remain impartial under pressure. Therefore the Clause provides that the Contractor's consent may be required before the Purchaser can switch from an independent Project Manager to one of his own employees during the Contract.

Clauses 11.4–7

Under Clause 11.5 the Project Manager may appoint or change a Representative (or Representatives) at any time during the Contract. The Project Manager's Representative is more than simply a 'representative'. He is given the basic authority necessary for day-to-day management of the Contractor, the right to reject work done by the Contractor which is not in accordance with the requirements of the Contract, subject to a right of appeal to the Project Manager.

Clause 11.6 then permits the Project Manager to give additional powers to a Representative. Most common will be powers to approve designs or Documentation, or to issue instructions relating to matters such as site safety or Variation Orders.

Clause 11.7 provides a simple validation procedure in case a Representative should exceed his authority.

Finally Clause 11.8 provides that only the Project Manager/Representative and Contract Manager/Site Manager, or those authorised by them in accordance with the Contract, are authorised channels of communication unless the recipient of an unauthorised communication is willing to acknowledge it formally. For instance the Purchaser cannot normally intervene, except in cases where specifically permitted by the Conditions such as Clauses 36.6 and 43.3.

CLAUSE 12

Clause 12 deals with the project management personnel to be provided by the Contractor. There are two identified managers, a Contract Manager responsible for running the Contract, and a Site Manager, responsible for the day-to-day management of operations on Site.

The Conditions make very few references to the Contract Manager or Site Manager. In general they refer almost exclusively to 'the Contractor', although there are many references to 'the Project Manager'. The reason is that the Conditions give the Project Manager powers to manage the Contract, and the Contractor has the obligation to carry out the Contract. Of course the more procedural parts of the Contract such as Schedules and Specification may well make many more references to the Contract Manager and Site Manager.

The Contract is based upon two management relationships. The Project Manager or a Representative will deal with the Contract Manager during the design and manufacturing stages, and then their work towards each other will be supplemented by that of a Representative and the Site Manager during operations on the Site.

There will need to be a Contract Manager in place up to the end of the Defects Liability Period. He will need to co-ordinate work in connection with performance tests and Acceptance Certificate, deal with any repairs, and handle the work needed to apply for and obtain the Final Certificate. The Contractor is less likely to change the Contract Manager than the Purchaser is to change the Project Manager.

The Contract Manager is named in the Contract (see Clause 10 of the Agreement). The Contract should also state his address and how he may be contacted. The Contract Manager is entitled to appoint a deputy to act for him during any absence from the project for any time, by written notice to the Project Manager. This is a normal provision given that the life of a process contract may well be measured in years rather than months.

The Contract Manager is again given 'full authority' to act on the Contractor's behalf.

Under Clauses 12.2–3 the Contractor must appoint a Site Manager to be permanently based upon the Site and supervise Site operations. He must work exclusively on the Contract and must have a deputy capable of acting in his place while he is absent. The Contractor must also provide any further site supervisory staff *named in the Contract*. The Contractor need not appoint the Site Manager until the start of work at the Site. Clause 12.3 includes an additional requirement that the Contractor should provide all other supervisory staff that may be needed. Note also that the supervisory team to be provided by the Contractor must remain at Site beyond the taking over of the Plant if needed, until the completion of any performance tests, or perhaps even longer.

Clause 12.4 then permits the parties to list 'key personnel' in the Contract (Schedule 8). If so the Contractor may not move them from the Contract until their contribution has been completed. The principle is that in a process contract what may persuade the Purchaser to give the Contract to the Contractor (and what the Purchaser often actually wishes to buy) is the abilities of the Contractor's design/project team. In that case the Contractor must be prepared to commit the key individual members of that team to the project for the duration, if required.

Clause 12.5 is the standard clause permitting the Project Manager to have any member of the Contractor's Site management team withdrawn for incompetence or serious misbehaviour. The dismissal of a member of the management team is bound to be contentious and therefore the Project Manager cannot delegate this function, especially because it is not subject to appeal.

3.2.2 Management control/manipulation

We have already said that the reimbursable contract will always permit control of the collaboration by the Project Manager, since it is the power to control the Contractor that will give the Purchaser *flexibility*. This control is given by Clause 11.2 of the Conditions.

CLAUSE 11.2

Clause 11.2 states the power of the Project Manager to exert day-to-day control over the activities of the Contractor. He may at any time instruct the Contractor to carry out any part of the Works including the Contractor's own activities (see the definition in Clause 1) in whatever way the Project Manager wishes, and the Contractor must comply within a reasonable period. (Of course the Contractor is protected by the reimbursable nature of the Contract from any increase in cost that such an instruction might cause.) The Clause then allows the Contractor to use the Variation procedure to obtain any necessary extension in time or other change to the terms of the Contract that might be necessary as a result. The result is that the Project Manager has very wide powers if he decides to use them to change how the Contract is to be carried out.

3.2.3 Programme and time management

The Conditions deal with the Contractor's obligations as to time in a number of different ways:

- The Contract will include Schedule 11 setting out the 'Times of Completion' of the Works. At the very least this should list the dates for the completion of various stages and sections of the Plant and Works, and it may also include bar charts or other preliminary programme information.
- The Contract will contain Schedule 12, setting out the liquidated damages that will attach to the date or dates set out in Schedule 11 that are of special contractual significance. Generally this will be the date(s) of readiness for or completion of take-over tests.
- The Contract may contain some form of more detailed programme for the Works.

117

CLAUSE 13

The Contract can and should include at least an outline programme. Clause 13, however, will apply, whether or not this is so. It requires the Contractor to prepare and submit a further and more detailed programme of the work to the Project Manager for approval, in whatever form or detail the Project Manager considers reasonable in the circumstances. The actual words used, '. . . sequence in which and date(s) by which . . . etc', are common to some of the other model conditions available and permit the Project Manager to call for a considerable degree of detail if necessary. In general terms the Project Manager should always insist on a programme being prepared which contains *adequate* detail for his purposes. The more complex the project, the greater the detail that may be required.

Clause 13.1 simply states that the time obligation of the Contractor is to comply with Schedule 11. Schedule 11 should specify:

- the date for submission of the programme;
- the date(s) for submission of Documentation for Approval;
- the date(s) of readiness of the Plant for take-over tests;
- any other key dates (perhaps the date for successful completion of take-over tests).

Schedule 12 will then state the liquidated damages for delay and the dates/events to which those damages will apply.

Clause 13.2 then sets out the procedure for the certification of events that may trigger milestone payments.

Clause 13.3 deals with the preparation of the programme and requires the Contractor to predict when he will require Documentation and other foreseeable items of information and work from the Purchaser during the Contract. This is necessary to enable the Purchaser to programme his own work under Clause 4.1. The Conditions do not require the Contractor to give any other notice to the Purchaser of when he will need any Documentation, information or facilities.

Then Clause 13.3 requires the Project Manager to approve the Contractor's Programme if it is reasonable and complies with the Contract. If the programme is not reasonable or does not properly comply then the Project Manager may of course reject it and, although the conditions are silent on the point, require the Contractor to re-submit. Finally the Clause imposes an obligation, at the reasonable endeavours level (i.e. to try reasonably hard) to comply with the Approved Programme.

One other comment that may be made about Clause 13.3 is that it leaves the period for the preparation of the programme by the Contractor to be stated in Schedule 11. This is very much a decision that should be made on a case-by-case basis. Perhaps in most contracts the time can be quite short, but in some contracts a longer time might be more appropriate.

Clause 13.4 provides for the possible submission by the Contractor of a schedule of the numbers and types of personnel and resources to be employed on the project and particularly on the Site. This information is useful to the Project Manager both to assess whether the Contractor's programme is reasonable and then for checking progress as the work proceeds.

Clauses 13.5–8

These Clauses give the Project Manager considerable powers to use in the event that the Contractor is in serious delay in carrying out the Contract.

Clause 13.5 is a standard clause common to many sets of model conditions which allows the Project Manager to demand a revision of the programme, i.e. the re-scheduling of the work, in the event that the Contractor has fallen behind schedule. In addition it also allows the Project Manager to instruct the Contractor to take proper action to achieve the current programme where practicable.

Clause 13.7 follows on from Clause 13.5, by allowing the Project Manager to make his own revision to the programme where the Contractor has failed to put forward a proper proposal for revision after having been instructed to do so.

Finally Clause 13.6 gives the Project Manager the power to demand that the Contractor take steps to avoid further slippage against the programme and also that the Contractor take all possible steps to accelerate work to recover lost time against the programme if he is satisfied that the Contractor's rate of progress is *inadequate*, and that it is the Contractor's fault that it is inadequate. The legal/contractual meaning of the phrase 'best endeavours' is that the Contractor will only be excused for failure to succeed where he can demonstrate that it was virtually impossible that he could succeed.

Of course the Contractor's costs of taking action under these Clauses would be payable by the Purchaser.

Clause 13.8 then confirms that whatever steps are taken by the parties, contractual liability for lateness is unaffected.

3.2.4 Documentation and approvals

Contracts for the supply of equipment usually include provision for the approval by the Project Manager of designs/drawings submitted to him by the Contractor of the Plant which the Contractor proposes to supply.

Many engineers find the concept of the Project Manager 'approving' the Contractor's designs somewhat confusing when they first meet it. The purpose of the approval procedure is not for the Project Manager to take the place of the Contractor as the designer or to reduce the overall responsibility of the Contractor for the design of his equipment. Instead the purposes are:

- to enable the Project Manager to extract from the Documentation any information which he needs in order to ensure that the Purchaser can comply with Clause 4.1–2;
- so that the Project Manager can raise any comments or queries that he may have regarding the design of the Plant;
- so that the Project Manager can question any aspects of the design that he feels may be incorrect or inadequate;
- so that the Project Manager can, possibly for the first time, see a detailed design for the Plant that the Purchaser will receive.

The approvals procedure increases the Contractor's obligations rather than reduces them. Before Documentation has been approved the obligation of the

Contractor is to supply a Plant which complies with the Contract. After Documentation has been approved his obligation is to supply a Plant which complies with the Contract *and* is in accordance with the approved Documentation.

The Purchaser and Contractor should agree the list of Documentation to be subject to the approval procedure before Contract. This list should then be included in Schedule 2 to the Contract. Schedule 11 will then include the date or dates by which the listed Documentation must be submitted by the Contractor.

The Documentation to be submitted will generally be drawings but may well include other information as well—calculations, flow sheets, data sheets or diagrams for example.

Where the Contract is for a complex plant the Contractor will often also supply an actual or computer model of the Plant as an aid to construction. It would be possible to include a Plant model within Schedule 2, but this would be unusual. The model would normally be considered to be an item to be supplied after the Documentation had been approved.

Obviously it is for the Purchaser and Contractor to agree between themselves as to the number of documents and the detail to be included in Documentation, and therefore the quantity of information, to be approved by the Project Manager. There is a conflict here that can only be resolved by the Purchaser. Clearly the more information he includes within Schedule 2 and therefore within the approval process, the more he will learn about the precise physical characteristics of the Plant. However he must be prepared to pay the Contractor's charges for preparing the extra documents and to provide the man-hours necessary to examine those documents when they are submitted. He must also accept that the Contractor will certainly want additional time if the approval stage begins to expand beyond what is usual. There may also be limits to the practical value of the extra information that he obtains.

The basic procedure
CLAUSE 21

Clause 21.1 lays down a quality control procedure for all Documentation. Clauses 21.2–3 and 21.5 lay down the basic approval procedure. (Where documents are being transferred/submitted by electronic mail the Clauses will need to be suitably modified by a Special Condition).

The Documentation, number of copies, and so on will be described in Schedule 2. The Project Manager is given fourteen days to inspect each document. Effectively this means that he has fourteen days plus the rest of the day on which the item is submitted to him for approval; an item will be 'submitted' on the day on which it actually arrives at the Project Manager's address. By the end of that period the Project Manager must either:

- Return a copy to the Contractor endorsed as approved.
- Return a copy to the Contractor endorsed as not approved. The notification must reach the Contractor's address within the fourteen day period. If he does so the document must be amended and then re-submitted. As soon as the document has been re-submitted in a form which answers the objections of the Project Manager the document must then be approved by the Project Manager. Note that the Project Manager has very wide powers to ask for

re-design of the Plant/Works, including the right to require preferential engineering by the Contractor. (The Contractor can really only object when the Project Manager wants to go beyond what is good practice or laid down in the Contract). But then the Purchaser will pay the cost.

- Return a copy to the Contractor endorsed with any questions that he wishes to raise concerning the document. In this case the document is deemed to be approved subject to the question(s) being answered satisfactorily by the Contractor, and must then be approved by the Project Manager. If the Contractor is unable to answer any question satisfactorily then the document is not approved and should be re-submitted.
- Notify the Contractor of any comment that the Project Manager wishes to make concerning the document. In that case the Contractor should take due note of the comment and the document will be deemed to be approved subject to the Contractor confirming to the Project Manager that he will do so.
- If the Project Manager fails to approve any document or deliver to the Contractor any valid notification within the fourteen day period then the document is automatically approved.

Clause 21.3 then lays down two further basic principles. Once Documentation has been approved it binds the Contractor unless or until alternative Documentation has been approved by the Project Manager (usually as a part of a Variation). Approval of Documentation does not in any way reduce the Contractor's responsibility for the design of the Plant.

Dispute
Clause 21.4 deals with the problems that may arise because of disputes about any unwillingness by the Project Manager to accept the design proposed by the Contractor. The preferred route for any dispute is that of reference to an Expert.

Drawing inspection
Clause 21.6 gives the Project Manager an additional power to inspect, but not to keep or copy, all Documentation, except that which he is not permitted to see by the specific terms of the Contract. The right is useful to the Project Manager because it enables him to check on any minor details that he may need to know, and also because it enables him to verify the Contractor's progress in completing the design work. Note also that this Clause extends not simply to the Contractor, but also to Subcontractors. The Contractor will therefore need to pass the obligations under the Clause on in his Subcontracts.

In addition, under Clause 21.7 (if Schedule 2 provides) the Project Manager may also have access to, and copies of, other Documentation.

Final drawings/manuals
Clauses 21.9–10 then cover the supply of as-built drawings of the Plant and Works and operating and maintenance manuals. The form and content of this Documentation and manuals should be included in Schedule 2 to the Contract. In any event it should take account of whatever legislation is applicable. In the UK, for instance, the Health and Safety at Work Act requires that all equipment

supplied for operation in the workplace must be supplied with all information necessary to enable it to be operated and maintained safely. It should be supplied *before* taking-over (in other words if the documents are not supplied take-over should be delayed), reviewed by the Project Manager and any defects remedied by the Contractor.

Variations/changes
Clause 21.11 deals with the problem of ensuring that Documentation is kept reasonably up-to-date whatever changes are made to the design of the Plant.

Other documents
Clause 21.8 ensures that the Purchaser has suitable access to any Documentation necessary for insurance or safety-related purposes.

Mistakes
Clauses 21.12–14 deal with the problems caused by mistakes in Documentation produced either by the Contractor or by the Purchaser. The particular problem of the process plant is that it is a very large and complex construction, and it is all too easy to make mistakes when producing drawings. Some degree of correction will be almost inevitable.

Clause 21.12 simply provides that the Contractor will correct any mistake in Documentation prepared by him. Clause 21.13 provides that the Contractor will also correct errors in the Purchaser's documents, if requested to do so by the Purchaser, at the cost of the Purchaser, unless the mistake arises from any error by the Contractor, in which case Clause 21.14 shall apply.

Clause 21.14 then provides that the costs of any rectification work by the Contractor shall be paid by the Purchaser except where:

- it can be back-charged to a Subcontractor; or
- it is covered within a fixed fee; or
- it is necessary because of 'substandard' work by the Contractor (see my comment on Clause 37.3 in section 3.6).

3.2.5 Subcontracting
The general principles underlying Clauses 9 and 10 are as follows:

- The Contractor should be responsible for placing and managing the Subcontracts.
- The Purchaser is however reimbursing the Contractor's costs, and the bulk of those costs will be the costs of subcontracted work and Materials, rather than costs directly incurred by the Contractor. Therefore while the *Contractor* is paid on a reimbursable basis, the *Subcontractors* should be chosen wherever possible on the basis of competitive fixed-price bidding. This helps both to reduce overall cost and also to reduce price risk.
- As far as the choice of Subcontractor is concerned, he who pays the piper calls the tune. Therefore the Project Manager, representing the Purchaser,

should have the right to make or approve the final choice—to decide which bidder should get a Subcontract.

* Nominated Subcontractors are to be permitted, but are not to be encouraged.

In any major contract there will be a clash of opinions in regard to possible subcontracts. The Purchaser, who has to live with the final Plant for many years, will want to have some say in the choice of companies whose equipment will be incorporated into his Plant. He may want to standardise on certain suppliers or types of equipment for simplification of spares holdings and maintenance. He will not want to see equipment on his Site supplied by companies that he does not like dealing with. And so on.

The Contractor wants freedom of choice, for process reasons, and also to give himself the maximum chance to buy suitable equipment at the best prices.

This clash may be resolved in one of a number of different ways:

* complete freedom of choice for the Contractor;
* freedom of choice for the Contractor subject to approval of major Subcontracts by the Purchaser;
* inclusion in the Contract of lists of approved suppliers; and
* the use of nominated Subcontractors.

In the case of a reimbursable contract the clash is resolved very firmly in favour of the Purchaser.

CLAUSE 9
Assignment
Clause 9.1 provides that neither the Contractor nor the Purchaser may assign, i.e. dispose of, the Contract to a third party. The only exception to this is that the Contractor can assign the right to receive payments due under the Contract (for instance to an associated company of the Contractor or to a debt-factoring company).

Procurement
Clauses 9.2–8 then lay down a basic consultation/procurement procedure involving both the Contractor and the Project Manager in the selection of Subcontractors.

Clauses 9.2–4 define the procedure. Clauses 9.5–8 set out the main outlines of the Subcontract terms that the Contractor is to use. Finally Clauses 9.9–12 deal with ancillary matters.

CLAUSES 9.2 and 9.4
Clauses 9.2 and 9.4 provide for the following procurement procedure:

* The procurement procedure (including Subcontract Conditions, enquiry document, enquiry response times, etc) should be agreed between the Contractor and Project Manager in line with Schedule 7.
* If no procedure is agreed then the Contractor should adopt a standard competitive fixed-price procedure.
* All subcontracting should be done on the basis of this procedure unless unavoidable.

- The Contractor should obtain a reasonable number of bids from 'qualified' suppliers, ('qualified' in this context is almost indefinable, but will be easily understood by the engineer. It means that the supplier is reasonably competent to supply the equipment or services required.)
- The Contractor will assess the bids received, and then send the bids to the Project Manager, together with a statement setting out his assessment of the various bids and his recommendation as to which bidder should be selected. The assessment should also draw the attention of the Project Manager to any bids that the Contractor considers technically inadequate.
- The Project Manager will, if he wishes to do so, assess the bids for himself and then inform the Contractor of the supplier that he approves.
- The Contractor will then place the Subcontract with the approved supplier.

Clause 9.4 is silent as to the number of suppliers that should be approached, or whether the Project Manager has the right to decide suppliers that should be approached. These points are left for the Contractor to decide, unless the procurement procedure deals with the matter, or the Project Manager elects to issue an instruction under the terms of Clause 11.

Two comments should be made concerning Clause 9.2.

The Project Manager is given the power to give 'general approval' to purchases by the Contractor. This power is valuable and is generally used to reduce the volume of tenders that the Project Manager has to handle so that he can concentrate on important items. He will therefore usually give 'general approval' to the purchase of low-value items, or 'off-the-shelf' standard materials by the Contractor on the basis of the lowest-price tender.

The last sentence of the Clause makes it clear that the Contractor has the obligation to ensure that the Plant will still meet its guarantees whichever supplier is used or selected by the Project Manager. Therefore the Contractor should take care in his choice of suppliers to approach for bids, in the specifications that he uses to buy equipment and in his bid assessments. (Indeed in one sense in a fixed-price contract the Contractor runs the risk of under-specifying equipment, and in a reimbursable contract the Purchaser runs the risk of over-specification.)

Clause 9.2 then adds to the Project Manager's powers in respect of procurement by providing that the Contractor must procure any subcontracted Site work in a manner agreed with the Project Manager.

CLAUSES 9.5–8

Clauses 9.5 and 9.7–8 are straightforward in that they deal with some specific issues, price discounts, guarantees and the Purchaser's rights to terminate under Clauses 42 and 43. Clause 9.6 is more difficult, as it lays down a general principle concerning the terms on which Subcontracts should be let. This is that the Subcontracts should be let on 'similar' contract conditions to those of the Contract and that the Subcontractors should be required to observe any provisions of the Contract 'which apply to Subcontracts'. The Clause requires the Contractor to ensure that the conditions of the Subcontracts relate closely to the Contract conditions. It does not *demand* that the Contractor should endeavour to place Subcontracts that seek to be 'back-to-back' with the Contract conditions. (For further discussion of this problem see Chapter 5.)

CLAUSE 9.3

This Clause is straightforward. It deals with the potential clash of interest between the Contractor as an impartial procurement organisation working on the Purchaser's behalf and the Contractor as a possible supplier or sister-company to a possible supplier. The solution is straightforward—that the Contractor is entitled to benefit from possible Subcontracts provided that the issue is dealt with openly.

CLAUSE 10

This is largely a standard nominated Subcontractor clause that allows the Purchaser to select the suppliers of particular items of work or equipment who are to be employed as Subcontractors by the Contractor. There are two ways that this can happen. The first is where the Contract itself requires the Contractor to employ a particular named Subcontractor, in other words it states that a particular supplier is to be used, *and* states that the supplier shall have 'nominated' status under Clause 10.1. The second is where Clause 10.2 applies.

The opening lines of Clause 10.2 are the key to the whole of the Clause. They state that a Subcontractor may only have nominated status where the Contract specifically states that certain items will be provided by a Subcontractor to be nominated by the Project Manager *after the Contract has come into being*.

Clauses 10.3–4 provide a procedure for the Contractor to object to a nomination if he feels that there are substantial grounds for believing that the actual company nominated will cause him commercial or technical problems in carrying out the Contract. Clause 10.3 lays down the procedure to be followed by the Contractor. The Contractor must notify the Project Manager of his objection within four weeks after nomination, and must give reasons for objecting. Clause 10.4 then requires the Project Manager to respond to a valid objection in appropriate fashion.

Clause 10.5 closes the door to further claims by the Contractor once he has accepted any nominated Subcontractor. Of course in a reimbursable contract the risks posed to the Contractor by a nominated Subcontractor are much reduced.

Clause 10.7 requires the Purchaser to accept the responsibility, or risk, for any extra cost incurred by the Contractor because of a failure by a nominated Subcontractor to perform properly. This is in fact justifiable in the context of the process plant where there may be potential process implications affecting the selection of almost every equipment item.

Clause 10.6 emphasises the special status of the nominated Subcontractor by, in effect, giving the Subcontractor a possible right of appeal to the Project Manager in the event of any dispute between himself and the Contractor.

It has to be said that the nominated Subcontractor is a difficult beast to manage at the best of times for both Contractor and Purchaser, however reasonable the theoretical position. Clause 10.7 could leave the Purchaser responsible for cost overruns caused by a Subcontractor with whom he had comparatively little real bargaining power. Therefore there are two precautions that the Purchaser who intends to nominate should always consider taking:

- To ensure that the potential nominated Subcontractor is not informed of his position in case he should allow his 'monopoly' status to influence his bargaining position vis-a-vis the Contractor, or
- To set up a separate contract between the Purchaser and the potential Subcontractor in advance of or at the time of nomination. This would require the Subcontractor to accept the appropriate Subcontract terms and also create direct responsibility from the Subcontractor to the Purchaser, in case Clause 10.7 should ever be activated.

Subcontract terms

Finally we come to a small group of Clauses that deal with some standard situations.

Clauses 9.10–11 provide that wherever confidential information is passed between the Purchaser and a Subcontractor, in whichever direction, then the recipient will be directly responsible to the other party for any breach of confidentiality, under the terms of the Contract (Rights of Third Parties) Act. The practical arrangements for this of course are the responsibility of the Contractor, through the terms of the Subcontracts and his communications with the Project Manager.

Then Clause 9.7 requires the Contractor to obtain guarantees in the names of both the Contractor and Purchaser from all Subcontractors in respect of the items that they supply. The supplier of structural steelwork or ready-mixed concrete might, in practice, be asked for very different guarantees to those of a pump or vessel manufacturer. The period of those guarantees is to be as close to those of the Contract as possible. (Bear in mind that Materials might be delivered by the Subcontractor long before the Plant is taken over). These guarantees are enforceable by the Purchaser directly under the terms of the Contract (Rights of Third Parties) Act.

Finally Clause 9.9 bars 'pay-when-paid' Subcontracts.

3.2.6 Vesting

CLAUSE 25 and CLAUSES 34.3–5

In one sense it is illogical to deal with these Clauses at this point, because they are more concerned with the problem of the possible liquidation of the Contractor than the delivery of equipment to Site. They provide a standard 'vesting'/'devesting' procedure. Its purpose is, so far as possible, to try to minimise the disruption to the project in the event of the financial collapse of the Contractor. They are dealt with here only because they have to be taken into account during procurement.

Essentially a vesting procedure seeks to minimise the problems that might be caused by a seller's financial disaster. It can do no more than that. If a company goes into liquidation control of all the assets of the company will pass to a liquidator who has a duty to convert the company's assets into money for distribution to creditors. He will therefore sell those assets, including any work in progress, to the highest bidder. The purpose of a vesting clause is to transfer ownership of equipment from a seller to a buyer, while it is still work in progress. If then the seller then gets into financial difficulties and is put into liquidation (or receivership) the buyer would have the right to take possession of the equipment, as it is his property, and remove it from the seller's premises. Then any necessary work can be carried out by another manufacturer and the equipment put into use. Of course the liquidator would have the right to recover reasonable payment from the buyer for any work done by the seller, but would not have any other legal power to delay the project.

Clause 25.1 provides that where the Purchaser is due to make phased payments for equipment under the Contract, and does actually make such a payment, then the ownership of the equipment will transfer to the Purchaser. The Clause applies to all equipment, both manufactured by the Contractor and by Subcontractors, therefore this Clause needs to be taken into account in Subcontracts by the Contractor. (By 'phased payments' we mean any advance, stage, or progress payments.) Clause 25.3 is self-explanatory.

If the Contract does not include for phased payment then ownership will transfer on delivery to the Site (not on installation/erection).

Clause 25.2 deals with the marking/storage considerations. If a vesting clause is to work properly it must allow the Purchaser to be able to identify precisely which items have become his property, otherwise a liquidator would quite properly refuse to release them.

Clauses 34.3–4 then deal with the situation that arises when items are no longer needed for the project or need to be removed so that they can be replaced or reworked. They are reasonably self-explanatory. Finally Clause 34.5 deals with the question of surplus materials that are to be left on Site.

3.2.7 Project/site meetings

The aim of Clause 29 is to outline an arrangement to ensure monthly (at least) progress meetings to monitor progress on the Contract. The Clause states that meetings are only at the option of the Contractor or Project Manager, but in practice regular meetings, probably held a few days after the submission by the Contractor of his monthly progress reports under Clause 3.7, are very worthwhile.

CLAUSE 3.7
The last paragraph is a straightforward procedural clause requiring monthly (at least) progress reports, supported by whatever backup Documentation is necessary in the circumstances, to be submitted by the Contractor. Usually the Contract would allow the Project Manager or the parties to fix or agree precise timing for reports. Usually too the aim would be for progress reports to be submitted a few days in advance of project meetings.

CLAUSE 29
Clause 29.1 needs no comment. Note that the meetings will, or may, be attended by four different groups of people—the representatives of both project management teams, Subcontractors and then any others who need to be there on an ad-hoc basis.

Clause 29.2 provides for the meetings to be minuted by the Project Manager, and for minutes to be signed by both parties. The Clause is very cumbersome in the way it deals with the minutes of progress meetings—but it is very difficult to think of an alternative that would not be equally cumbersome.

Note that, under Clause 29.3 the agreed minutes of progress meetings are automatically contractually binding, where they record any notice or instruction, once they have been signed in accordance with Clause 5.3.

3.2.8 Pre-delivery inspection

Repairing or replacing defective equipment is always far more expensive in time and money once that equipment has left the factory. Therefore Clause 22 assumes that the Contract will include, in Schedule 13, specific descriptions of the pre-delivery tests and pre-installation tests which will be carried out on any critical items of equipment, plus probably a general provision that all equipment will be subject to normal pre-delivery tests before being accepted for delivery to the Site. Clause 22 is a standard procedural clause, similar to the pre-delivery inspection clauses found in other sets of model conditions.

The Clause also allows the Project Manager to nominate inspectors who will exercise his functions under the Clause, if he wishes.

Principles

Clause 22.1 gives the Project Manager, and any inspector nominated by the Project Manager under Clause 22.8, access to the premises of the Contractor and also those of his Subcontractors. (The Contractor must take Clause 22 into account when preparing his Subcontracts.) The Clause gives the Project Manager the right both to observe tests, and also to inspect equipment in the course of manufacture and other work such as calibration. The Clause does not make any specific provision for the right to reject any equipment found to be defective by the Project Manager during any inspection, leaving the Project Manager and Contract Manager to settle the matter by discussion. It would, of course, be extremely unusual for the Contract Manager to refuse to take note of any reasonable objections raised by the Project Manager during any inspection. Indeed the Contractor could well be in breach of Clauses 2.4 and 3.2 (and 3.8) of the Conditions in doing so.

Clause 22.2 sets out the basic obligation of the Contractor to arrange and carry out tests.

Procedure

Clauses 22.3 and 22.5–6 set out the procedure for giving notification of readiness for test and the testing of equipment. The Clauses are reasonably self-explanatory. Note that the Clause does not deal with the costs of carrying out or witnessing any repeat tests. The conditions assume that each party would bear its own costs.

Additional tests

A process contract will cover many different types and items of equipment, many of which may not have been identified at the time of Contract. It is impossible for the Contract to set out in detail what pre-delivery tests are to be carried out on every single item. Therefore Clause 22.4 allows the Project Manager to require any item of equipment to be given any pre-delivery tests that the Project Manager wishes, in addition to the tests specified in the Contract.

The Project Manager must notify the Contractor of any additional tests in adequate time to allow the Contractor to arrange for the tests. With respect to the equipment manufactured by the Contractor himself this could mean at almost any time up to delivery itself; if however a test would involve the use of scarce test-bed facilities, notice would in practice need to be given much earlier. With respect to equipment manufactured by a Subcontractor the problem is much more difficult because the Contractor would almost certainly be charged extra for *any* test not written into the purchase order. This would then lead to a claim by the Contractor for a Variation to the Contract. Therefore the Project Manager should, as far as possible, be prepared to indicate any tests that he might require at the time of procurement by the Contractor, so that the Contractor can make adequate provision when ordering.

As regards the cost of additional tests, Clause 22.4 provides that tests that are normal practice should not be charged for. Other tests may be charged for, as stated in the Clause. Of course the question will always arise of exactly what is 'normal practice', but few serious problems arise. Clause 22.7 repeats the basic cost principle.

3.2.9 Site activities

Any engineer looking at the Conditions for the first time will wonder why they have so little to say about the construction of the Plant, especially compared, for example, to the ICE or RIBA model conditions. All that the Conditions do is to specify in outline the facilities that the Contractor is to provide and then to lay down general rules about the way that he is to organise the Site and his workforce. In fact the Site activities clauses occupy only two to three pages in the Conditions, compared with two pages on insurance/responsibility for Site damage, three pages on Variations, or over four pages on Site tests.

The reasons are simple:

- the Contractor must, to some extent at least, be left to run the project his way, and can be manipulated if necessary;
- the terms of the Contract relating to administrative detail and work quality and supervision can be safely left to the Schedules and Specification;
- as the Conditions are for use by professionals they concentrate upon the essentials—the testing procedures to demonstrate that the Plant will produce what the Contract requires it to produce—rather than the control of the construction process.

Since all the Clauses that deal with Site activities are concerned with setting out general rules, they are reasonably straightforward.

Availability and access
CLAUSE 23
In general terms this Clause speaks for itself.

Clause 23.1 deals with the date for access to the Site. It lists the possible options open to the parties for fixing the date in order of precedence. The Conditions do not make any specific provision for the consequences of delay by the Purchaser in making the Site available to the Contractor. Simple failure to provide access would of course be breach of the Purchaser's obligations, allowing the Contractor to claim costs, plus time. The Purchaser does have other options such as suspending the Contract under Clause 42, and/or allowing the Contractor to deal with delay under Clause 14.2(d), or, if justified, claiming force majeure.

Clause 23.2 then provides for the access route to the Site, stating that it is the responsibility of the Purchaser to provide an adequate access route to the Site boundary from a convenient point on a public road. Clauses 23.2 and 23.3 then make the Contractor responsible for the suitability of the route up to that convenient point. There are two problems with the suitability of any route—the weight of traffic or individual loads that it must carry, and its ability to take unusually wide, long and high loads. Should any Plant require the bringing to Site of 'extraordinary traffic' this would obviously need special consideration, and probably a Special Condition.

Clauses 23.4 and 23.7 are straightforward and need no comment.

Control and access

Clauses 23.5–6 are self-explanatory. The Contractor has possession of the Site under Clause 23.1 and therefore control of it. Under Clause 23.6 he can and must exclude from it any third party who does not have specific authorisation from the Purchaser and anyone who has no need to to be there, and under Clause 23.5 he can *and must* also refuse access to other contractors where their work would unreasonably impede his own. Of course this will often be of great importance to the Contractor. He has a large and complex construction/ erection job to do, and the presence of others on the Site will almost inevitably impede his work at some time or another. Apart from that he must allow reasonable access to the Site to the Purchaser and other contractors. The consequences of Clauses 23.5–6 are that the Contractor will need to set up facilities for controlling access to the Site.

CLAUSE 24
Clauses 24.1, 24.2 and 24.4 need no comment.

One comment upon Clause 24.3 is necessary. It provides that the Contractor may not move anything on to the Site in advance of the Approved Programme without the consent of the Project Manager. This is because the Purchaser may need to prepare the Site or access route and arrange for permission for the Contractor's traffic to use the route from the owner of the land. The Purchaser will almost certainly use the Approved Programme as guidance as to when the Site and access route must be ready for the Contractor.

Construction
CLAUSE 3.3
The Clause is straightforward and needs no comment.

CLAUSE 26

This Clause is of major importance, but needs very little comment. The principles are straightforward and will be well known to all Contractors and Purchasers. Also note Clause 7.2.

CLAUSES 26.1–4

These Clauses combine with Schedules 4 and 5 to set up a Site regime in line with best practice. It will be obvious from the wording of Clause 26.1 that the Clauses are drafted to comply with UK law—but there are no significant differences between UK law and law throughout the rest of the European Union, and probably very few between European law and law in the rest of the world. Therefore the Clauses would need modification in any Contract where the Plant was to be constructed on a Site outside the UK, but they provide a good framework to begin from. In particular the references to UK legislation in Clause 26.1 would need amending. Note especially the requirements of Clauses 26.3 and 26.4(c).

CLAUSE 26.5

This Clause requires the Contractor to accept responsibility for pollution and hazardous material, and all consequential costs, arising from the Works, subject however to a number of limits, as follows:

- where pollution occurs as the inevitable result of the Works;
- where pollution occurs as the inevitable result of instructions by the Project Manager or Purchaser;
- where the pollution was already in existence at the Site but could not have been foreseen; or,
- where the sheer extent of the pollution was more than could reasonably have been foreseen.

The effect of the Clause is to underline the need for both parties to plan for the risks of pollution and hazardous materials that might arise during the Contract, and to carry appropriate insurance cover.

CLAUSE 27

This Clause deals with the subject of the resources needed to construct, erect and test the Plant, apart from the Site management team called for by Clause 12. The principle is very simply that the Contractor is to provide everything required to carry out the Work on the Site unless it is specifically stated in the Contract that a particular item is to be provided by the Purchaser. There is no mention of any right for the Contractor to use any power supplies or lifting gear or other facilities of the Purchaser on the Site.

Clause 27.1 is simply a clear statement of the general principle. The Contractor will provide all the Materials at the Site as stated in the Contract, together with all resources such as labour, construction equipment and services necessary to carry out the Works, other than those which the Purchaser is to provide.

Clauses 27.2 and 27.3 are a straightforward list of the main support services that the Contractor is expected to provide for the construction operation.

In effect the Contractor is being asked by these Clauses to ensure that the Site can operate as a complete, safe, self-contained unit without needing any support from the Purchaser.

Clause 27.4 needs no comment.

Clause 27.5 requires the Contractor to be able to produce certification for his construction equipment, such as safety inspection certificates for cranes and slings, whenever requested.

Clause 27.6 requires the Contractor to make the necessary arrangements to ensure that no construction equipment will be removed from Site until no longer needed. In particular this may require special arrangements to be made with the suppliers of equipment under hire, so that the hiring agreements can be transferred from the Contractor to the Purchaser in case of the Contractor's receivership or liquidation.

Employment conditions

Clause 28 is really not so much a clause as an outline statement of a number of agreements in principle that may need to be covered at greater length in Special Conditions.

CLAUSE 28

Clause 28.1 requires the Contractor to provide, and to require his Subcontractors to provide, reasonable pay and conditions for personnel working on the Site. Clause 28.3 then adds to this by stating that where the Site on which the Contractor is working is covered by a general agreement on working conditions the Contractor will conform to that agreement. (On very large construction sites, or sites where a number of different contractors are working, general agreements are sometimes used to minimise disputes over problems such as differential pay rates, poaching of labour, job demarcation, etc. A general agreement will provide for common or co-ordinated recruitment of labour, generally similar pay structures for all contractors, co-ordinated safety procedures, common policies for personnel matters, etc.)

Then Clause 28.2 requires the Contractor to keep the Project Manager/ Purchaser advised of any potential or actual industrial relations problems on the Site.

Clause 28.4 allows the removal of *any other person* from the Site (compare Clause 12.5) for unsafe conduct, incompetence or serious misconduct of any other kind, at the cost of the Contractor.

Clause 28.5 is self-explanatory.

Site clearance

CLAUSES 34.1–2

These Clauses are standard and need no comment.

3.3 Completion and testing

The Clauses to be covered in this section are those listed under the heading 'Tests' in Figure 2 (see page 102).

3.3.1 General approach

The completion and testing phase is the most critical part of any process Contract for both parties.

For the Contractor it is the crunch, the culmination of everything that he has been trying to achieve, and it happens so late in the Contract that there is very little time to put things right if they go wrong.

For the Purchaser the position is much the same. If the Plant passes its tests then he has to accept it, even if it is not really what he wants, and if it fails then his project is potentially a disaster.

Consequently there is a change of emphasis as the test period approaches. In the design and manufacturing periods the question is always 'does the Plant (or Works or Materials) meet the Specification?' At the testing stage that question changes to 'will it pass the tests?' The tests become the definitive requirement of the Contract in place of the Specification.

The Conditions assume that the Contract will contain or result in an agreed test or tests which will be a fair examination of whether or not the Plant does comply with the Contract. It is critical to both Contractor and Purchaser to ensure that this is so. If the tests are too stringent or lax the result will be unfair to one or the other. The issue is of particular importance because of the scope of testing provided by the Conditions.

3.3.2 Defining the tests

Every Contract Specification has to deal with three separate aspects of the equipment or Plant that it describes. These are *physical* dimensions and characteristics, *quality* of finish or manufacture, and *performance*.

When a Specification deals with something very simple, such as a knife or fork, the Specification will be very simple. It concentrates on the physical nature and quality of the item being described. It will not mention performance at all. When the buyer wishes to check whether the item meets the Specification the test that he will carry out will be equally simple. He will merely inspect the item to check that it is made from the proper materials to the proper dimensions, the quality of finish, and that there are no obvious defects.

When a Specification deals with something slightly more complex, such as a bicycle, the Specification/tests will cover more ground. In addition to physical characteristics and quality, the Specification will now also deal with performance required, and the buyer's checks will now include a running test to ensure that the wheels go round and the brakes work.

Go to something more complicated such as a machine tool and the Specification will change again. It will concentrate less on detailed physical description, though it will still deal with the physical characteristics that are required. Instead it will deal more with reliability, quality and performance. Also the running test will now concentrate on the ability of the machine to produce the product. (If a performance test is a test to demonstrate whether anything performs in accordance with the requirements of the Contract, then a running test is a performance test for a machine.)

Once the Specification has to deal with a Plant, it will include only the minimal amount of physical description. It will put far more emphasis upon the general characteristics, quality and performance required. Also the running tests on the Plant will change. Because a Plant comprises a large number of separate items of equipment which must operate as a single integrated unit there will now need to be tests to show that each item of equipment works and then tests to show that integration has been achieved. This is difficult to do properly without putting the Plant into operation, and a series of tests now need to be carried out.

3.3.3 The tests in context

The testing Clauses are part of a series of design/approval/testing stages that accompany or are allowed for by the Conditions.

The very first stages take place pre-contract. There may be a formal pre-qualification stage. Negotiations for the Contract will certainly include discussions on the Contractor's ability to design and construct the Plant, together with the design of Plant that he will supply. The Purchaser will wish to be sure that the Contractor can do the job. He will check that the Contractor understands what it is that is required, and that he can and will construct a Plant that is at least approximately what the Purchaser wants it to be.

These negotiations will also need to settle a number of specific contractual questions. These are:

- the wording of the Specification;
- the description of the Works (Schedule 1);
- the description of the various items and services to be provided by the Purchaser in accordance with Clause 4 and Schedules 2 and 3, both to assist the Contractor in the design/construction of the Plant, and also during the test stages;
- detailed descriptions, so far as can be achieved at this early stage of the project, of the various inspection and testing procedures to be carried out before delivery and at each test stage, comprising:
  - pre-delivery tests under Clause 22.2 (Schedule 13);
  - construction completion tests (Schedule 14);
  - take-over procedures and take-over tests (Schedule 15);
  - performance tests (Schedule 16).

The next two stages are then those of Documentation approval and pre-delivery inspection under Clauses 21 and 22, when the Project Manager is given the opportunity to query the Contractor's detailed designs, and when the Materials are inspected and tested.

Then come three test stages following construction of the Plant—construction completion, take-over tests and performance tests. (The Conditions state that performance tests are optional, but this is an option that the Purchaser will almost always use unless his process is secret.) The purpose of these stages is to demonstrate progressively the fitness of the Plant to meet the requirements of the Contract.

The construction completion procedures demonstrate that the construction of the Plant has been completed and that it is in good and safe condition for commissioning.

The take-over test demonstrates that the Plant is in operating condition and can be run on a production basis. As the Plant can now run the Purchaser is getting benefit from it, therefore the risk in the Plant will transfer from the Contractor to him and the Defects Liability Period will commence.

The performance test demonstrates that the Plant is capable of meeting the output/quality guarantees given by the Contractor in the Contract, once the Plant has been run up to full operating condition and any final adjustments or modifications have been made by the Contractor.

3.3.4 Test specifications

It is always entirely a question for the parties to agree upon what the tests are to be, though of course in practice one party will tend to impose its own ideas upon the other. There is no such thing as a standard test. Therefore it is impossible to set out any precise rules for defining any test under the Conditions.

Tests will also vary depending on precisely when they are carried out. This is a question to be decided by the Purchaser. Practice varies considerably. In some industries, such as the water or food industry, it is normal practice for the Contractor to carry out the take-over test on a Plant that is in full normal production. In other industries, such as the pharmaceutical industry, the Purchaser might not put the Plant into production until after the Contractor has withdrawn from the Site. Nevertheless there are a number of general suggestions that can be made.

3.3.5 Construction completion tests

The purpose of the Construction Completion Certificate procedure is to demonstrate that the Plant is complete and in good condition. It also needs to show that the Plant is in a *safe* condition because no process material can be allowed into the Plant if there is danger of leakage or accident.

Therefore following the issue of any draft Construction Completion Certificate by the Contractor the Project Manager should conduct a complete inspection of the relevant parts of the Plant to check, so far as he has not done so already, that:

- those parts have been completely constructed;
- nothing is in poor or damaged condition;
- the parts have been correctly constructed (for instance non-return valves operate in the correct direction);
- there is no internal obstruction or dirt left inside them;
- all work is of the correct quality.

Next the Project Manager will wish the Contractor to demonstrate that the various items of equipment are in working order, that valves open and close, etc. Finally the Contractor may be required to carry out appropriate tests to demonstrate mechanical integrity, perhaps pressure tests or leak tests using water or air rather than the process fluids, and perhaps tests to demonstrate that the control and safety systems and equipment are in operational order.

The specific requirements for this programme of inspections, demonstrations and tests should be included in Schedule 14.

3.3.6 Take-over tests

The take-over tests are important for both sides. The Purchaser will usually want to get the Plant into operation as soon as it is in working order, because delay in bringing the Plant on stream can have a serious effect on the economics of the project by delaying and then extending the pay-back period for the Plant. However he will not want to take over a Plant which is not capable of being put into production, and the Project Manager will not want to release the Contractor from his obligations until the Plant is in operating condition.

The Contractor will obviously want the Plant to be taken over as soon as he has put it into operating order. The Take-Over Certificate will almost certainly trigger a payment and also transfers responsibility for the Plant to the Purchaser, starts the guarantee period running, and gets the Contractor off a major Contract hook. However once the Plant has been taken over, the Contractor will lose control over it and will still be responsible if it fails the performance test. Therefore the Contractor will not want to carry out a take-over test until the Plant is generally fit for the performance test.

The take-over procedures in Schedule 15 will normally do two things. First the Contractor will be required to demonstrate that all the various parts of the Plant, electrical and mechanical equipment, control systems, etc, are in proper order. Then the Contractor will be required to carry out a running test on the Plant, either using process materials or using a non-process material such as water, to demonstrate that the Plant is capable of normal operation.

3.3.7 Performance tests

The performance test is a test to prove that the Plant is capable of manufacturing the products for which it is designed under all normal operating conditions foreseen by the Contract.

That is the theory. In practice of course no Purchaser can expect this. The Plant is still at the teething stage, in need of fine tuning and being run by operators who are not yet used to its little ways, and perhaps not yet fully experienced in the process or the equipment. Most companies would expect the production from any Plant to be measurably higher after a year or two of normal operation than at the time when the Plant is first put into production.

Also no test can really reproduce all normal operating conditions.

Therefore every performance test (and take-over test) has to be something of a compromise. It has to be for a comparatively short operating period, and probably the Plant will only make a limited selection of the possible product range, or operate under a part of the full range of operating conditions. But it has to be a test from which the parties can make deductions about the capability of the Plant to make the full range of products over its normal operating life.

Again there are a number of general principles:

- The test should not be unreasonably long. Obviously it needs to be for long enough to enable proper measurement of performance and to give some indication of equipment and process reliability. However a test that goes on for too long proves very little and risks being interrupted by something that has nothing to do with the Plant at all, when the whole thing has to start all over again at the Purchaser's cost.

- The test must be selective. The Purchaser can never expect any test to cover the whole of the Plant's product range.
- There has to be a limit to the number of parameters that the parties seek to measure during the test.
- The test should be run using the Plant's own controls and instrumentation. It is seldom practicable to try to install supplementary instrumentation to measure additional parameters during the test.
- Finally the most important. Unless you can design a test that will measure something accurately there is no point in asking for it to be guaranteed.

3.3.8 Performance guarantees and liquidated damages

The main reason why any performance test must be selective is that the test is used to do two entirely distinct things. First it is used to determine whether the Plant operates in accordance with the Contract. Secondly it is used to measure the degree of any shortfall in the performance of the Plant.

Should there be a major shortfall, the Plant will fail the test and must be modified or adjusted before being re-submitted.

Should there be only a minor shortfall in performance however the Plant may be accepted by the Purchaser, subject to the payment by the Contractor of liquidated ('agreed' in legal jargon) damages. Liquidated damages may be fixed for a number of different parameters, such as production quantity, degree of impurities, wastage of raw materials, usage of power or chemicals, etc. The problem for the Purchaser is that the more complex the test he uses, or the more parameters he tries to measure for liquidated damages, the more tempting it becomes for the Contractor to set the Plant up to minimise his exposure to damages rather than to make the product.

Again there is no standard way of setting up a liquidated damages structure, but there are some general principles:

- unless a parameter can be measured accurately it should not carry liquidated damages;
- unless a parameter has *real* significance in process *and* economic terms it should not carry liquidated damages;
- always allow a measuring tolerance—no instrument outside a laboratory ever measures with complete accuracy;
- one, or perhaps two, parameters may be treated as mandatory, with no shortfall allowed (except for a measurement tolerance);
- one, two, or perhaps three at the most, other parameters may then be subject to liquidated damages.

If it is the intention of the Purchaser to include provision for liquidated damages in the Contract then Schedules 16 and Schedule 17 should be completed. In other words the performance test and liquidated damages should be defined in the Contract and not left to be agreed later.

FORMS OF CONTRACT: USER GUIDE

The Conditions set out a practicable testing scheme. Clearly no two projects and no two Plants will ever be the same and therefore the Clauses will often be modified or supplemented by the parties.

The scheme is as follows. The Contractor issues a draft Construction Completion Certificate under Clause 32 when the Plant, or any part of the Plant, is fully erected. That work is then inspected. Once the Plant has been fully constructed, take-over procedures are carried out under Clause 33 including any take-over tests specified in the Contract. On successful completion of the take-over procedures, a Take-Over Certificate is issued by the Project Manager and the Plant then passes over to the Purchaser and the guarantee period commences. When the Purchaser, or perhaps in practice both parties, is ready, performance tests are then carried out during the early part of the guarantee period under Clause 35, and an Acceptance Certificate is issued once those performance tests have been properly completed.

3.3.9 The testing procedure

Construction
CLAUSE 32
This Clause requires few comments. Clauses 32.1–4 set out a procedure for the approval by the Project Manager of a series of Construction Completion Certificates as the work of constructing the different parts of the Plant is carried out. Clause 32.5 deals with the cost of repeat tests. Clause 32.6 deals with the certification procedure for tying back the completion of construction to the Contract dates set out in Schedule 11, if appropriate. Finally Clause 32.7 suggests that any dispute concerning certification should be decided by an Expert.

Clause 32.1 establishes that the Plant may be treated as a single construction exercise, or as a number of separate exercises. This allows for two possibilities that can often happen in practice, that the various sections of the Works might be carried out at different times, or that they might be treated as entirely separate exercises. For instance preliminary civil engineering work to prepare the Site might be carried out by a different workforce well before the erection of the Plant begins. The erection of a tank farm might be carried out over the same time-scale as the main Plant, but by a separate workforce.

Clause 32.2 then sets out a further basic principle, that approval of construction can, and probably will, be carried out on a piecemeal basis, rather than as a single all-embracing exercise.

The procedure is initiated by the Contractor who may issue a Construction Completion Certificate for all the Plant (or a section of the Plant if Clause 32.1 applies), or any 'appropriate part' of the Plant, when he considers that it is 'substantially' complete. An appropriate part of the Plant will be any area or part that can reasonably be inspected and tested as a unit. Something is 'substantially' complete when it is sufficiently complete to be capable of use for its intended purpose, though not necessarily absolutely complete.

In the Certificate the Contractor will define the part of the Plant being offered for inspection and tests and will set out his programme for the tests.

The Project Manager is allowed a week's grace to make whatever preparations are necessary before the inspection/test period begins, unless he is prepared to respond more quickly.

Clause 32.4 then provides that if the part fails on inspection and test the Project Manager must identify the shortcomings that he has found so that the Contractor knows precisely what to correct before re-submitting the part.

Clause 32.3 then deals with the proper form to be used by the Project Manager when accepting that construction of any part of the Plant is complete and also reminds him of the whole purpose of the construction completion exercise. He is to endorse the Construction Completion Certificate with the statement that the part is complete and *safe for the taking-over work to commence,* and then return the Certificate to the Contractor. When returning the Certificate he may also attach a snagging list—a list of minor items, that do not affect the safety of the Plant or taking-over procedures, that need correction.

Certification of completion of construction

Under Clause 32.6, if completion of construction is of contractual significance—that is if it is referred to in Schedule 11 to the Contract—the Project Manager is required to issue a Certificate when construction of the entire Plant or a section is complete.

Taking over

CLAUSE 33

Clause 33.1 allows for the Plant to be taken over in sections where stated in the Contract. Sectional taking-over is, to some extent at least, always an advantage to the Contractor, because it enables him to concentrate his resources on each part of the Plant in turn, rather than having to bring the entire project up to taking over simultaneously. It gives the Contractor the added benefits perhaps of obtaining some payments earlier than might otherwise be the case, and also getting part of the Plant through its Defects Liability Period earlier.

Of course sectional taking over also benefits the Purchaser, simply because the sooner he can put some part of the Plant into production the sooner he can obtain a return on his investment. This consideration is the key to the approach any Purchaser should take towards sectional taking over. Ideally, though in practice it may not always be the case, where a Contract allows sectional taking over, each section should produce something that the Purchaser can *use.*

The basic procedure

The basic procedure for taking over is set out in Clauses 33.2–4, and 33.6–7.

Following the completion of construction, the Plant is prepared by the Contractor for take-over. When he is satisfied that the Plant is ready, he gives notice to the Project Manager under Clause 33.2 and the procedures specified in Schedule 15 are carried out, including any taking over tests (that is, running tests) specified.

If the Contract does not include a Schedule 15 then the Project Manager can still introduce take-over tests and procedures by using the Variation procedure. It is, however, questionable whether it is advisable to use this route.

When successful procedures (and tests) have been carried out a Take-Over Certificate is issued by the Project Manager under Clause 33.7. The Plant is now taken over by the Purchaser and the Defects Liability Period commences. From this point the Contractor is no longer responsible for the care, maintenance or operation of the Plant, but will be responsible for correcting any defects or damage under Clause 37.

Although the Clauses are logical and clear in what they say, they need to be operated carefully by the parties.

Clause 33.4 sets out the basic principle that the Contractor provides everything necessary for the take-over tests except where the Purchaser has agreed to supply it.

Clause 33.2 simply permits the Contractor to give the Project Manager reasonable notice of when the Contractor intends to commence the take-over procedures, provided that the Contractor cannot do so until after the approval by the Project Manager under Clause 32.2 that construction has been completed. Clause 33.3 then entitles the Project Manager to observe the procedure, and obliges the Contractor to ensure that it is possible for him to do so. In the somewhat unlikely event that the Project Manager fails to attend the procedures, Clause 33.6 allows the Contractor to proceed without him.

If the Plant passes the take-over procedures and tests then under Clause 33.7 the Project Manager must issue a Take-Over Certificate to the Contractor, although the Project Manager does not have to issue the Certificate until after the Contractor has dealt with the construction completion snagging list. The Project Manager cannot however withhold the Take-Over Certificate for minor defects that emerge during taking over. These are to be dealt with by another snagging list, which must then be dealt with promptly by the Contractor under Clause 33.8.

The Plant then passes from the Contractor to the Purchaser.

Failure of a test

Clause 33.5 provides the usual procedure to require the Contractor to repeat whatever take-over tests the Project Manager considers reasonable, if the Plant fails the tests.

Issue of a Take-Over Certificate in other circumstances

Clause 33 then provides, in Clauses 33.9 and 33.10, two possible ways in which the take-over tests may be postponed or shelved, one by agreement and the other by default.

Under Clause 33.9 the Project Manager may, with the Contractor's consent, issue a Take-Over Certificate without the Plant having completed the take-over procedures. The Certificate may be issued even if the Plant has actually failed procedures. This allows the Purchaser a route to bring the Plant into operation if he is in serious need of it, without waiting for take-over to run its course. The only condition is that this can only be done with the Contractor's consent, which cannot of course be unreasonably refused. The Contractor's consent is required because the Contractor must be satisfied that the Plant is in proper condition for future take-over procedures and tests, and probably also for performance tests, and that the Purchaser is able to run it *safely* before he allows it to be put into operation. The Contractor will then remain liable to carry out the remaining take-over procedures during the Defects Liability Period, if requested to do so, but any extra costs will be borne by the Purchaser (Clause 33.11).

Clause 33.10 provides the usual protection for a Contractor who is prevented from carrying out any take-over procedure, by allowing him to bypass that procedure and claim his Take-Over Certificate. However the Clause contains two safeguards for the Purchaser. First the Contractor is only permitted to bypass those procedures that he is actually prevented from carrying out, and where the Contractor is acting reasonably in claiming the Certificate. (It might be unreasonable to claim the Take-Over Certificate if the Purchaser had delayed the commencement of the test by one day—it might be very reasonable if the start of the test was delayed for several days or weeks.) Any other procedures must be completed. Secondly the Purchaser can require the Contractor to carry out the remaining procedures during the Defects Liability Period as under Clause 33.9. In other words delay by the Purchaser in providing facilities for the tests does not mean that the Contractor can avoid the need to carry out the tests altogether, only that they may be postponed.

The final safeguard is added by Clause 33.12, which permits the revocation of any Take-Over Certificate which has Acceptance Certificate status (see below) in the event that any deferred take-over test fails.

Finally Clause 33.11 deals with the question of the extra costs of any testing procedures which have been deferred under Clauses 33.9 and 33.10.

Performance tests

The performance test/Acceptance Certificate stage is covered by Clauses 35 and 36. Clause 35 deals with the tests themselves and Clause 36 deals with the issue of the Acceptance Certificate, confirming that the Plant is accepted by the Purchaser as complying with the requirements of the Contract.

CLAUSE 35

Under Clause 35.1 performance tests are, in theory anyway, optional. The Clause only applies if the Contract calls for performance tests. In practice the performance test is one of the main benefits of these Conditions for the Purchaser.

Clause 35.2 allows performance tests to be specified in Schedule 16, or to be agreed during the Contract. In theory both methods offer equal advantage to both sides. (Before Contract the Purchaser has more negotiating power to demand whatever tests he thinks appropriate. After Contract he learns more about the Plant and the process, so that he can negotiate with greater knowledge.) In practice most Purchasers prefer to include details of the performance tests in Schedule 16.

Procedure

The basic procedure is set out in Clauses 35.3–6 and Clause 35.8–9. The procedure is intended to ensure that the performance tests are carried out as quickly as possible after the Plant has been taken over, so that the Plant can then be put into normal operation.

Under Clause 33.7 the Purchaser is required, when the Plant is taken over to *start up* the Plant and *prepare* it for performance tests, and then *carry out* the performance tests. (Clause 35.9 follows on from this by requiring the Purchaser not to cause unreasonable delay to performance tests.) Clause 35.4 then requires the Purchaser to carry out the performance tests as soon as practicable after the Plant or section has been taken over. (Possible sectional performance tests are covered by Clause 35.2, and the same considerations apply as for sectional take-over tests.)

In practice the Purchaser will obviously exercise some control over the timing of the performance tests. This is important because the Purchaser has to provide all the resources necessary for the test. The actual procedure for initiating a test is that the Purchaser must give notice under Clause 35.5, which must then be acknowledged and accepted by the Contractor.

Strictly speaking the Contractor will not be entitled to make any further adjustments to the Plant between take-over and the commencement of the performance test. In practice his Site personnel will almost inevitably advise either the Project Manager or the Purchaser of anything that they consider needs doing before the performance tests begin.

The reasoning behind these Clauses is straightforward. The Contractor has demonstrated that he has constructed the Plant and put it through its preliminary tests (construction completion and take-over). It is now the responsibility of the Purchaser to complete the testing sequence and to do so with reasonable speed so that an Acceptance Certificate may be issued and the Contractor may be paid whatever sum is due to him.

The test will then be run in accordance with Clause 35.4. Note the words in the last sentence of Clause 35.4 that the test will be run 'as far as practicable' in accordance with the Contract. This is reality—no Plant is ever run precisely in accordance with the Contract or Specification.

During the test the performance of the Plant will be monitored and recorded by both sides acting together. Then, once the test is complete, the results will be jointly evaluated by both sides. The reasons for joint evaluation are so that:

- The parties can reach an agreed interpretation of what the results of the test actually show. In some processes the simple output figures will not tell the whole story.
- The parties can agree measurement tolerances and allowances.
- The parties can agree any necessary adjustments to the test results. No test ever runs totally smoothly, and minor hitches in operation seldom justify the trouble, time and expense of repeating the whole test.

Problems

Clause 35.6 deals with the question of whether or not a test that is failing to achieve its required parameters may be terminated. Of course it may be terminated if the Contractor and Project Manager agree that it should. Unless they agree then the test may not be terminated unless there is risk of damage or injury, or it is unacceptable to either party (for good reason) to allow it to continue. The reason for this is that the results of even a complete failure are of importance, because they enable the Contractor to analyse what is wrong and to plan corrective action.

Clause 35.9 allows the Contractor only a limited period after taking over within which to achieve a successful performance test. Obviously there is a conflict here. The Purchaser has overall control of the tests, since he has to provide resources and trained operators, and give notice of any test. However if a test fails and has to be repeated, especially if it needs to be repeated more than once, it will be the Contractor who will be eager to move as quickly as possible. The answer to this conflict lies in Clause 35.4, that tests must always be carried out as quickly as possible.

The problem is also covered by Clauses 35.10–11. Clause 35.10 allows the Project Manager to defer the work of carrying out modifications to the Plant if the Purchaser is not willing to take the Plant out of production during the test period allowed by the Contract. Any extra costs caused to the Contractor by the deferment will of course be met by the Purchaser. Any deferment to beyond the end of the Defects Liability Period brings the Contractor's obligations to an end.

Where the results of any test falls short of the requirements of the Contract, but are within the limits of the performance liquidated damages specified in Schedule 17, the Contractor has a choice (Clause 35.9). He can either pay the appropriate liquidated damages, or seek to modify or adjust the Plant to improve performance and then repeat the test, provided that this can be done within the Contract period. If he decides to pay liquidated damages then under Clause 35.9 the Plant has to be accepted by the Project Manager and an Acceptance Certificate issued.

If the results of the tests are outside the limits of Schedule 17, or the Contractor chooses to carry out further work on the Plant, then Clause 35.7 will apply. The Contractor has to decide what further work to carry out and must, if the Project Manager requests, inform the Project Manager of what he intends to do and get his approval before doing it. The Contractor must then be allowed reasonable opportunity to carry out the adjustments or modifications before the Plant is put back into operation and the test repeated. In the meantime the Purchaser is entitled to operate the Plant.

If the Plant fails the performance tests then Clause 35.9 allows the Purchaser to reject the Plant, or to accept it on whatever terms are agreed between the parties or fixed by an Expert.

Clauses 35.11–13 then deal with the question of what happens if the Purchaser, or events outside the Contractor's control, prevent the Contractor from successfully completing a performance test within the Contract period. Essentially if that happens the Project Manager must issue an Acceptance Certificate so that the Contractor can be paid, but the Contractor will remain liable to carry out the tests when possible during the Defects Liability Period. The extra costs to the Contractor of delayed tests will be met by the Purchaser. The Project Manager can require the Contractor to provide security for any payments or liquidated damages that might be involved before issuing the Acceptance Certificate so that, if the Plant fails when the test is finally carried out, the Purchaser can recover the payment from the Contractor.

143

3.3.10 Acceptance Certificate

CLAUSE 36

The Acceptance Certificate is the last stage of the approval/testing process. In one sense it is purely a formality, because it follows and is governed directly by the performance test. But it is a very important formality because it will virtually always be a payment document. It also acts as conclusive evidence that the Plant is accepted by the Purchaser as complying with the requirements of the Contract.

If there are no performance tests required by the Contract then the Take-Over Certificate will double as the Acceptance Certificate.

The Acceptance Certificate must be issued by the Project Manager as soon as the Contractor has complied with the terms of Clause 35. Like all other Certificates up to this point, it may contain a snagging list of items to be corrected by the Contractor in the usual way.

3.4 Variations, changes and claims

The Clauses to be covered in this section are those listed under the heading 'Claims & Variations' in Figure 2 (see page 102).

3.4.1 General approach

These Clauses cover two areas, first the procedure for dealing with Variations to the Contract, and secondly the procedure for dealing with claims under the Contract. Remember that the Conditions use the Variation Order procedure to do two different things. It is used to order a change to the Works by the Project Manager. It is also used to record and formalise *other changes* to the Contract, see for example Clause 14.1.

Change is the most likely area for project management problems. At least one in three project managers will say that change management is the most difficult problem they face. Of course in a reimbursable contract change presents different problems to those in the price-based contract. In the price-based contract the problem is managing the effects of change, especially on project cost/price and timescale, within a potentially adversarial relationship. In the reimbursable contract, with a more collaborative relationship and a reimbursable pricing/payment structure, the cost/price effects are easier to manage, but the scope/extent of change is more difficult simply because change is so easy—and reimbursable contracts are, of course, often used for projects involving a significant level of uncertainty.

Change is a function of the complexity (not size) and duration of the project. A simple contract, however large, that takes merely a few days or weeks to carry out is unlikely to be subject to any changes. A complex contract that takes a few years to carry out, especially if there is a degree of uncertainty about the objectives, is likely to be subject to a whole range of different types of change. Some changes may be outside the parties' control, such as a change in legislation, or the loss of a particular feedstock for the Plant. Others will be partly or wholly within control, such as a change to the product range to meet market requirements, or a modification to the Plant to improve its performance.

The Conditions assume that some change is virtually inevitable. They give the Project Manager a range of options to use in initiating Variations. They also assume that the Project Manager is sufficiently process-skilled to be able to manage the Contractor and negotiate Contract amendments. In case problems arise which cannot be solved quickly by the parties they allow for the use of an Expert as the preferred option to resolve the matter.

For ease of reference the Clauses covered in this section can be divided into the following groups:

- changes in legislation (Clauses 4.5 and 7.3–4);
- Site problems (Clause 6);
- Variations:
  - definition and limits to the Project Manager's powers (Clauses 16.1 and 16.7);
  - initiation by the Project Manager (Clauses 16.1–3, 16.5–6 and 37.3–4);
  - feasibility studies (Clause 16.4);
  - Contractor's proposals (Clauses 3.5 and 17);
- claims for extensions of time.

3.4.2 Changes in legislation

CLAUSE 4.5
This Clause needs no comment.

Clauses 7.3–4
Clause 7.3 allows the Contractor to claim what is in effect a Variation, to cover any increases in cost plus any consequent extension to the programme as a result of legislation which is passed or comes into force during the period of the Contract. No special procedure is required for the Contractor's claim.

The Clause is not limited to legislation in one particular country. Therefore the Clause could apply if legislation in Japan, which made the export of a key item of equipment more costly, affected a UK contract.

The effect of Clause 7.4 is to exclude all tax and related charges from Clause 7.3. They remain with the Contractor. If therefore the Contract was likely to be affected by any exceptional tax it would need to be dealt with by a Special Condition.

3.4.3 Site problems

Unforeseen ground conditions will always be a problem in Contracts involving site construction work. The higher the ratio of civil/building work to structural/process/electrical/mechanical work, the worse the potential problem. Within the chemical or oil industries the problem is small because the ratio is often low. In other process industries the position may well be different.

CLAUSE 6
Clause 6.1 requires the Contractor to behave professionally with respect to the Site. He is expected to inspect the Site properly. This means that he must take account of:

- the information actually in his possession concerning the Site;
- information available from a visual inspection of the Site;

- information resulting from reasonable enquiries prompted by that visual inspection;
- information in the public domain, such as geological maps of the area.

The phrase 'visual inspection of the Site' means precisely what it says. All that the Contractor is required to do is to look at what is visible on the Site at and above ground level and then draw reasonable conclusions and ask whatever reasonable questions are prompted by that inspection.

If then at any time during the Works, usually but not necessarily during the Site construction period, the Contractor comes up against unforeseeable problems on the Site, other than weather (though of course truly exceptional weather or the *result* of weather, such as flooding, could qualify) which cause extra cost then the Contractor will be entitled to claim additional costs. Of course unforeseeable conditions would usually be ground-related, though the Clause will also cover other Site problems, such as a pollution problem caused by other premises in the vicinity.

The Clause lays down a precise procedure that the Contractor must follow in making his claim, and also lays down a strict time limit for any claim.

Project Manager's instructions

Clause 11.2 permits the Contractor to trigger the Variation procedure in the event that manipulation by the Project Manager affects his ability to meet any time or other requirements of the Contract. Again the Clause sets out a timescale and procedure that the Contractor must follow in making his claim.

3.4.4 Variations

Definition of a Variation and the limits to the Project Manager's powers
CLAUSE 16.1

The first principle laid down by Clause 16.1 is that only the Project Manager, or a Project Manager's Representative specifically authorised by the Project Manager under Clause 11.5, can initiate a Variation.

Secondly Clause 16.1 defines a Variation. Clarifications will not constitute a Variation, nor will an instruction to carry out work already covered by the Contract. However any change, even minor, to the Specification or work to be carried out by the Contractor will constitute a Variation. Also any changes to methods of working, which are not simply to rectify unsafe methods being used or proposed by the Contractor, will be Variations.

Therefore *any* order or instruction by the Project Manager to the Contractor to make any material change, whether an amendment, increase or omission, will constitute a Variation Order. In particular any instruction that is in conflict with the Contract, and especially in conflict with Schedule 1 or the Specification must be deemed to be a material change and therefore to be a Variation.

Under Clause 5.1 a Variation can only be ordered in writing. Therefore Clause 16.1 allows the Contractor to insist that the Project Manager issues formal written Variation Orders to cover any material changes instructed by him.

CLAUSE 16.7

This Clause deals with the limits to the Project Manager's power to order Variations by allowing the Contractor to object to Variations in certain circumstances. It is unacceptable for the Project Manager to have the right to use Variations to change a Contract by more than is reasonable, since this could place excessive strain on the Contractor's organisation and his ability to plan the Contract properly. Therefore Clause 16.7 allows the Contractor to object to any Variation once the cumulative effect of Variations is to increase or reduce the cost of the project by more than 25% of the original estimate of the Contract Price, or 5% in the case of Variations issued after take-over. In effect once this percentage change in estimated Contract Price is reached the Contractor is able to pick and choose which Variations he wishes to carry out. (Of course if the Contractor is happy to carry out Variations above the 25% limit then there is nothing to prevent him doing so.)

In addition Clause 16.7 allows the Contractor to refuse to comply with any Variation when it would have the effect of requiring the Contractor to infringe the terms of any agreement with a third party, such as its process licence, or any third-party patent or other intellectual property right.

Finally Clause 16.7 allows the Contractor to refuse to comply with any Variation which would have the effect of pushing the Contractor into areas where he lacks the appropriate technology or expertise, unless the Project Manager agrees that a suitable nominated Subcontractor may be brought in (when Clause 10.7 would protect the Contractor against claims).

The Clause then sets out the proper procedure for objections to Variations by the Contractor. Essentially the Clause requires the Contractor to set out his objections in writing by at the latest two weeks after any order and even before the order if possible.

Initiation of Variations by the Project Manager

Normally the Purchaser should consult the Contractor in advance about the way in which the Contract may need to be amended to take account of a Variation (Clause 16.5).

The principles followed by the Conditions are then straightforward. They are that Variations to a complex process plant may well be complex in themselves. Therefore the Purchaser may need assistance from the Contractor in deciding whether a particular Variation is feasible (Clause 16.4). The Contractor may notify the Project Manager of any problems likely to be caused by a Variation (Clause 16.6).

Even more important, perhaps, is the principle set out in Clause 16.2 that the Project Manager must decide clearly what changes to the Plant he wants before the Contractor can be expected to begin work.

CLAUSES 16.2–3

These Clauses state the basic principles. Firstly that the Variation Order, whatever form it may take, must define clearly what Variation is required by the Project Manager. Any purported Variation Order issued by the Project Manager that did not clearly define the 'Variation' would be invalid and must not be acted upon by the Contractor. Secondly that the Contractor must proceed to carry out any Variation properly ordered, subject of course to Clauses 16.6–9. Thirdly that the Contractor is entitled to receive payment for carrying out the Variation in accordance with the terms of Clause 18. Finally the Contractor is entitled to an appropriate adjustment of Programme (and other Contract requirements).

CLAUSE 16.5

In the normal course the Project Manager would discuss any proposed Variation with the Contractor in some detail and agree the necessary Contract amendments and perhaps even a cost for the extra work before issuing a Variation Order.

However the Clause gives the Project Manager another option. If he decides that the Variation is sufficiently urgent he may order it, provided that it can be fully defined, without agreeing anything or giving the Contractor any opportunity even to comment/quote in advance.

CLAUSE 16.6

Clause 16.6 provides the machinery by which the Contractor can raise any contractual/process/technical problems caused by a Variation with the Project Manager. In effect it is the Clause that allows the Contractor to bring any or all 'knock-on' consequences of the Variation to the Project Manager's attention, so that the problems can be dealt with *immediately*. Therefore the Clause only allows the Contractor *seven days* to notify the Project Manager of any problems, plus a further seven days to define them. If the Contractor does invoke the Clause then the Variation is put into abeyance until any confirmation by the Project Manager that the Contractor is to proceed with the Variation. In that case the Contract must be suitably modified to take reasonable account of the problem raised by the Contractor, either by agreement or in accordance with Clause 16.8.

CLAUSE 37.4

This Clause deals with a further power of the Project Manager, to require the Contractor to repair defects in equipment supplied by the Purchaser or damage caused by the Purchaser in the Plant or equipment as a part of the defects repair service by the Contractor, but paid for as a Variation. It covers defects that arise both during the construction period and the guarantee period.

Feasibility studies

Any process plant is best known to its designer, and the designer of the Plant is the Contractor. Therefore the Conditions give the Project Manager the right to call upon the Contractor's expertise to investigate potential Variations.

CLAUSE 16.4

If required by the Project Manager the Contractor will draft or collaborate with the Project Manager in drafting the technical content for a possible Variation Order. The Contractor will also provide a statement on the Contract implications in line with Clause 16.5.

Contractor's proposals for Variations

CLAUSE 3.5

Clause 3.5 is very much a 'teamwork' clause. It requires the Contractor to make the Project Manager aware of any possible improvements/modifications to the Plant, Works or methods of operation which would either eliminate defects or hazards, or which could benefit the Purchaser. If appropriate the Contractor will then take action under Clause 17.

CLAUSES 17.1–4

Clause 17.1 recognises a situation that may often arise in a process context—that the Contractor may find himself in a position to recommend an improvement in equipment or process to the Purchaser. (Of course this Clause partly overlaps Clause 3.5.) If this should be the case the Contractor must put forward a brief proposal for the improvement to the Project Manager. If the Project Manager then wishes to take the idea further he can use Clause 17.2 to develop further details. The choice of whether the improvement is to be incorporated in the Plant is then for the Purchaser/Project Manager to make within the time-scale(s) provided in Clause 17.3.

The Clause would also be used by the Contractor to put forward a proposal for any Variation to correct any error in the Plant which was the responsibility of the Contractor.

Clause 17.4 would then permit the Contractor to insist upon the right to carry out a Variation which he has proposed under Clause 17.1 where there were safety or operating implications, and if necessary to appeal the point to an Expert.

CLAUSE 17.5

This Clause then deals with another problem, where the Contractor has detected an error in the Contract. (This could of course be due either to an error by the Purchaser or the Contractor, but is more likely to be used by the Contractor in the case of an error by the Purchaser.) It is straightforward and needs no comment.

Valuation of Variations

In a reimbursable contract the costing/pricing of Variations is much less of a problem than in a price-based contract. Of course, many Variations will in practice be carried out largely on the basis of fixed prices quoted by Subcontractors and agreed in advance between the parties. The Conditions do not therefore include any price claim procedure. Clause 16.10 simply requires the Contractor to compile and keep costing records for each separate Variation—not always as easy as it sounds in a large and complex project.

Variations would then simply be paid for under Clause 39 (see pages 165–166 below).

3.4.5 Claims and disputes

Even in the collaborative relationship, disputes can still arise about the effects of a Variation, cost, delay, Specification, etc.

What often happens is that the parties leave resolution of the problem until the end of the Contract, often because the project management teams on either side are just too busy to handle the extra work involved while the Contract is still live. This always causes difficulties for both sides. Claim/Variation problems are best settled at the time they occur. The Conditions therefore suggest (Clause 16.9) that any disputes should be settled quickly by reference to an Expert.

Extensions of time

In this section we have only mentioned in passing the question of the Contractor's rights to claim an extension to the Contract programme or period. Claims for an extension of time for a Variation will be discussed in more detail in the next section.

At this point it is only necessary to point out that the Contractor must always remember that if he wishes to claim an extension of time for any Variation, and in most cases this will be the case, then he must notify the Project Manager of his claim in accordance with Clause 14.2 *as soon as reasonably possible.*

3.5 Delays and lateness

3.5.1 Lateness law

See section 1.5.

3.5.2 The Conditions

The Clauses to be covered in this section are those listed under the heading 'Delay' in Figure 2 (see page 102).

For ease of reference the Clauses can be divided into the following groups:

- suspension (Clause 41);
- extensions of time (Clause 14);
- liquidated damages (Clause 15 (and Schedule 12)).

3.5.3 Suspension

In one sense Clause 41 is closely allied to the Variation procedures discussed in section 3.4. There is always the risk in a Contract with a long time-scale that some unexpected but serious (either actually serious or potentially serious) problem will be found. Perhaps the Contractor may be found to have committed a serious error that has put the success of the Contract into question. Perhaps a change in market conditions means that the Purchaser needs time to consider whether the Plant should be modified to manufacture a different product. Perhaps a serious problem has arisen on Site. Perhaps the Plant may need modification to handle different raw materials. When that happens it may sometimes be advantageous to the Purchaser to, so to speak, stop the clock for a short time while he considers how best to tackle the problem. The suspension clause allows him to do just that.

Of course one can never stop the clock, or more accurately one can stop the clock only to some extent, in the sense of asking the Contractor to suspend work, but one cannot stop the Contractor's costs increasing. Therefore the Clause should only be used when *really* necessary, because there will always be a cost to the Purchaser, unless the suspension is because of a serious error by the Contractor.

From the Contractor's point of view also the Clause is a difficult one. He must keep his Contract team and his Subcontractors idle but ready to recommence work if and when requested to do so, and probably in a situation of considerable uncertainty. He may be able to employ *some* resources on other contracts, but will not be able to transfer major resources to other contracts in case they need to be transferred back again.

Neither party can therefore allow a suspension of the Contract to last indefinitely.

CLAUSE 41

Clause 41.1 needs no comment. It is a simple enabling clause allowing the Project Manager to suspend the Works, subject to any safety implications.

Clause 41.2 deals with the consequences of a Suspension Order. Where the Suspension Order is due to breach/error by the Contractor, the Contractor must bear the consequences. Otherwise the Contractor is entitled to extra time, which should be claimed in writing as soon as practicable in accordance with Clause 14.1, and also to his extra costs resulting from the suspension.

Clause 42.3 then allows the Contractor to require the Project Manager to decide whether or not the Contract is to be resumed if suspension continues for three months, so avoiding indefinite suspension, and Clause 41.4 deals with the programme implications of a suspension/resumption.

Disputes on cost and time should go to the Expert.

3.5.4 Extension of time

There are two groups of reasons which allow an extension of the Contract dates or periods. There is 'force majeure', which permits both the Contractor and the Purchaser to claim an extension of time if they are delayed by causes beyond their reasonable control. Then there are other delays that entitle the Contractor to a reasonable extension of time.

CLAUSE 14.2

The term 'force majeure' is regularly used commercially as meaning events generally beyond a party's control. The Conditions define the term as events which are beyond a party's control and which affect that party's ability to perform the Contract to time. The Clause lists a number of circumstances that are within the definition and some others that are not.

There will always be some difficulty in defining, in the abstract, all the possible circumstances that could be considered to come within this definition of force majeure. In purely contractual terms the problem is one of exactly how the Clause should be interpreted. Would it, for instance, include terrorist activity— near the Site or near a route to the Site—which was making people reluctant to stay on the Site?

The answer is, of course, that nobody does know what the abstract answer is, but that the abstract answer is unimportant. Like all 'force majeure' clauses, Clause 14.2 is not intended to define the parties' rights with legal precision. All it does is to lay down the basic principle, which is that if some fairly serious event or chain of events causes delay to either party then that party should have a defence against claims by the other party arising out of the delay. It is up to the parties to the Contract, or an arbitrator, to reach a common-sense and fair decision between them about any actual circumstances that may arise.

CLAUSES 14.1 and 14.3–5
Clause 14.1 sets out the *procedure* for claiming an extension of time and also deals with the *rights* of the Contractor to claim an extension to the Contract in a range of situations, including force majeure, but mainly situations which arise out of the natural interplay between the parties in a complex long-term Contract.

The Clause lists the different circumstances that allow an extension of time:

- Clause 14.2(a)—Clause 6.1 deals with the consequences of problems on the Site;
- Clause 14.2(b)—the parties would need to use Clause 16 to amend the Contract;
- Clause 14.2(c)—straightforward;
- Clause 14.2(d)—breach of the Contract by the Purchaser covers a range of Clauses, such as a failure to do work or provide information (Clause 4), or lateness in providing access to the Site (Clause 23). See also Clause 14.4;
- Clause 14.2(e)—see Clause 10.7. The Contractor would also receive an indemnity against extra costs, but must be able to demonstrate proper management by him of the nominated Subcontractor.

The procedure is that the party (Contractor or Purchaser as the case may be) claiming extra time should give notice of the delay to the Project Manager under Clause 14.1 'forthwith' (as soon as is practicably possible) after delay has actually occurred. The Contractor should then follow this with a further notice of the extension of time caused and therefore claimed. The Project Manager must then investigate the impact of the delay upon the Contract, and grant a reasonable extension by means of a Variation Order. (In other words the extension granted by the Project Manager may be for a shorter or longer period than the actual duration of the situation causing the claim.)

Clauses 14.3–4 are reasonably self-explanatory and need no comment.

Finally Clause 14.5 allows either party to bring the Contract to an end if force majeure circumstances, claimed or not, cause the Works to be completely or substantially stopped for a *continuous* four-month period. In that case the Purchaser would be required to pay the Contractor his costs/profit up to termination. (Note that there is a difference between Clause 14.5 and Clause 41.3. Under Clause 14.5 *either* party can terminate after 120 days stoppage. Under Clause 41.3, after 90 days stoppage, the Contractor can ask the Project Manager to make a decision in a further 28 days whether to terminate or re-commence work.)

3.5.5 Liquidated damages

Clause 15 then deals with the question of delay by the Contractor in carrying out the Contract. In commercial terms the Clause is of enormous importance because it provides that delay by the Contractor is to be recompensed by liquidated damages. Little comment is necessary here, however. Clause 15.1 simply allows the parties to decide and negotiate their liquidated damages, as Schedule 12 to the Contract.

Clause 15.2 sets out a procedure to deal with one difficult point, where an excusable delay occurs after liquidated damages have become payable. It simply suspends damages until the excusable delay has ceased.

Clause 15.3 suggests the Expert as the proper route to settle disputes on time problems.

3.6 Defects, Site accidents, insurance and exclusions

3.6.1 The law

See section 1.5.

3.6.2 The Conditions

The Clauses to be covered in this section are those listed under the headings 'Defects/Final Certificate', 'Insurance etc' and 'Liability' in Figure 2 (see page 102).

For ease of reference the Clauses can be divided into the following groups:

- guarantees:
  - guarantee period (37.1–2 and 37.12–3);
  - normal defects procedure (Clauses 37.2);
  - Contractor's responsibility (Clause 37.3–4);
  - extension of guarantee period (Clause 37.6 and 37.10);
  - repetition of tests (Clause 37.5);
  - repair by the Purchaser (Clauses 37.7–9);
  - access to Site (37.11);
- access to Plant and records (Clause 33.13);
- Final Certificate:
  - procedure (Clause 38.1);
  - purpose/effect (Clause 38.4);
  - time of issue (Clauses 38.1–3);
  - disputes (Clause 38.5);
- insurance:
  - responsibility for cover (Clauses 31.1–4);
  - administration (Clauses 31.2 and 31.5);
- Site work—accidents and responsibilities:
  - Contractor (Clauses 4.6 and 30.1–4);
  - Purchaser (Clauses 30.3–4 and 30.9);
  - limits of Contractor's liability (Clauses 30.3–4 and 30.7–9);
  - employee risk (Clauses 30.5–6);
- overall exclusions of liability (Clauses 15, 43 and 44).

3.6.3 Guarantees

Guarantee period
CLAUSES 37.1–2 and 37.12–3
Clause 37.1 allows for sectional defects liability periods. The basic Defects Liability Period is then set by Clause 37.2. It starts when work commences or Materials arrive at the Site and continues until one year after take-over. If a different period or periods is agreed, a Special Condition will be necessary to modify the Clause.

Then there are two clauses that allow for limits to the extent of the Contractor's liability. Clause 37.12 and Schedule 10 deal with items that have a limited life, such as filters. Clause 37.13 limits the Contractor's liability if he is unable to obtain full back-to-back guarantees from Subcontractors.

Normal defects procedure
The Clause enables the Purchaser to ensure that the Contractor repairs or replaces equipment that is found to be defective as a result of some error in design or manufacture, for which the Contractor is responsible, during the guarantee period. Clauses 37.2 and 37.4 do this, and they also cover two other situations as well, firstly that of a defect which comes to light before the guarantee period commences, and secondly that of a defect which is not due to the fault of the Contractor. There is a cross-relationship between these Clauses and the testing and Variation Clauses.

CLAUSE 37.2
The Project Manager may notify the Contractor in writing of a defect in work/Materials or failure of the Plant/section to conform to the requirements of the Contract. Therefore 'defect' has a very wide meaning. It includes a deterioration in the performance of the Plant as well as equipment breakdown or failure. Clause 37.4 then extends the meaning of 'defect' further by including defects which have been caused by the Purchaser or others, for instance by incorrect operation of the Plant.

The notice by the Project Manager must describe the defect and must be given quickly. The Project Manager is not entitled to delay notification because it might be more convenient to delay repair, since this could increase the cost of repair to the Contractor. If the Purchaser does delay then the Contractor is entitled to charge him with the increase in his repair costs.

The Contractor must then be given all necessary access to the Plant and must carry out whatever work is necessary to correct the defect. The Contractor has the right to decide what corrective action to take—whether to repair or replace a defective item for example—but must inform the Project Manager of what action he intends to take if the Project Manager asks him to do so and obtain his approval.

Contractor's responsibility
The allocation of responsibility for the cost of correcting a defect is dealt with in a totally different manner under the Green Book Conditions to that of the

Red Book Conditions. Under the fixed-price contract the Contractor bears the risk of defects, and will meet the cost. He will be expected to have allowed for this in his price and to protect himself by suitable terms in his Subcontracts.

In the reimbursable contract the Contractor cannot protect himself against the full risk of defects. Equipment is passed on to the Purchaser at cost. His work is charged for on a rate or fee basis. Therefore his ability to build contingencies into his prices is severely limited. In addition the Purchaser/Project Manager has considerable influence over the final design of the Plant and the final choice of Subcontractors.

Therefore the allocation of defects risk is very different. The Contractor is expected to place Subcontracts under Clause 9 that include adequate guarantees to the Contractor and the Purchaser, and then to enforce those guarantees if necessary. In addition to this he is expected to take whatever other action may be necessary to correct any defect in the Plant that comes to light during the Defects Liability Period. However the Contractor's costs of doing so will be reimbursed by the Purchaser, unless the Contractor has specifically agreed to accept the cost or the Contractor has failed to exercise a proper standard of skill and care.

There will always be some doubt as to when a particular defect is to be considered to be due to a failure by the Contractor to exercise proper skill and care. Nevertheless the basic risk of defect repair cost will lie with the Subcontractors and the Purchaser.

CLAUSE 37.3
Clause 37.3 states that any cost to the Contractor of making good defects will be paid by the Purchaser, except in two situations:

- Firstly, and most importantly, where an item of equipment is defective, and equipment defects will make up the vast majority of defect claims, the Subcontractor is to be required to comply with the terms of the guarantees included in his Subcontract (Clause 9.7 etc.).
- Secondly, where the Contractor has failed to exercise proper skill and care. The process plant is a large and complex thing. The job of designing and constructing it is also large and defects are bound to occur. The cost of those 'inevitable' or 'normal' defects is to be met by the Purchaser. If, however, the Contractor makes mistakes of the type that a contractor should never make, or makes far too many mistakes ('mistakes' meaning 'mistakes which result in defects') then the Purchaser may wish to hold the Contractor liable for the cost of their repair.

CLAUSE 37.4
Clause 37.4 then deals with defects that are not the Contractor's fault, but due to actions by others. The Contractor will take the necessary corrective action but the work must be dealt with as a Variation.

Extension of guarantee period

Clearly if the Plant becomes defective the Purchaser suffers in two ways. He may lose part of his original guarantee protection because an item of equipment will have been changed or replaced. Also he may lose part of his guarantee period because the Plant will have been put out of action for a time. The Conditions deal with both of these problems.

CLAUSE 37.6

This Clause gives the Purchaser a new Defects Liability Period of one year upon any repair, as opposed to re-adjustment, and on any item of equipment or work which is replaced under Clauses 37.2–3. The Clause is fair—since repair/replacement implies a greater degree of failure than re-adjustment—but it will obviously influence the Contractor's thinking when faced with the decision how to make good any particular defect.

CLAUSE 37.10

This Clause then provides that any Defects Liability Period will be extended by the time that the Plant or relevant section has been put out of use due to a defect.

To a certain extent this remedies the possible shortcoming of Clause 37.6, in that it applies to delay due to re-adjustment, but it does raise one problem of its own. It only applies where the defect is sufficient to put the Plant/section out of use. In other words where the defect or corrective work by the Contractor does not actually stop the Plant operating or producing, but only *limits* or *restricts* its use then the Purchaser is not entitled to any extension, even though the restriction in output may be relatively serious.

Repetition of tests

It is normal to provide for the possible repetition of Contract tests on the Plant, in case serious defects show themselves during the guarantee period, to demonstrate that the corrective action taken by the Contractor is adequate to ensure that the Plant has been put back into proper order.

CLAUSE 37.5

The Project Manager may require the Contractor to repeat take-over tests to establish that defects have been properly corrected. The Clause refers only to take-over *tests*, however, not to take-over *procedures* or *performance tests,* and also allows the Project Manager only to require *appropriate* take-over tests. In other words, Clause 37.5 will apply only where the defect is of such a type that a take-over test is suitable to decide whether the defect has been properly corrected and the defect will normally have to be fairly serious to justify a repetition of a complete test. Clause 37.10 then allows an appropriate extension to the Defects Liability Period to allow for these tests.

Repair by the Purchaser

Clauses 37.7 and 37.9 provide the Purchaser with the usual remedy against the Contractor who fails to honour his defects obligations. He can carry out repairs for himself and then back-charge the costs to the Contractor. The Purchaser will often wish to retain some form of security against this possibility, usually in the form of a bond/bank guarantee or a cash retention. Clause 37.8 deals in the same way with urgent repairs.

CLAUSES 37.7–9

Where a repair is urgent the Purchaser can carry out repairs himself (Clause 37.8) without invalidating the guarantee, if the Contractor cannot or will not do so. Furthermore if the Contractor fails to correct *any* defect with reasonable speed, even a defect which has been caused by the Purchaser, Clause 37.7 permits the Purchaser to carry out the repair, provided that he must first give the Contractor fourteen days notice that he will do so. In both cases the Purchaser is then entitled to recover his costs of corrective action from the Contractor under Clause 37.9.

The Clauses pose two practical problems for the Purchaser. The first is how to assess whether the Contractor is moving with reasonable speed in carrying out corrective work. The second is that the Purchaser's ability to use the powers given to him by the Clauses may be limited by a lack of knowledge of the process or technology involved.

Access to Site
CLAUSE 37.11

If the Purchaser, for whatever reason, does not give access to the Contractor to carry out the necessary work to correct a defect, then the Contractor does not have to carry out that work. If the Purchaser simply *postpones* the correction work then the Contractor will carry out the work at the end of the postponement and will be entitled to the extra costs of the delay.

There are three problems. The first is the difference between refusing or not allowing access, and deferring access. This is all a matter of degree in one sense, but one test of refusal/deferment is whether or not, when access is denied, a date is set when access will be given (and is then given). The second is that delay in repairing a defect may simply mean that the defect becomes more serious and difficult to repair. The third is that repairing defects often involves equipment manufactured by Subcontractors, who are considerably less than enthusiastic about extending the guarantees on their equipment (under Clause 37.6) in these circumstances.

Access to plant records

A process plant is a highly complex unit. This means that it may not always be easy to diagnose the root cause of a process problem or defect. Therefore the Contractor must have access to the Plant and to all operating data. It may also be necessary to investigate the way in which equipment is performing to assist in diagnosis.

CLAUSE 33.13

Clause 33.13 lays down the general principles of the Contractor's right of access to the Plant and its associated operating records, and also sets out the procedure to be followed. The right is primarily there for use in case of defects problems, but is a general right of the Contractor and could be used at any time during the Defects Liability Period.

157

3.6.4 Final certificate

Procedure

The procedure for issuing a Final Certificate is essentially the same as for any other certificate. It is to be issued by the Project Manager to both the Contractor and Purchaser. It should be issued when it is due without any need for application by the Contractor, unless a payment is also due, though the Contractor will normally apply for it anyway.

CLAUSE 38.1

The Clause states the procedure in simple terms and needs no comment. The Clause does not require any application from the Contractor for the Certificate per se. Where take-over is by sections then a separate Certificate should be issued for each section.

Purpose and effect

The Conditions operate on the principle that the Contractor's obligations end once the Defects Liability Period or Periods have been completed. The purpose of the Final Certificate is therefore to confirm formally that the Contractor has carried out all his obligations, *and therefore* to bar the Purchaser from any actions against the Contractor for breach of the Contract once it has been issued. As a result the Project Manager must take great care in issuing the Final Certificate.

CLAUSE 38.4

The Final Certificate performs a number of functions:

- it brings to an end the Contractor's obligation to do any further work on the Plant or relevant section under the Contract, except for any 'insurance' repair work;
- it confirms that the Plant or section as constructed complies with the Contract;
- it confirms that the Contractor has properly performed his obligations during the Defects Liability Period;
- the Certificate (or, where take-over has been by sections, the *last* Certificate) will act as a formal legal document which the Contractor can use to prevent any litigation/arbitration by the Purchaser for breach of Contract ('conclusive evidence . . . in any proceedings that the Contractor has completed the Works').

This last function actually raises a problem in the Clause. The Clause *requires* the Project Manager to issue the Certificate once the Defects Liability Period is complete. However the Clause does not formally permit the Project Manager to qualify a Certificate. Therefore there could be a problem where the Project Manager is required to issue a Final Certificate under a Contract which is the subject of a dispute. Effectively the Project Manager would have to issue a qualified Certificate.

Time of issue

The Clause provides that in principle a Final Certificate is to be issued by the Project Manager when the relevant guarantee period has been completed, but this is subject to a number of qualifications that are listed in the Clause.

CLAUSE 38.1

This Clause provides for the basic time of issue of the Certificate—when the defects liability has expired. It then allows the first qualification, that the Certificate may be delayed until all corrective action in respect of any defects being carried out by the Contractor under Clause 37 has been completed.

CLAUSE 38.2

This Clause then provides a further qualification. Where any equipment or work has been replaced or renewed under Clause 37.6 it is to be treated separately from the rest of the Plant or section, and separate Certificates issued as the different guarantee periods terminate.

CLAUSE 38.3

Clause 38.3 deals with the question of delayed performance tests, by simply allowing the Project Manager to delay any Certificate until any matters relating to delayed tests have been resolved.

Disputes

Clause 38.5 states that any disputes about whether the Plant qualifies for the issue of a Final Certificate or not—that is about issues of technical fact—should go to the Expert rather than to arbitration.

3.6.5 Insurance

Responsibility for cover

The discussions in sections 1.4 and 1.5 have already emphasised the importance of avoiding legal disputes, or at least minimising their impact upon the project as a whole. One of the most serious areas of risk is that of accidents and damage occurring during the construction of the Plant on the Site and while the Contractor is repairing defects.

There are a number of reasons why the risk is substantial in Contracts for process plants. Firstly, there is the sheer number of different companies that may be involved in Site work at any one time, the Contractor, the Purchaser, and any number of Subcontractors. Secondly there is the fact that all these different parties may be working in close physical proximity to each other. Thirdly there are the linked problems of double insurance, under-insurance and non-insurance.

The intention of Clause 31 is therefore to provide a framework within which the parties can organise a coherent insurance scheme for the project. The aim is to achieve adequate cover for the work and to avoid, wherever possible, the risk of cross-claims—disputes between different insurance companies as to which of them has to meet the costs of making good any damage. The problem is that when insurance companies argue, their clients become sucked into the dispute whether they want to or not.

CLAUSES 31.1–2

The Clauses set out the scheme as follows:

- the Purchaser is to be responsible for arranging the principal project insurance package for the Works through insurers acceptable to both parties;

159

- the package is in the joint names of all parties involved, Purchaser, Project Manager, Contractor and Subcontractors, simply to eliminate cross-claims and consequent delay in settling a claim;
- the insurance cover is to be against all normal insurable risks;
- the period covered by the package will be primarily that of Site construction, but the package will also cover defects in the Plant and any work done by the Contractor or any Subcontractor during the Defects Liability Period;
- the package will include the main areas of construction risk, the Documentation, the Materials and Plant;
- the insurance will be for full replacement cost, *unless* the Contract states differently (in which case the parties will need to make other arrangements for any risk in excess of the agreed amount).

Note that if under the terms of the Contract the Contractor has to remove any items of equipment belonging to the Purchaser from the Site, for example because they require refurbishment, then special insurance might need to be arranged.

CLAUSE 31.3

The second main area of cover is that of the Site, other than the Works and other property of the Purchaser adjacent to the Site. This is to be kept covered against all normal risk by the Purchaser, subject to the Contractor being liable for the first £5million of any damage caused by him in any single accident. It is therefore very much the responsibility of the Purchaser to make certain that he has an adequate level of insurance cover for his other property on or in close proximity to the Site, particularly because of the indemnity given by him to the Contractor under Clause 30.9.

CLAUSE 31.4

The Contractor is responsible for providing adequate insurance cover against the risk of accidental damage etc, both to the Purchaser and also to third parties. He will need adequate cover against the risk of damage to third-party property, especially if the Site is adjacent to high-value plant or equipment not owned by the Purchaser or its affiliated companies. (This is often the case. Major process sites regularly house plants belonging to different groups of companies, quite apart from the possibility of damage to property on adjacent premises.)

The only major areas omitted from this package are that of the Contractor's construction equipment, tools, site facilities, etc, which the Contractor and his Subcontractors will be expected to hold covered anyway, and the risk of injury to the employees of the various parties (which is covered, within the UK at any rate, by compulsory Employer's Liability insurance).

Administration

The administration of the insurance package is straightforward. The Purchaser, who has set up the package, is responsible for paying the necessary premiums. Clause 31.1 then provides for the management of claims by the Purchaser on behalf of all parties. But the decision on settlement of any claim must be with the agreement of the Contractor. Any payments made by the insurers will be to the Purchaser, who will then use the money to fund the work by the Contractor under Clause 30.2–3.

CLAUSE 31.5
This Clause needs no comment.

3.6.6 Site work–accidents and responsibilities

Contractor
The Contractor has full responsibility for managing the Site during construction, and must repair any damage that may occur to the Works for any reason during that time. He is therefore responsible for meeting the costs of repair, subject to the limits stated in Clause 30.7, but will be assisted by payments received from the insurers under the Clause 31 insurance package.

CLAUSE 4.6
This Clause is straightforward and needs no comment.

CLAUSE 30.1
This is the basic 'responsibility/control' clause. It needs no comment.

CLAUSE 30.2
This Clause sets out the Contractor's obligations to repair or make good any accidental (and also deliberate—for example, vandalism, theft or sabotage) loss or damage to the Plant and to Materials. Up to take-over the Contractor must repair and make good *all* loss and damage (Clause 31.2). After take-over the Contractor must repair/make good where Clause 37.2 is applied by the Project Manager.

CLAUSES 30.3–4
These Clauses confirm the principle laid down in Clause 30.1, that the Contractor is in control of the Site and therefore responsible for carrying out repairs to all accidents and damage. They then list certain categories of loss or damage that the Contractor will repair, but at the cost of the Purchaser, if the Purchaser invokes Clause 37.2:

- political instability, sonic and nuclear risks (which are in any event uninsurable commercially) are best dealt with by the Site owner;
- problems arising from the use of the Site by the Purchaser need no comment;
- damage caused by the fault/negligence of the Purchaser, or designs/information provided by the Purchaser, which would be breach of the terms of the Contract and need no comment (although it is worth pointing out that the Clause 31.1 insurance policy would probably indemnify/protect the Purchaser).

Limits of the Contractor's liability
The Conditions put a number of limits to the Contractor's liability for loss or damage on Site. These are all straightforward.

CLAUSE 30.7

(The Purchaser's property and premises)

This Clause is easy to deal with. In the insurance policy required to be maintained by the Contractor under Clause 31.4, the Contractor is required to insure against damage to the property of the Purchaser for an amount to be agreed between the parties. Clause 30.7 then limits the Contractor's liability for this damage to £5million, unless otherwise agreed. Effectively therefore what Clause 30.7 does is to limit the Contractor's liability for damage to the property of the Purchaser to the amount of insurance cover agreed between the parties pursuant to Clause 31.4.

However Clause 30.8 makes the Contractor liable for all *third-party* claims, even when made against the Purchaser, because third parties suffering damage will usually find it easier to claim against client than contractor.

Employee risk

CLAUSES 30.5–6

These Clauses deal with the risk of injury to the employees of the different parties involved during work on the Site. They provide simply that each party will accept responsibility for its own employees. This is normal practice in view of statutory Employer's Liability Insurance, and avoids cross-claims.

3.6.7 Overall exclusions

Liability

Liability of one party to the other under a Contract, and the liability of either of the parties to any third party, is always a highly emotive and contentious area, but it is an area with which all model forms have to deal.

Clauses 15 and 43 of the Conditions have already been discussed.

CLAUSE 44

The intention of Clause 44 is to put certain clear limits to the Contractor's liability.

Clause 44.1 excludes the Contractor's liability for various types of what may be called 'consequential' damage, together with damage caused because the Purchaser has imposed direct requirements upon the Contractor (subject to recovery under insurance).

Clause 44.2 then puts a general limit to the Contractor's liability. He is only to be liable for those damages allowed by the Conditions.

Perhaps, therefore, it is desirable to summarise the liability of both parties as set out by the Form:

• Performance of the Plant—if the Plant fails to pass its performance tests by a small amount, the Contractor will be liable to the Purchaser for breach of the Contract and his liability will be as agreed by the parties in Schedule 17 to the Contract. If the Plant fails to pass its performance tests by a significant amount, or fails to pass its take-over tests, the Contractor will be in breach of the Contract. (In each case the Contractor will certainly be liable for damages, and perhaps also to termination or cancellation of the Contract.)

- Third-party intellectual property—each party is liable to the other if it causes any infringement of any patent or other right owned by a third party, essentially to indemnify the other party against any claim.
- Delay—if the Purchaser delays the Contractor other than by reason of force majeure, the Purchaser is liable for the Contractor's extra costs. If the Contractor is late other than by force majeure or various other acceptable reasons, then the Contractor will be liable to the Purchaser and his precise degree of liability will be set out in Schedule 12 to the Contract.
- Disruption—if the Purchaser disrupts the Contractor's work on Site by failing to supply work or information then the Purchaser will be liable to meet the Contractor's extra costs.
- Damage to property—damage to the Plant by either party during construction should be covered by joint insurance arranged under the Contract. The Contractor would then be expected to insure his own Site facilities and construction equipment. Damage to the Plant during the guarantee period by the Contractor would be covered by the joint insurance package. Damage by the Purchaser would be insured separately by the Purchaser. Damage to third-party owned property would be insured separately by the parties. If this insurance were inadequate then the parties would be liable for the excess.

3.7 Payments and money

The Clauses to be covered in this section are those listed under the heading 'Money' in Figure 2 (see page 102).

3.7.1 General approach

In a reimbursable contract the principle is that the Contractor is to be reimbursed for his work, and that reimbursement should be on a 'transparent' basis. This means that payment is dealt with in a completely different way to a price-based contract. There are perhaps four separate payment questions to be dealt with.

- The first is how the Contractor's work is to be priced. Essentially this can be done in two ways, on the basis of *cost*, actual or presumed, plus a profit, or on the basis of *rate/charge/fee* per unit of work. The Conditions do not deal with this as such, because there is no need to do so. They refer to the Contractor's right to be paid his cost/expenditure, and leave the parties to define the way in which cost/expenditure is to be calculated in Schedule 18.
- The second is the procedure for deciding when and how much money should be paid by the Purchaser to the Contractor. The Contract is a 'reimbursable' contract. The aim of the Contract therefore is to ensure that money is transferred to the Contractor as necessary to fund the Works, to ensure a neutral cash flow. This problem is dealt with by the Conditions, in Clause 39, for

reimbursable payment, and also in Schedule 19, for any lump sum or milestone payments.

- Thirdly is the problem of maintaining an open system of cost control. This is dealt with primarily in Clause 3.7 and Clause 19, supported by Schedule 20 to contain the detail.
- The final problem is that of the terms of payment that will apply to Subcontractors. In a process contract probably well over fifty percent of the total cost of the Works will be payments to Subcontractors, rather than for work done by the Contractor. This is not dealt with by the Conditions. What should happen is that the Project Manager and the Contractor will decide between them upon the payments policy to be adopted by the Contractor when letting Subcontracts. Terms of payment will then be agreed by the Contractor with each Subcontractor.

The Conditions are written on the basis that payments will be made to the Contractor on a monthly basis, with enough money being transferred each month to enable the Contractor to finance his own operations and then meet Subcontractors' invoices when they become due.

3.7.2 The 'Contract Price'

CLAUSES 18 and 40

Clause 18.1 states the basic principle, that in a reimbursable contract there is no real Contract Price. The Contract Price will only be known when all work under the Contract has been completed and paid for. It is to be calculated in accordance with Schedules 18–20.

Clause 18.2 then simply complements Clause 18.1 by stating that any further items required will be priced either on the basis of the Schedules or by agreement between the Contractor and Project Manager. Finally Clause 18.3 deals with dispute.

Clause 40 allows for any prime cost and provisional sums required by the Purchaser to be included in the Contract in Schedule 18. The Clause is straightforward and needs little comment.

A provisional sum is a sum, stated in the Contract, that is available for use if the Project Manager decides that he wishes the Contractor to carry out certain additional work. Provisional sums are often allowed for in contracts when the Purchaser or Project Manager realise at the start that additional or ancillary work may be needed, but when it is impossible to decide precisely what may need to be done until the Contract is well advanced. Typical examples are optional items of equipment or 'site improvement' work, such as landscaping, fencing or paths, etc. A provisional sum might also be used to cover more important items of work, which are known to be necessary but which cannot be accurately priced at the date of the Contract, such as building or foundation work.

A prime cost sum is an amount included in the Contract Price to be used for a specific purpose as instructed by the Project Manager. Prime cost sums are regularly used where the Purchaser/Project Manager may wish to nominate a Subcontractor.

3.7.3 The payment procedure

CLAUSE 39

Clause 39 is the main payment clause. It does two things. Firstly, it lays down the procedure for monthly transfers of money to the Contractor. Secondly it sets out the rights of the Contractor in the event of non-payment.

Clause 39.1 and 39.2 need no comment.

Perhaps the best way to comment upon Clauses 39.3–5 is to describe the payment procedure.

Firstly, the time-scale. Near the end of each month during the Contract, say about the 20–24th of the month (if the parties are adopting calendar months as their payment periods) the Contractor will submit a request for the transfer of the funds needed by him during the following month. The request will take the form probably of a draft invoice or statement setting out the Contractor's estimate of the funds that he will require during that month supported by the appropriate back-up information called for in Clause 39.3. The Project Manager is allowed two weeks to check the Contractor's request/invoice/estimate and must then certify to the parties the amount that he accepts as being payable. The Purchaser then has two weeks to pay the amount certified to the Contractor. The result is that the Contractor will receive payment of the amount on or around the 20th of the month. He will then use that money during the last ten days of the month to pay any Subcontractors whatever is due to them, and also to meet his own costs and salaries.

Secondly the request. The request for payment will be in two parts, and will refer to two quite different months. Assuming that a Contract is signed on the 1st February the Contractor will immediately submit an invoice for that month's estimated costs, which will be paid without certification. Then at the end of *February* he will submit a request setting out his estimated expenditure (his own costs and any invoices from Subcontractors due for payment) during *March* (Clause 39.3(a)). A request submitted in *March* will then set out the Contractor's estimated expenditure during *April* (Clause 39.3(a)), *together with* details of actual charges and payments during *February* (Clause 39.3(b)). The request submitted in *April* will set out the Contractor's estimate for *May* (Clause 39.3(a)) and actual charges and payments for *March* (Clause 39.3(b)) *together with* the amounts certified by the Project Manager for that month (Clause 39.3(c)). The request submitted in *May* will set the Contractor's estimate for *June* (Clause 39.3(a)), actual charges and payments for *April* (Clause 39.3(b)), together with the amounts certified by the Project Manager for that month (Clause 39.3(c)), and so on.

Given that the Project Manager will have detailed knowledge of Subcontracts under Clause 9, and monthly reports of the Contractor's progress under Clause 3.7, as well as access to the Contractor and his records and forecasts, the request for payment procedure will quickly enable the Project Manager to build up a comprehensive cost/price/cash flow picture of the Contract.

Thirdly, the supporting 'relevant documentary evidence'. For actual expenditure this might comprise receipted copies of Subcontractors' invoices or payment documents, together with the Contractor's timesheets, etc.

165

For estimated expenditure this might comprise predicted manning levels and charges, plus Subcontractors' invoices awaiting payment.

Fourthly, the organisation. It will be clear that all the parties involved will need to have adequate organisation. The Contractor has to be able to submit regular monthly invoices with a mass of supporting detail. The Project Manager then has only a few days to assimilate that detail before certifying payment. The Purchaser then has to arrange transfer quickly.

3.7.4 Non-payment

Clause 39.6 and 39.8–9 deal with the Contractor's rights in the event of delay in payment. Under Clause 39.6 interest is payable on any amounts overdue at rapidly-increasing rates. In addition, under Clauses 39.8–9, the Contractor has the right to suspend performance and ultimately terminate the Contract if *either* the Project Manager delays certification *or* the Purchaser delays payment.

3.7.5 Set-off

Clause 39.7 allows the Purchaser a right of set-off, in respect of sums due to him from the Contractor *under the Contract*. This of course is provided that the Purchaser can justify his claim—see Clause 4.3.

3.7.6 VAT

Clause 39.10 is straightforward and needs no comment.

3.7.7 Audit

CLAUSES 3.7, 19 and 39.11

Clause 19 needs little comment in one sense. Most complex contracts that include a reimbursable element include a clause allowing the Purchaser to exercise a degree of financial oversight of the way in which the Contractor controls and spends the funds that he provides.

Clause 19.1 combines with Clause 3.7 and Schedule 20 to require the Contractor to keep records of the Contract which are both complete and detailed and satisfactory to the Purchaser, that will enable the Purchaser to check progress under the Contract and its financial position. Note that the Contractor's records do not have to be in any specific form. They can be of any form or kind the Contractor chooses, subject to Schedule 20, so long as they provide the Purchaser with the reasonable ability to ascertain progress.

Clause 19.2 then allows the Purchaser to check on progress should he wish to do so, and Clause 39.11 provides the procedure to rectify any errors that are discovered.

The Burgundy Book

4

4.1 General introduction

The text of the Burgundy Book contract is almost entirely based upon the Green Book reimbursable contract. Virtually the entire text of the Green Book Conditions is repeated in the Burgundy Book. Given that Target Cost contracts are essentially collaborative relationship contracts, but with an incentive to the Contractor to minimise cost as far as realistically possible, this is quite correct.

But there are a large number of additions to the original text to incorporate the necessary references to Target Cost. The Target Cost principle implies the following stages:

- working out, hopefully in considerable detail, exactly what work the Contractor is to carry out under the Contract, or within that part of the Contract that is to be subject to a Target Cost;
- calculating the Target Cost that is to be set for that work, and the bonus/penalty, or 'gain share/pain share', arrangement that is to apply to that Target Cost;
- recording and paying the Actual Cost of carrying out the work as the work proceeds;
- adjusting the Target Cost to take account of any changes to the Actual Cost caused by changes and delays for which the Purchaser is responsible;
- finally, when the work is complete, comparing the total Actual Cost with the final Target Cost, and applying the gain share/pain share formula to any difference between the two to arrive at the final Contract Price.

This means that there are a large number of clauses with minor changes to them. Where the Green Book deals with change, the clauses have to be modified. Where the Green Book refers to 'Contract Price' the Burgundy Book refers to 'Actual Cost' and perhaps also to 'Target Cost'. Some clauses relating to payment or termination also need to have additional paragraphs added.

The Conditions are a little bit more complicated because they have to cover two or three different situations. The Contract may include a fully agreed Target Cost at the moment of signature. It may not include a Target Cost at all, but

167

provide for one to be agreed during the Contract. It may include an initial assessment of the Target Cost but with provision for this to be finalised and agreed between the parties during the Contract.

The conditions make two assumptions that may not always apply in practice:

- That the Target Cost will apply to the whole of the Works. It will often be the case that various parts of the Works may be carried out outside the scope of the Target Cost, either on a fixed fee or reimbursable basis.
- That the final calculation of the Contract Price will take place after the work is finished, at or around the time of the issue of the Final Certificate. Often the parties will not wish to wait for so long. Instead they will agree, perhaps at the time of taking over or Acceptance (on the successful completion of a test stage), upon a reasonable sum to cover the cost of making good defects and use that sum to make the final gainshare/painshare calculation. This has the benefit of getting things settled while the full project teams are still in place.

Remember too that the project relationship between the parties will be bound to change once the Target Cost has actually been agreed. Until agreement of the Target Cost the relationship may be reimbursable and collaborative. Once Target Cost has been agreed the relationship may still be collaborative but will almost inevitably become slightly more adversarial and arms-length simply because of the inherent conflict between being flexible and minimising cost to protect a potential bonus. As we have already said, this transition from one management style to another makes the Target Cost contract a very difficult beast to manage for the project teams on both sides.

4.2 Procedural and general clauses

4.2.1 Target Cost contracts

The Burgundy Book is the only set of model conditions specifically designed for Target Cost contracts for capital plant published within Europe.

Being result-orientated rather than work-orientated the Conditions, like the Red and Green Conditions, are truly multi-disciplinary and are suitable for projects involving work in several different engineering disciplines, such as process/chemical engineering, civil/structural engineering, electrical/mechanical engineering.

4.2.2 The Agreement

I would always recommend you to consider the form of Agreement on pages 6–7 when setting up the Contract. Of course you may very well choose another contract form, such as a Purchase Order, but the Agreement is important. It is a reminder of the points that must be covered and of the various additional documents that are necessary to complete it properly. It also sets out the shape that the Contract should take, so that its various parts will relate correctly to one another. The heading and preamble to the Agreement set the scene, and Clause 1 incorporates the Burgundy Book conditions and lists the other Contract documents.

Clause 2 of the Agreement is self-explanatory, but states an important principle. Nothing counts that is not a part of the Contract.

Clauses 3–12 are straightforward and need little comment. Clauses 3 to 5 set out the extent of the Contractor's risk/liability. There could be considerable cost and other implications arising from the date fixed by Clause 7, as it sets a date from which certain things switch from the risk of the Contractor to that of the Purchaser. The point to be remembered here is that 'the date of the Contractor's tender' is a slightly artificial concept. The Contractor will often submit not one but two or more 'tenders' as the negotiations proceed towards a conclusion and the parties explore different technical or commercial possibilities. Often the Contractor's initial tender will have been submitted anything up to a year before the Contract is made. The date inserted in Clause 7 should be either the date of the Contractor's initial formal tender for the project or the date of a later tender by the Contractor that has been submitted after proper consideration of all the circumstances, as opposed to a simple price update or re-validation exercise.

The additional documents listed in Clause 1 are as follows.

The Specification

The Specification can be anything from a complete detailed description of the Plant and Works downwards. The important thing however is that, by the time the Target Cost is agreed, the parties must have agreed upon the detailed description *and* a detailed cost structure. The reason for this is simply that detailed costs are essential to keeping control of *changes* to the Target Cost when they occur. The Specification needs to deal with:

- the Plant that is to be constructed;
- any other work which the Contractor is to carry out;
- the process requirements, performance, raw materials, products, operating and safety considerations and so on;
- the design standards and other requirements that the Plant must meet; and
- testing and inspection standards.

The Special Conditions

Although the form of Agreement adds the words '(if any)' to paragraph 1(b), it is virtually certain that every Contract will need to include Special Conditions to adapt the Conditions to the particular needs and circumstances of the project.

The Schedules

Pages 59–76 give guidance on compiling the Schedules with reference to the appropriate Guide Notes. I particularly recommend reading the guide notes to Schedules 18, 19 and 20. The list of Schedules is not quite as formidable as it looks. Its purpose is to act as a reminder of the various issues to consider, and as a framework to organise the Contract contents so that the right information ends up in the correct pigeonhole.

First-time users of the Forms should find the Guide Notes invaluable in explaining how to go about the task of producing the Contract. Certainly no other Institution produces anything comparable to them.

4.2.3 The procedural clauses

The clauses to be covered in the remainder of this section are those described as Procedural and General Clauses in Figure 3 (see page 171). For ease of reference they can be split into the following groups:

- Contract interpretation (Clause 1);
- co-operation (Clause 2);
- responsibilities (Clauses 3.1–2, 3.4, 3.6, 3.8-9, 4.1–2, 4.4–5, 7.1–2 and 7.4);
- intellectual property (Clauses 8 and 20);
- termination (Clauses 42 and 43);
- notice procedures (Clauses 1.7 and 5);
- disputes provisions (Clauses 45, 46, 47 and 48).

4.2.4 Contract interpretation

Clause 1 defines a number of words and expressions. 'Defined Terms' as they are called are used in every set of model conditions. They are verbal short-hand. Defined Terms always mean their *definition,* whenever and wherever they are used, that is anywhere in the Contract and also in any correspondence between the parties arising from the Contract. They help to ensure consistency between the different parts of the Contract and accuracy in correspondence during the Contract. Always be careful when using any Defined Term that you are clear as to precisely what it means, and then that you use it correctly. Then in Clause 2 a number of other points of interpretation are also laid down.

Definitions
CLAUSE 1

The definitions set out in Clause 1 are all reasonably straightforward but note the following points.

'Actual Cost' is the amount(s) payable to the Contractor as the work proceeds. Once the work is complete, total Actual Cost is then compared with the Target Cost (updated to take account of changes). If total Actual Cost equals updated Target Cost then that is the Contract Price. If total Actual Cost is different to updated Target Cost it is adjusted in accordance with the gainshare/painshare formula and the *adjusted* total Actual Cost is then the Contract Price.

'Agreed Rate' defines the starting point for the calculation of interest payable on late payments under Clause 39.13. Essentially the viewpoint of the Conditions is that overdue payments should carry interest at a rate that is sufficiently high to make deliberate delay in payment unappealing. Remember, too, that there is legislation on the point *within the UK*, the Late Payment of Commercial Debts (Interest) Act (1998).

START		SITE COMMENCEMENT	TAKING OVER	FINAL CERT.
Procedural & General Clauses	1 2 3.1-2 3.4 3.6 3.8–9 4.1–2 4.4-5 5 7.1-2 7.4 8 20 42 43 45 46 47 48			
	DESIGN / MANUFACTURE	SITE CONSTRUCTION / COMMISSIONING	DEFECTS REPAIR	
Main Project Activity II	3.7 9 10 11 12 13 21 22 29	29		
Site Work		3.3 23 24 25 26 27 28 34		
Tests		32 33	35 36	
Claims & Variations	3.5 4.7 7.3–4 16 17 18.6 37.3–4	3.5 4.7 6 7.3–4 16 17 18.6 37.3–4		
Delay	14 41	14 15 41		
Defects/Final Certificate			33.13 37 38	
Insurance etc	31	4.6 30 31	30 31	
Liability	15 43 44	15 43 44	43 44	
Money	3.7 18 19 39 40	3.7 18 19 39 40	3.7 18 19 39 40	

Figure 3 The Burgundy Book

171

'Applications Software/Contractor's Software/Standard Software'. Note the three definitions of different categories of software referred to in Clause 8.

The definition of the 'Contract', and other definitions as well, refers to an 'Agreement'. See the earlier comments on the advisability of using the recommended form of Agreement set out on pages 6–7 of the Form.

(For comments on the significance of the 'Acceptance Certificate' see page 215.)

'Contract Manager' means the manager appointed by the Contractor to manage the project.

'Contractor's Equipment' is an expression used to describe everything that the Contractor may bring on to the Site to assist in the construction of the Plant (as distinct from items brought on to the Site for inclusion within the Plant). The expression is therefore very comprehensive, covering everything from a spanner to site huts or heavy lifting or construction equipment.

Note that 'Documentation' means *both* drawings *and* other technical documentation, such as data, calculations or diagrams and also non-technical documentation, as appropriate in the circumstances, both in hard copy and electronic form.

'Initial Target Cost' and 'Target Cost'. The 'Initial Target Cost' is the original Target Cost agreed between the parties, which may be written into the Contract or agreed later. The 'Target Cost' is the Initial Target Cost adjusted to include changes under the Contract.

'Plant', 'Works' and 'Materials'. The purpose of the Contract will be that the Contractor will carry out Works including the provision of:

- services of various kinds (such as design, manufacture, procurement, site supervision, testing);
- the supply of Materials;
- the construction, installation and erection work necessary to build the Plant on the Site from the Materials and any equipment or other items provided for that purpose by the Purchaser;
- the testing of the Plant.

'Materials' means everything that the Contractor supplies that is to be incorporated into the Plant and/or necessary for its operation. It includes such things as equipment, piping, structural steelwork, control systems, computer programmes (or at least the discs or chips containing the programmes), and civil engineering/building materials. It may also cover such things as operational spare parts, lubricants, fuel, chemicals or catalysts.

The 'Works' will, together with any other work done and equipment provided by the Purchaser, result in a process plant that can be put into operation by the Purchaser.

The 'Project Manager' should always be known and identified, even if not formally nominated, well before the Contract is made. He *can* be a firm or company, but should really be a person, as this gives the Contractor a clear point of contact and decision-making.

'Subcontractor' means any and every company that carries out any work or supplies any Materials or Contractor's Equipment to the Contractor.

'Site' means the area both where the Plant is to be built and any other areas to be used by the Contractor for the purposes of construction. It may be either the whole or only a part of the Purchaser's own site, and may also include other areas to be used by the Contractor for the purposes of the Contract.

Note the difference between the Specification and the Description of Works, which is set out in Schedule 1, together with a description of the Site. In essence it is that the Specification is a statement of the technical requirements for the Plant. The Description of Works is a statement of what input is required from the Contractor (and therefore also from the Purchaser) towards achieving that final result. The two fit together—and of course the description could be anything from a simple statement that 'the Contractor shall do everything' downwards.

Clause 1.2 provides for the Contract to be governed by English law, but of course there would be no difference if another UK law were to apply. The IChemE Conditions can easily be adapted to non-UK contracts and non-UK law—the changes that would be necessary present few problems to the professional draftsman and in most cases there would be little difference in meaning.

Clause 1.3 defines the order of priority that is to apply between the different parts of the Contract. Special Conditions, i.e. Conditions specially written into the Contract, prevail over these Conditions. These Conditions then prevail over the Specification and the Specification over the Schedules. It is therefore important to minimise overlap between the Specification and Schedules.

The consequence is that changes to these Conditions *must* be made by a Special Condition—*it is not enough to try to do so by writing possible changes into a Schedule or the Specification*.

What Clause 1.5 means is that before either party can refuse any approval or consent he must have a valid reason for doing so. The only reasons that will normally be valid are the intervention of force majeure, that the other has failed to comply with the relevant terms of the Contract or good engineering practice, or has overlooked something and is not therefore entitled to be given the approval or consent which he has requested.

4.2.5 Co-operation

CLAUSE 2

This is perhaps the most important principle in any Target Cost contract. The Contractor will become responsible for trying to keep the Actual Cost of the Works as low as possible in order to earn his bonus but this is impossible in a collaborative framework without the help of the Purchaser. Clause 2.1 therefore sets out a co-operative principle *with both parties undertaking to look for and employ low-cost solutions and methods.* Clause 2.2 stresses the need for openness and prompt disclosure.

These matters are always a question of degree, of course, but any clear failure by either party would be breach of the Clause.

4.2.6 Responsibilities

Basic principles
CLAUSES 3.1–2 and 3.4

Clauses 3.1–2 and 3.4 set out the Contractor's obligations in broad terms.

Clause 3.1 simply establishes the basic principle that the Works must be carried out in accordance with the Contract.

Clause 3.2 then says that all work must be carried out by the Contractor *both* safely and in accordance with good engineering practice *and* to the reasonable satisfaction of the Project Manager. There is a big difference between a Contract based on a Specification which sets out in great detail exactly what the Contractor has to achieve (the Red Book) and a Contract which requires the Contractor to carry out his work to the satisfaction of the Project Manager (the Burgundy). The Contract cannot do both. Either the Specification or the Project Manager must have the ultimate power to decide what the Contractor is to do. The Red Book, as a firm/fixed-price contract should, resolves this conflict in favour of the Specification. It provides that if the Specification sets out what is to be supplied then the Project Manager is not empowered to change that. In effect the Contractor can supply whatever he wants, provided only that it meets the Specification. The Burgundy Book goes the other way—but note Clause 2.1.

CLAUSE 3.6

This Clause is obvious in meaning but important in principle. Essentially it allows the Purchaser the right to insist that the Contractor retains the necessary resources within the project, and also perhaps even to terminate for breach if the Contractor fails to do so, even if the Contractor is not actually in breach of the terms of the Contract in any other way. (In addition, by making a specific reference to *financial* resources, it links to Clause 43.1 which gives the Purchaser a way of closing out the Contract if the Contractor is having financial problems that are sufficiently serious to affect his ability to carry on the project properly.) Quite apart from the obvious problems that can result from receivership or administration, effective procurement by a Contractor usually requires a reasonable degree of financial credibility.

CLAUSE 3.7

The first part of this Clause deals with an important function within a reimbursable contract—cost control and cost reporting. Of course the Clause can only lay down the basic principles, but it will inevitably link back to Schedules 18–20. Note in particular paragraph (d) and the final part of the Clause.

CLAUSES 3.8–9

Clauses 3.8–9 need no explanation, but underline two important principles, the provision of training in the operation and maintenance of the Plant, and the establishment of an adequate quality assurance system by the Contractor. In addition Clause 3.8 makes provision for *validation* of the Plant by the Contractor. Broadly speaking validation comprises the provision of whatever documentation is necessary, as the project proceeds, to prove precisely:

- the design of the Plant;
- the Materials used in its construction;
- that the Plant has been constructed in accordance with the design; and
- the accuracy and repeatability of the process, and therefore of the products made by the Plant.

Validation is often an essential stage in product approval in industries such as pharmaceuticals.

CLAUSE 3.10
Finally this Clause simply clarifies designer liability under UK law.

4.2.7 Purchaser's obligations
CLAUSES 4.1–2 and 4.4
Clauses 4.1–2, supplemented by Schedule 2, is a simple description of the contribution to the project to be made by the Purchaser. The words need little comment. Nevertheless while the Clause is simple it deals with an area that is always likely to give rise to claims by the Contractor. The problem is that any failure to comply with the terms of Clause 4 (except where due to 'force majeure' under Clause 14.2) is a breach of contract, for which the Contractor is entitled to claim damages, i.e. the cost of any extra work caused to the Contractor (plus Profit), together with any extension of time needed by the Contractor under Clause 14.1(d). Therefore the supply of services and information by the Purchaser is one area where the Project Manager will always need to exert close control.

The Clause adopts a similar approach to Clause 3.2. Where there is an express description in the Contract of what is to be provided by the Purchaser then that is precisely what must be supplied—no more and no less—and other considerations do not apply. Where there is no express description ('express' meaning a description in clear technical terms) then the clause lays down a number of general and obvious rules for the Purchaser. These are that the Purchaser must carry out his work in a proper way, reasonably quickly, and in a manner that will cause the Contractor no unreasonable time, quality, design or safety problems in carrying out the Contract.

Clause 4.1 refers to the supply of any or all designs or technical or other information to be supplied by the Purchaser under the Contract and does so in much the same terms that Clause 4.2 uses for the supply of Materials or Work. The Purchaser will be responsible for the information which he supplies to the Contractor in a number of ways:

- under Clause 8.4 he may be responsible if he has provided 'drawings or instructions' to the Contractor which result in an infringement of a third-party intellectual property right;

- then under Clauses 30.4(b) he may also be responsible if designs or information lead to an accident on Site, or are responsible for a failure of the Plant to meet its guaranteed performance.

Clause 4.1 lays down one very important principle. The only permissible route for the transfer of information to the Contractor is through the Project Manager. The consequence is that the Contractor should *only* act upon information provided by the Project Manager, or authorised members of his staff.

4.2.8 Compliance with legislation

CLAUSES 7.1–2, 4.5 and 7.4

The first sentence of Clause 7.1 reflects recent changes in safety law, and in particular the responsibilities imposed by law on both sides to the project. In all projects within the European Union, both parties will have obligations under legislation arising from Council Directive 92/57/EEC (in the UK the Construction (Design and Management) Regulations of 1994) in respect of the way the work on the Site is organised and carried out. The second part of Clause 7.1 refers both to planning permission and any permissions that may be needed from the owners of adjacent land, such as wayleaves or rights of way or permission to bring services to the Site. Outline planning permission is usually obtained by the Purchaser, but there will often be logical reasons for the Contractor to be involved in the application for detailed planning permission, due to his process knowledge. In practice if the parties decide that the Contractor should apply or assist the Purchaser in any particular case, then it is a simple matter to amend the clause. Clause 7.2 is self-explanatory, and so too is Clause 4.5.

Clause 7.4 is straightforward, but is of very great importance, especially in any Contract with an export/import content.

4.2.9 Intellectual property

The Conditions deal with a number of issues relating to the use and protection of intellectual property by the parties. Clause 8 deals with four—the licensing and use of third-party processes used in the design and operation of the Plant; responsibility for third-party claims; the ownership and possible further use by the Purchaser of the Contractor's design information outside the Contract; and finally the ownership of and rights to use software. Clause 20 then deals with confidentiality.

CLAUSE 8

Clause 8.1 establishes the principles that apply where the design of the Plant uses any processes, know-how or software which are the property of a third party. The Purchaser (not the Contractor, as in the Red Book) will agree terms with the third party for the supply of the necessary design package and assistance. This will usually be done under the terms of a licence agreement that will allow the Contractor to use information to carry out the Works including testing and commissioning the Plant.

If the licence agreement is on the basis of a single 'all-in' lump sum fee then there will be no further fees payable by the Purchaser. Otherwise the Purchaser will then agree with the licensor any output or use-related royalties or fees required by the licensor and will accept responsibility for their payment.

In practice, of course, wherever a significant third party process is involved, it will normally be necessary for the Contractor and Purchaser to incorporate a whole series of Special Conditions into the Contract to deal with the issues involved and a series of discussions between the Purchaser, Contractor and process owner will probably be necessary to agree them before the Contract can be signed.

Clauses 8.2–4 are standard intellectual property infringement/liability clauses that require each of the parties to be responsible if the information and design input which it makes towards the Contract is claimed to infringe the rights of a third party. In other words each party carries the cost/risk of any dispute over infringement of patent or design rights which he may cause.

Note, by the way, the general obligation of the Contractor under the last sentence of Clause 8.2. The purpose is clear—but it is uncertain for how long the Contractor's obligations under the Clause will last. The answer is not very long. Realistically no third party right can adversely affect the Purchaser's right to use or operate the Plant unless it pre-dates the design or construction phase of the Contract. The longest timescale of any intellectual property right is that of the patent which can take some three to four years to obtain/publish.

In case of any claim of infringement the third party claimant would almost certainly take action against the Purchaser as well as, or even instead of, the Contractor. The Purchaser will always be the more vulnerable of the two. He has invested heavily in a production plant that could in theory be rendered useless or prohibitively expensive to operate by a successful claim, and might not have the technical knowledge to defend the claim himself. This is the reason behind Clause 8.3 which sets out a procedure by which the Contractor will, in consultation with the Purchaser, take over the responsibility for dealing with any infringement claim made against the Purchaser which relates to the Contractor's design of the Plant. The Clause is intended to ensure three things:

- there must be no unreasonable delay by the Contractor in initiating action to deal with any dispute;
- the Contractor must deal with the claim as efficiently as possible; and
- the Contractor must keep the Purchaser informed of his policy and progress in dealing with the claim,

because the result of a successful claim would probably be to prevent the Purchaser from operating the Plant, or being able effectively to use or market products from the Plant, except at a very high price. If process information is provided by the Purchaser, of course, the Clause might need to be reversed.

CLAUSES 8.5–6

Clause 8.5 simply provides that the Contractor and Subcontractors retain copyright in the drawings and other documents which they supply (subject only to

177

pre-existing rights—which could include any licensor or the Purchaser, for instance). This is necessary to ensure that they retain ownership of their design information. It also ensures that they keep the right to take action if there is any attempt to use their designs which is not authorised by the Contract, either by the Purchaser or by any other person who has acquired copies from the Purchaser. Afterall the Contractor, who is in the business of building plants, has a much greater interest to protect than the Purchaser who is only concerned with operating one plant.

Clause 8.6 then gives the Purchaser two rights to use those drawings and documents. Firstly he is given the right to use them in the operation and maintenance of the Plant. Secondly he is given the further right, subject to the restrictions stated in the Clause, to use the drawings to debottleneck, enlarge or improve the Plant.

Two comments should be borne in mind here:

- This second right must always to some extent affect the willingness of the Contractor to hand over *detailed* drawings. It is also very much a compromise. The Contractor is reluctant to see information that may contain his valuable know-how being released by the Purchaser to other contractors or suppliers in order to buy equipment. The Purchaser wants to have freedom to modify or carry out work on his own Plant, and to use information that he has paid for in order to achieve that. It has to be said that the compromise can sometimes give rise to problems, although not insoluble problems;
- The clause will usually be deleted, or heavily modified, wherever a third party process licensor is involved.

CLAUSES 8.7–8
Clauses 8.7–8 deal with the ownership of or the copyright in computer software which forms part of the Materials, typically the programmes forming part of the Plant's control system. The basic law is that the copyright in computer software vests in the writer until transferred. Therefore, unless a Contract says otherwise, the copyright in the control programmes will normally remain the property of the Contractor (or his Subcontractor) and a Purchaser of that software would simply receive an implied licence to use it for the purposes for which it is purchased.

The Clauses modify this basic position as follows:

- the Purchaser obtains the *ownership* of all software written by the Contractor or Subcontractors *as a part of the Contract*, which usually includes the Plant's operating/control systems;
- the Purchaser gains a specific licence to use all necessary software for the lifetime of the Plant;
- the Purchaser receives the information and source codes that he needs to be able to modify and update the software.

CLAUSE 20
Little comment is necessary on this Clause. It requires both parties to respect *all* confidential information received from the other during the Contract, both technical and commercial.

The Contractor is allowed to use the Purchaser's confidential information only during the period of the Contract and for the purposes of carrying out his work. The Purchaser is permitted to use the Contractor's confidential information during the lifetime of the Plant but only for the purposes of operation and maintenance. Maintenance does *not* include 'repair', therefore the Purchaser would not be entitled to use information provided by the Contractor, or by Subcontractors, to have spare parts manufactured.

Note that Clause 20.2 specifically provides that the Purchaser may at any time require confidentiality undertakings from the Contractor's personnel and also from Subcontractors if he wishes. There is no equivalent clause giving the Contractor the same rights in respect of the Purchaser's personnel. If this were to be required, say where a process licence was involved, it would need to be included by a Special Condition.

Photographs etc.

Clause 20.4 bans the use of cameras and imaging software by the Contractor without prior consent. This looks old-fashioned, especially since when properly used a camera is an invaluable means of recording a situation, and therefore a vital project management tool. There are two reasons for the Clause. The first is that photographs/images of the Purchaser's Site should not to be used for publicity without his consent. The second is that a photograph should not be taken of any secret process or equipment belonging to the Purchaser without his consent.

4.2.10 Termination

There are two completely separate termination clauses in the Form—Clause 42 which permits termination where there has been no breach by the Contractor, and Clause 43 which provides for termination by the Purchaser where there has been breach of Contract by the Contractor.

Termination 'for convenience'

CLAUSE 42

This Clause gives the Purchaser the right to terminate the Contract at any time before it is completed; however this is at the Purchaser's expense. This will obviously be a very costly exercise and means that the Purchaser may have to pay the Contractor a considerable amount for something that is of very little use. Therefore this is really a solution of last resort which the Purchaser will only use when he has absolutely no practicable alternative but to end the Contract.

The Clause is long and complex in wording and procedure but little different in content from similar clauses appearing in other sets of model conditions. What the Clause does is to set out the basis and procedure for calculating and paying a reasonable termination payment to the Contractor.

The termination payment as defined in Clause 42.5 will cover the cost of all work done by the Contractor up to termination, plus that of closing down the

Contract and dealing with any long-term commitments made by the Contractor for the Contract, plus profit on that work. That payment will then be adjusted in accordance with the Contractor's performance against the Target Cost as at termination. A Target Cost for the work done up to termination will be fixed and the termination payment adjusted in accordance with the gainshare/painshare formula. Of course if no Target Cost has been agreed at the time of termination then the payment will not be subject to adjustment.

Termination for breach
CLAUSE 43

Clause 43.1 allows the Purchaser to terminate the Contract where the Contractor is in major financial difficulties (and see also Clause 3.6) on whatever terms will allow the Purchaser to get the best out of the disaster that has hit his Contractor. The Clause does this by allowing the Purchaser to terminate the Contract if he wishes, which means that the Purchaser can deal with an administrator or liquidator from a position of strength, supported perhaps by the terms of Clause 25.

Clause 43.2 then deals with the Purchaser's right to terminate the Contract in the case where a Contractor ceases to continue the proper performance of the Contract or is in 'material', i.e. rather more than insignificant, breach of Contract. The Clause then lays down the procedure to be followed. If after written notice by the Project Manager the Contractor fails to take reasonable action to correct the breach then the Purchaser can terminate the Contract, also by written notice.

Clauses 43.3–4 then make practical provision for the completion of the Works by the Purchaser in the event of termination and then closing down what may well be a substantial construction operation.

Then Clauses 43.5–13 deal with the consequential financial settlement that will take place after termination—deciding what the costs of termination and completion of the work are, and therefore how much is owed by one party to the other. The Clauses are complex but straightforward and need little explanation.

There are two comments that I would make:

• Although there is a clause like this in virtually every set of model conditions, it is a clause that will only be used in the most extreme cases. The risks and problems of changing horses in mid-stream are normally so great that, termination of any Contract for breach is very much a solution of last resort. A Process Contract tends to lock the Purchaser into the Contractor at least for most of the Contract period.
• The complex demands that a process Contract makes on both parties are such that, however skilled their project management, both the Purchaser and Contractor will regularly be in breach of their contractual obligations. Documentation will be incorrect or delivered late. Approvals will be delayed or wrongly refused. Incorrect information will be given. Equipment will be faulty. There will be mistakes and errors on both sides throughout the Contract. It is very rare for any party to a complex Contract to be blameless. Therefore termination by the Purchaser for breach of Contract can often be strongly contested by the Contractor.

Clause 43.5 simply puts a stop on further payments until the project is finished. Then there are two alternative procedures that can be used by the Purchaser. Under Clauses 43.6–7 he can allow the Project Manager to get the project completed, or complete it himself, and then prepare a statement of the financial position, balancing what is owing to the Contractor, taking into account the Target Cost (if agreed) and the extra cost of completion caused by his default. Alternatively, under Clause 43.8, he can have the statement prepared without waiting for the project to be completed.

The financial statement then leads to a Default Certificate showing whatever sum is payable by either party, which is then payable under Clause 43.12.

4.2.11 Notice procedures

CLAUSE 1.7

This Clause deals with the correspondence/communications between the parties during the Contract. Everything that might be important must be in writing. Then the Clause defines 'writing'. Writing means a permanent record and the more common types of permanent record are listed in the Clause. Note the reference to 'secure e-mail'. Secure e-mail means an e-mail system that retains a permanent copy of the e-mail text originally transmitted, so that any subsequent alterations of that text can be identified. Note also that a drawing is writing.

CLAUSE 5

This Clause needs no comment. It is procedural and self-explanatory. But the Clause is vital as it lays down the basic rule for all formal documents that may need to be exchanged between the parties and the Project Manager. Disregard the rule at your peril.

Two comments should be made regarding the procedure set out in the Clause:

- The Clause simply states that *oral* communications must be confirmed in writing within seven days *by the issuing party* in order to become valid.
- Problems often arise with communications made during progress meetings (Clause 5.3) because it may not always be clear to the receiving party that a notice has actually been given to him. Therefore to avoid doubts the authorised minutes of the meeting should always be written in such a manner as to make it absolutely clear when a notice or instruction has been given by either side. Note that it is only properly approved minutes that have 'decision/instruction/notice' status.

4.2.12 Dispute provisions

(See also section 1.4.)

The IChemE Forms have an unusually good record in the dispute area, with possibly the lowest rate of serious dispute of any of the major model forms. In nearly thirty years of existence the Green Book contract has never been the subject of litigation. In nearly forty years the Red Book has been to court twice. One court case every twenty years is quite good going.

CLAUSE 45

Clause 45 is the essential preliminary clause. Clauses 45.1–2 and 45.5 set the scene by stating that both sides should try to avoid the escalation of problems into dispute. Clearly this is in one sense a pious hope, but it is always better to say it and hope, than to say nothing and expect the worst.

Clauses 45.3–4 set up a formal procedure to identify any dispute. The aim here is to ensure that neither side leaps into any dispute procedure without both parties realising that an identifiable issue has arisen which has assumed 'dispute' status. This is actually of great practical importance in the case of adjudication. There is nothing worse for the adjudicator than to have to waste precious days trying to identify what the dispute is actually all about.

Then Clauses 45.6–7 offer the first alternative settlement routes, negotiation and mediation.

Adjudication
CLAUSE 46

This Clause simply makes provision for adjudication in accordance with the Housing Grants Act. Of course in doing so it assumes two things—that the Site is within the UK and that the Contract does include some element of 'construction operations'. If either of these is not the case then Clause 45 should really be deleted by a Special Condition.

The Expert
CLAUSE 47

This provides for the referral of certain disputes to an Expert. A number of Clauses in the Conditions allow disputed decisions by the Project Manager or claims by the Contractor to be referred to the Expert for independent assessment if the Contractor and Project Manager cannot agree upon the matter reasonably quickly. The parties may also agree to ask him to decide other questions as well. The device enables such points to be settled fast (often simply by submitting documents to the selected Expert for his decision) and cleanly without the need to struggle through a mediation or arbitration procedure which is not designed for settling that type of dispute.

Therefore the Expert is given the power to decide questions submitted to him by whatever procedure he thinks fair, and to demand from both parties whatever assistance he requires for that purpose. He can therefore deal with the matter in whatever way he feels to be conducive to a speedy but equitable decision and consistent with the rules of natural justice.

He is also given the right by Clause 47.3, for very practical reasons, to decide any ancillary contractual issues that relate to the dispute. He can also decide who pays his charges for deciding the dispute.

His decision will also be binding on the parties and is not open to appeal. The whole aim of the Clause is to provide a speedy method of solving essentially factual disputes. It does appear to be extremely effective and extremely fair.

The Clause allows the parties to agree upon their own Expert, but if they are unable to do so either party can require an Expert to be appointed by

IChemE. If so asked, IChemE would appoint some person with the appropriate qualifications, knowledge and experience to decide the issue, possibly but not necessarily an engineer, and probably competent to act as an arbitrator.

Arbitration
CLAUSE 48
Properly handled by an arbitrator who knows his stuff (and it must be said by solicitors and barristers who understand the differences between arbitration and litigation—of whom there are fewer than might appear at first glance), an arbitration can be quicker than going to the courts, much more confidential, rather more informal and likely to produce a more accurate decision on technical issues. However it is no less complicated to carry out than litigation. Arbitration will also be less expensive than litigation, but do realise that any argument between the parties that has to be settled through formal methods, whether arbitration or the courts may be horribly expensive both in money and man-hours. The legal profession makes a very expensive and often commercially unsatisfactory subcontractor.

4.3 Project/contract management
The Clauses to be covered in this section are those listed under the headings 'Main Project Activity' and 'Site Work' in Figure 3 (see page 171).

For ease of reference the Clauses can be divided into the following groups:

- management personnel (Clauses 11 and 12);
- management control/manipulation (Clause 11.2);
- programme and time management (Clause 13);
- drawings and approvals (Clause 21);
- subcontracting (Clauses 9 and 10);
- project meetings (Clauses 3.7 and 29);
- pre-delivery inspection (Clause 22);
- Site activities (Clauses 3.3, 23-28 and 34).

4.3.1 Management personnel
The Conditions provide the same management/control relationship as the Red Book Conditions, but with one critical difference—that the Project Manager is given much wider powers to control/manipulate the way in which the Contractor carries out his work.

The structure comprises a project manager appointed by each party and dealing with each other, both having full power to control the running of the Contract together with authority to act on behalf of the company which they represent. These two project managers, the Project Manager for the Purchaser and the Contract Manager for the Contractor, are responsible for the overall management of the Contract.

The Project Manager is then supported by one or more representatives who may either be responsible for the day-to-day management of the Contract, or responsible for managing various aspects of the Contract, such as work on Site, or the process control system, for example.

In other words the Project Manager may run the project on the basis of a two-tier management structure, with a Representative carrying out all day-to-day management and the Project Manager simply making the major 'policy' decisions; or he may carry out day-to-day management himself using Representatives as his assistants, or indeed without any Representatives at all.

The Contract Manager is supported by a Site Manager who is responsible for the control of construction and testing work on the Site.

CLAUSE 11

This Clause deals with the Purchaser's project management personnel.

The Contract is to be managed by the Project Manager, who must be named in the Contract (Clause 9 of the Agreement). The Contract should also state his address and how he may be contacted. This is important because the Project Manager is going to have to be responsible for a complex operation. If he is named in the Contract then he should have helped to set the project up or at least be reasonably well acquainted with its details. Therefore he will be able to take informed decisions from the start. There is nothing more annoying or disruptive to the Contractor than having to deal with a Project Manager who does not understand the basics of the project.

The Project Manager may then appoint one or more Representatives. A large project may well require the appointment of several Representatives, and Representatives may be changed as the project advances from the design to construction and testing stages. Often a Representative will be located at the Site once construction begins, as the Purchaser's Site Manager.

Clause 11.4 gives Representatives the basic power to reject, and therefore also to approve, any work by the Contractor, together with the authority to receive copy-notices from the Contractor. Under Clause 11.5 the Project Manager can delegate powers to his representatives. Obviously if a Representative is to act as the day-to-day project manager or Site Manager he will need some additional powers, to order Variations for instance. This is for the Project Manager to decide. The greater the powers delegated by the Project Manager, the lower the degree of direct control he has over the project.

The Conditions allow for the Project Manager to be either an employee of the Purchaser (or a sister-company of the Purchaser) or someone independent of the Purchaser, such as a consulting engineer. If this is to be the case it is prefer-able for both the Purchaser and Contractor if an individual *person* is named as the Project Manager rather than an organisation (see the definition of Project Manager in Clause 1). The reason for this is that if an organisation is appointed as Project Manager there will always be doubt as to precisely by whom and how authority may be exercised. Quite apart from this, project management requires firm and consistent decision-making to drive the project, which is inherently more likely with an individual than a committee.

The Purchaser needs to have a Project Manager in place for the whole dura-tion of the Contract. He has to issue the Final Certificate. The Purchaser may wish to name a different person as Project Manager once the Plant has passed its take-over and performance tests, and passes into the control of a production department, but the Final Certificate process requires knowledge of the Contract history.

The Conditions stress the need for fair treatment of the Contractor by the Project Manager and the Purchaser during the Contract, and Clause 11 deals with two aspects of this, in Clause 11.1, and in Clauses 11.3 and 11.4.

Clause 11.1

Clause 11.1 sets out the conduct expected from the Project Manager in managing the Contract. In addition Clause 11.1 also makes it clear that the Purchaser is legally responsible for any failure by the Project Manager to act properly. The Clause states the following:

- The opening lines give the Project Manager 'full authority' to act on behalf of the Purchaser. The words 'full authority' are a little uncertain in their meaning (could someone else also have authority, for instance?) but the wording of the Clause makes it quite clear that the Purchaser is bound by any decisions made by the Project Manager.
- Paragraphs (a), (b) and (c) then make it clear that the Purchaser takes full responsibility to the Contractor for any failure or neglect of duty by the Project Manager by giving the Contractor the right to claim direct against the Purchaser if the Project Manager fails to perform properly.
- Finally, under Paragraph (d), the Project Manager is required to act using professional judgement and with impartiality as between Purchaser and Contractor. Obviously in practice no Project Manager can ever be *totally* impartial. Every Project Manager is the prisoner of his or her background and experience. Nevertheless the Clause requires the Project Manager to avoid any *significant* degree of bias when making any decision that affects the technical or commercial interests of the Contractor. Any failure will be a breach of the Contract for which the Purchaser will be liable.

Clause 11.1 is a strong clause. The IChemE Conditions go further than any other model conditions in spelling out the duty and obligations of the Project Manager.

Clauses 11.3–4

As is normal in any contract, Clause 11.3 permits the Purchaser to replace the Project Manager.

In the process industry the Purchaser will often be a member of a group of companies and may buy in project management services from another company within the same group. Therefore Clause 11.4 treats any Project Manager employed by any other company within the same group as being employed by the Purchaser. The Clause also deals with a problem that may arise as a result of a change of Project Manager during the Contract. Experience has shown that, in certain situations, a Project Manager who is not employed by the Purchaser may find it rather easier to remain impartial under pressure. Therefore the Clause provides that the Contractor's consent may be required before the Purchaser can switch from an independent Project Manager to one of his own employees during the Contract.

Clauses 11.4–7

Under Clause 11.5 the Project Manager may appoint or change a Representative (or Representatives) at any time during the Contract. The Project Manager's Representative is more than simply a 'representative'. He is given the basic authority necessary for day-to-day management of the Contractor, the right to reject work done by the Contractor which is not in accordance with the requirements of the Contract, subject to a right of appeal to the Project Manager.

Clause 11.6 then permits the Project Manager to give additional powers to a Representative. Most common will be powers to approve designs or Documentation, or to issue instructions relating to matters such as site safety or Variation Orders.

Clause 11.7 provides a simple validation procedure in case a Representative should exceed his authority.

Finally Clause 11.8 provides that only the Project Manager/Representative and Contract Manager/Site Manager, or those authorised by them in accordance with the Contract, are authorised channels of communication unless the recipient of an unauthorised communication is willing to acknowledge it formally. For instance, the Purchaser cannot normally intervene except in cases where specifically permitted by the Conditions, such as Clauses 36.6 and 43.3.

CLAUSE 12

Clause 12 deals with the project management personnel to be provided by the Contractor. There are two identified managers, a Contract Manager responsible for running the Contract, and a Site Manager, responsible for the day-to-day management of operations on Site.

The Conditions make very few references to the Contract Manager or Site Manager. In general they refer almost exclusively to 'the Contractor', although there are many references to 'the Project Manager'. The reason is that the Conditions give the Project Manager powers to manage the Contract, and the Contractor has the obligation to carry out the Contract. Of course the more procedural parts of the Contract such as Schedules and Specification may well make many more references to the Contract Manager and Site Manager.

The Contract is based upon two management relationships. The Project Manager or a Representative will deal with the Contract Manager during the design and manufacturing stages, and then their work towards each other will be supplemented by that of a Representative and the Site Manager during operations on the Site.

There will need to be a Contract Manager in place up to the end of the Defects Liability Period. He will need to co-ordinate work in connection with performance tests and Acceptance Certificate, deal with any repairs, and handle the work needed to apply for and obtain the Final Certificate. The Contractor is less likely to change the Contract Manager than the Purchaser is to change the Project Manager.

The Contract Manager is named in the Contract (see Clause 10 of the Agreement). The Contract should also state his address and how he may be contacted. The Contract Manager is entitled to appoint a deputy to act for him during any absence from the project for any time, by written notice to the Project Manager.

This is a normal provision given that the life of a process contract may well be measured in years rather than months.

The Contract Manager is again given 'full authority' to act on the Contractor's behalf.

Under Clauses 12.2–3 the Contractor must appoint a Site Manager to be permanently based upon the Site and supervise Site operations. He must work exclusively on the Contract and must have a deputy capable of acting in his place while he is absent. The Contractor must also provide any further site supervisory staff *named in the Contract*. The Contractor need not appoint the Site Manager until the start of work at the Site. Clause 12.3 includes an additional requirement that the Contractor should provide all other supervisory staff that may be needed. Note also that the supervisory team to be provided by the Contractor must remain at Site beyond the taking over of the Plant if needed, until the completion of any performance tests, or perhaps even longer.

Clause 12.4 then permits the parties to list 'key personnel' in the Contract (Schedule 8). If so the Contractor may not move them from the Contract until their contribution has been completed. The principle is that in a process contract what may persuade the Purchaser to give the Contract to the Contractor (and what the Purchaser often actually wishes to buy) is the abilities of the Contractor's design/project team. In that case the Contractor must be prepared to commit the key individual members of that team to the project for the duration, if required.

Clause 12.5 is the standard clause permitting the Project Manager to have any member of the Contractor's Site management team withdrawn for incompetence or serious misbehaviour at no cost to the Purchaser. The dismissal of a member of the management team is bound to be contentious and therefore the Project Manager cannot delegate this function, especially because it is not subject to appeal.

4.3.2 Management control/manipulation

We have already said that the reimbursable contract will always permit control of the collaboration by the Project Manager, since it is the power to control the Contractor that will give the Purchaser *flexibility*. This control is given by Clause 11.2 of the Conditions.

CLAUSE 11.2
Clause 11.2 states the power of the Project Manager to exert day-to-day control over the activities of the Contractor. He may at any time instruct the Contractor to carry out any part of the Works (including the Contractor's own activities, see the definition in Clause 1) in whatever way the Project Manager wishes, and the Contractor must comply within a reasonable period. (Of course the Contractor is protected by the reimbursable nature of the Contract from any increase in cost that such an instruction might cause.) The Clause then allows the Contractor to use the Variation procedure to obtain any necessary extension in time or other change to the Target Cost or other terms of the Contract

that might be necessary as a result. The result is that the Project Manager has very wide powers, if he decides to use them to change how the Contract is to be carried out.

4.3.3 Programme and time management

The Conditions deal with the Contractor's obligations as to time in a number of different ways:

- The Contract will include Schedule 11 setting out the 'Times of Completion' of the Works. At the very least this should list the dates for the completion of various stages and sections of the Plant and Works, and it may also include bar charts or other preliminary programme information.
- The Contract will contain Schedule 12, setting out the liquidated damages that will attach to the date or dates set out in Schedule 11 that are of special contractual significance. Generally this will be the date(s) of readiness for or completion of take-over tests.
- The Contract may contain some form of more detailed programme for the Works.

CLAUSE 13

The Contract can and should include at least an outline programme. Clause 13, however, will apply whether or not this is so. It requires the Contractor to pre-pare and submit a further and more detailed programme of the work to the Project Manager for approval, in whatever form or detail the Project Manager considers reasonable in the circumstances. The actual words used, '. . . sequence in which and date(s) by which . . . etc', are common to some of the other model conditions available and permit the Project Manager to call for a considerable degree of detail if necessary. In general terms the Project Manager should always insist on a programme being prepared which contains *adequate* detail for his purposes. The more complex the project, the greater the detail that may be required.

Clause 13.1 simply states that the time obligation of the Contractor is to comply with Schedule 11. Schedule 11 should specify:

- the date for submission of the programme;
- the date(s) for submission of Documentation for Approval;
- the date(s) of readiness of the Plant for take-over tests;
- any other key dates, such as the date for successful completion of take-over tests.

Schedule 12 will then state the liquidated damages for delay and the dates/events to which those damages will apply.

Clause 13.2 then sets out the procedure for the certification of events that may trigger milestone payments.

Clause 13.3 deals with the preparation of the programme, and also requires the Contractor to predict when he will require Documentation and other foresee-able items of information and work from the Purchaser during the Contract. This is necessary to enable the Purchaser to programme his own work under Clause 4.1. The Conditions do not require the Contractor to give any other notice to the Purchaser of when he will need any Documentation, information or facilities.

Then Clause 13.3 requires the Project Manager to approve the Contractor's programme if it is reasonable and complies with the Contract. If the programme is not reasonable or does not properly comply then the Project Manager may of course reject it and, although the Conditions are silent on the point, require the Contractor to re-submit. Finally the Clause imposes an obligation, at the reasonable endeavours level (i.e. to try reasonably hard) to comply with the Approved Programme.

One other comment that may be made about Clause 13.3 is that it leaves the period for the preparation of the programme by the Contractor to be stated in Schedule 11. This is very much a decision that should be made on a case-by-case basis. Perhaps in most contracts the time can be quite short, but in some contracts a longer time might be more appropriate.

Clause 13.4 provides for the possible submission by the Contractor of a schedule of the numbers and types of personnel and resources to be employed on the project and particularly on the Site. This information is useful to the Project Manager both to assess whether the Contractor's programme is reasonable and then for checking progress as the work proceeds.

Clauses 13.5–8
These Clauses give the Project Manager considerable powers to use in the event that the Contractor is in serious delay in carrying out the Contract.

Clause 13.5 is a standard clause common to many sets of model conditions which allows the Project Manager to demand a revision of the programme, i.e. the re-scheduling of the work, in the event that the Contractor has fallen behind schedule. In addition it also allows the Project Manager to instruct the Contractor to take proper action to achieve the current programme where practicable.

Clause 13.7 follows on from Clause 13.5, by allowing the Project Manager to make his own revision to the programme where the Contractor has failed to put forward a proper proposal for revision after having been instructed to do so.

Finally Clause 13.6 gives the Project Manager the power to demand that the Contractor take steps to avoid further slippage against the programme and also that the Contractor take all possible steps to accelerate work to recover lost time against the programme if he is satisfied that the Contractor's rate of progress is *inadequate*, and that it is the Contractor's fault that it is inadequate. The legal/contractual meaning of the phrase 'best endeavours' is that the Contractor will only be excused for failure to succeed where he can demonstrate that it was virtually impossible that he could succeed.

Of course the Contractor's costs of taking action under these Clauses would be payable by the Purchaser.

Clause 13.8 then confirms that whatever steps are taken by the parties, contractual liability for lateness is unaffected.

189

4.3.4 Documentation and approvals

Contracts for the supply of equipment usually include provision for the approval by the Project Manager of designs/drawings submitted to him by the Contractor of the Plant which the Contractor proposes to supply.

Many engineers find the concept of the Project Manager 'approving' the Contractor's designs somewhat confusing when they first meet it. The purpose of the approval procedure is not for the Project Manager to take the place of the Contractor as the designer or to reduce the overall responsibility of the Contractor for the design of his equipment. Instead the purposes are:

- to enable the Project Manager to extract from the Documentation any information which he needs in order to ensure that the Purchaser can comply with Clause 4.1–2;
- so that the Project Manager can raise any comments or queries that he may have regarding the design of the Plant;
- so that the Project Manager can question any aspects of the design that he feels may be incorrect or inadequate;
- so that the Project Manager can, possibly for the first time, see a detailed design for the Plant that the Purchaser will receive.

The approvals procedure increases the Contractor's obligations rather than reduces them. Before Documentation has been approved the obligation of the Contractor is to supply a Plant which complies with the Contract. After Documentation has been approved his obligation is to supply a Plant which complies with the Contract *and* is in accordance with the approved Documentation.

The Purchaser and Contractor should agree the list of Documentation to be subject to the approval procedure before Contract and this list should then be included in Schedule 2. Schedule 11 will include the date or dates by which the listed Documentation must be submitted by the Contractor.

The Documentation to be submitted will generally be drawings but may well include other information as well—calculations, flow sheets, data sheets or diagrams for example.

Where the Contract is for a complex plant the Contractor will often also supply an actual or computer model of the Plant as an aid to construction. It would be possible to include a Plant model within Schedule 2, but this would be unusual. The model would normally be considered to be an item to be supplied after the Documentation had been approved.

Obviously it is for the Purchaser and Contractor to agree between themselves as to the number of documents and the detail to be included in Documentation, and therefore the quantity of information, to be approved by the Project Manager. There is a conflict here that can only be resolved by the Purchaser. Clearly the more information he includes within Schedule 2 and therefore within the approval process, the more he will learn about the precise physical characteristics of the Plant. However he must be prepared to pay the Contractor's charges for preparing the extra documents and to provide the man-hours necessary to examine those documents when they are submitted. He must also accept that the Contractor will certainly want additional time if the approval stage begins to expand beyond what is usual. There may also be limits to the practical value of the extra information that he obtains.

The basic procedure
CLAUSE 21

Clause 21.1 lays down a quality control procedure for all Documentation. Clauses 21.2–3 and 21.5 lay down the basic approval procedure. (Where documents are being transferred/submitted by electronic mail the Clauses will need to be suitably modified by a Special Condition.)

The Documentation, number of copies, and so on will be described in Schedule 2. The Project Manager is given fourteen days to inspect each document. Effectively this means that he has fourteen days plus the rest of the day on which the item is submitted to him for approval; an item will be 'submitted' on the day on which it actually arrives at the Project Manager's address. By the end of that period the Project Manager must either:

- Return a copy to the Contractor endorsed as approved.
- Return a copy to the Contractor endorsed as not approved. The notification must reach the Contractor's address within the fourteen day period. If he does so the document must be amended and then re-submitted. As soon as the document has been re-submitted in a form which answers the objections of the Project Manager the document must then be approved by the Project Manager. Note that the Project Manager has very wide powers to ask for re-design of the Plant/Works, including the right to require preferential engineering by the Contractor. The Contractor can really only object when the Project Manager wants to go beyond what is good practice or laid down in the Contract. But then the Purchaser will pay the cost.
- Return a copy to the Contractor endorsed with any questions that he wishes to raise concerning the document. In this case the document is deemed to be approved subject to the question(s) being answered satisfactorily by the Contractor, and must then be approved by the Project Manager. If the Contractor is unable to answer any question satisfactorily then the document is not approved and should be re-submitted.
- Notify the Contractor of any comment that the Project Manager wishes to make concerning the Document. In that case the Contractor should take due note of the comment and the Document will be deemed to be approved subject to the Contractor confirming to the Project Manager that he will do so.
- If the Project Manager fails to approve any document or deliver to the Contractor any valid notification within the fourteen day period then the document is automatically approved.

Clause 21.3 then lays down two further basic principles. Once Documentation has been approved it binds the Contractor unless or until new Documentation has been approved by the Project Manager (usually as a part of a Variation). Approval of Documentation does not in any way reduce the Contractor's responsibility for the design of the Plant.

Dispute

Clause 21.4 deals with the problems that may arise because of disputes about any unwillingness by the Project Manager to accept the design proposed by the Contractor. The preferred route for any dispute is that of reference to an Expert. Note the way in which the powers of the Contractor to challenge rejection of a design by the Project Manager are increased once the Target Cost is in place. The position changes, in fact, from a reimbursable to a price-based one.

Drawing inspection

Clause 21.6 gives the Project Manager an additional power to inspect, but not to keep or copy, all Documentation, except that which he is not permitted to see by the specific terms of the Contract. The right is useful to the Project Manager because it enables him to check on any minor details that he may need to know, and also because it enables him to verify the Contractor's progress in completing the design work. Note also that this Clause extends not simply to the Contractor, but also to Subcontractors. The Contractor will therefore need to pass the obligations under the Clause on in his Subcontracts.

In addition, under Clause 21.7 (if Schedule 2 provides) the Project Manager may also have access to, and copies of, other Documentation.

Final drawings/manuals

Clauses 21.9–10 then cover the supply of as-built drawings of the Plant and Works and operating and maintenance manuals. The form and content of this Documentation and manuals should be included in Schedule 2 to the Contract. In any event it should take account of whatever legislation is applicable. In the UK, for instance, the Health and Safety at Work Act requires that all equipment supplied for operation in the workplace must be supplied with all information necessary to enable it to be operated and maintained safely. It should be sup-plied *before* taking-over (in other words if the documents are not supplied take-over should be delayed), reviewed by the Project Manager and any defects remedied by the Contractor.

Variations/changes

Clause 21.11 deals with the problem of ensuring that Documentation is kept reasonably up-to-date whatever changes are made to the design of the Plant.

Other documents

Clause 21.8 ensures that the Purchaser has suitable access to any Docu-mentation necessary for insurance or safety-related purposes.

Mistakes

Clauses 21.12–14 deal with the problems caused by mistakes in Documentation produced either by the Contractor or by the Purchaser. The par-ticular problem of the process plant is that it is a very large and complex con-struction, and it is all too easy to make mistakes when producing drawings. Some degree of correction will be almost inevitable.

Clause 21.12 simply provides that the Contractor will correct any mistake in Documentation prepared by him. Clause 21.13 provides that the Contractor will also correct errors in the Purchaser's documents, if requested to do so by the Purchaser, at the cost of the Purchaser. (In other words the correction cost will be added to the Target Cost.) If however the mistake arises from any error by the Contractor then Clause 21.14 shall apply.

Clause 21.14 provides that the costs of any rectification work by the Contractor shall be paid by the Purchaser as part of Actual Cost, except where:

- it can be back-charged to a Subcontractor; or
- it is covered within a fixed fee; or
- it is necessary because of 'substandard' work by the Contractor (see my comment on Clause 37.3 in section 4.7).

4.3.5 Subcontracting

The general principles underlying Clauses 9 and 10 are as follows:

- The Contractor should be responsible for placing and managing the Sub-contracts.
- The Purchaser is however reimbursing the Contractor's costs, and the bulk of those costs will be the costs of subcontracted work and Materials, rather than costs directly incurred by the Contractor. Therefore while the *Contractor* is paid on a reimbursable basis, the *Subcontractors* should be chosen wherever possible on the basis of competitive fixed-price bidding. This helps to reduce overall cost and also to reduce price risk.
- As far as the choice of Subcontractor is concerned, he who pays the piper calls the tune. Therefore the Project Manager, representing the Purchaser, should have the right to make or approve the final choice—to decide which bidder should get a Subcontract.
- Nominated Subcontractors are to be permitted, but are not to be encouraged.

In any major contract there will be a clash of opinions in regard to possible subcontracts. The Purchaser, who has to live with the final Plant for many years, will want to have some say in the choice of companies whose equipment will be incorporated into his Plant. He may want to standardise on certain suppliers or types of equipment for simplification of spares holdings and maintenance. He will not want to see equipment on his Site supplied by companies that he does not like dealing with. And so on.

The Contractor wants freedom of choice, for process reasons, and also to give himself the maximum chance to buy suitable equipment at the best prices.

This clash may be resolved in one of a number of different ways:

- complete freedom of choice for the Contractor;
- freedom of choice for the Contractor subject to approval of major Subcontracts by the Purchaser;
- inclusion in the Contract of lists of approved suppliers; and
- the use of nominated Subcontractors.

In the case of the Target Cost contract the clash is resolved in favour of the Purchaser, *but with the proviso that if the Project Manager selects an expensive supplier option then the Target Cost will rise to reflect this.*

CLAUSE 9
Assignment

Clause 9.1 provides that neither the Contractor nor the Purchaser may assign, i.e. dispose of, the Contract to a third party. The only exception to this is that the Contractor can assign the right to receive payments due under the Contract (for instance to an associated company of the Contractor or to a debt-factoring company).

Procurement

Clauses 9.2–8 then lay down a basic consultation/procurement procedure involving both the Contractor and the Project Manager in the selection of Subcontractors.

Clauses 9.2–4 define the procedure. Clauses 9.5–8 set out the main outlines of the Subcontract terms that the Contractor is to use. Finally Clauses 9.9–12 deal with ancillary matters.

CLAUSES 9.2 and 9.4

Clauses 9.2 and 9.4 provide for the following procurement procedure:

- The procurement procedure (including Subcontract Conditions, enquiry document, enquiry response times, etc) should be agreed between the Contractor and Project Manager in line with Schedule 7.
- If no procedure is agreed then the Contractor should adopt a standard competitive fixed-price procedure.
- All subcontracting should be done on the basis of this procedure unless unavoidable.
- The Contractor should obtain a reasonable number of bids from 'qualified' suppliers ('qualified' in this context is almost indefinable, but will be easily understood by the engineer. It means that the supplier is reasonably competent to supply the equipment or services required.)
- The Contractor will assess the bids received, and then send the bids to the Project Manager, together with a statement setting out his assessment of the various bids and his recommendation as to which bidder should be selected. The assessment should also draw the attention of the Project Manager to any bids that the Contractor considers technically inadequate.
- The Project Manager will, if he wishes to do so, assess the bids for himself and then inform the Contractor of the bid that he approves.
- The Contractor will then place the Subcontract with the approved supplier in accordance with the approved bid.
- If the bid approved by the Project Manager is higher in price than the bid recommended by the Contractor, the Target Cost will be adjusted by the difference in price.

Clause 9.4 is silent as to the number of suppliers that should be approached, or whether the Project Manager has the right to decide suppliers that should be approached. These points are left for the Contractor to decide, unless the procurement procedure deals with the matter, or the Project Manager elects to issue an instruction under the terms of Clause 11.

Three comments should be made concerning Clause 9.2:

- The Project Manager is given the power to give 'general approval' to purchases by the Contractor. This power is valuable and is generally used to reduce the volume of tenders that the Project Manager has to handle so that he can concentrate on important items. He will therefore usually give 'general approval' to the purchase of low-value items, or 'off-the-shelf' standard materials by the Contractor on the basis of the lowest-price tender.
- The second part of the Clause requires adjustment of the Target Cost if the Project Manager chooses more expensive bids than those proposed by the Contractor.
- The last sentence of the Clause makes it clear that the Contractor has the obligation to ensure that the Plant will still meet its guarantees whichever supplier is used or selected by the Project Manager. Therefore the Contractor should take care in his choice of suppliers to approach for bids, in the specifications that he uses to buy equipment and in his bid assessments. (Indeed in one sense in a fixed-price contract the Contractor runs the risk of under-specifying equipment, and in a reimbursable contract the Purchaser runs the risk of over-specification.)

Clause 9.2 then adds to the Project Manager's powers in respect of procurement by providing that the Contractor must procure any subcontracted Site work in a manner agreed with the Project Manager.

CLAUSES 9.5–8

Clauses 9.5 and 9.7–8 are straightforward in that they deal with some specific issues, price discounts, guarantees and the Purchaser's rights to terminate under Clauses 42 and 43. Clause 9.6 is more difficult, as it lays down a general principle concerning the terms on which Subcontracts should be let. This is that the Subcontracts should be let on 'similar' contract conditions to those of the Contract and that the Subcontractors should be required to observe any provisions of the Contract 'which apply to Subcontracts'. The Clause requires the Contractor to ensure that the conditions of the Subcontracts relate closely to the Contract conditions. It does not *demand* that the Contractor should endeavour to place Subcontracts that seek to be 'back-to-back' with the Contract conditions. (For further discussion of this problem see section 5.1)

CLAUSE 9.3

This Clause is straightforward. It deals with the potential clash of interest between the Contractor as an impartial procurement organisation working on the Purchaser's behalf and the Contractor as a possible supplier or sister-company to a possible supplier. The solution is straightforward—that the Contractor is entitled to benefit from possible Subcontracts provided that the issue is dealt with openly.

CLAUSE 10

This is largely a standard nominated Subcontractor clause that allows the Purchaser to select the suppliers of particular items of work or equipment who are to be employed as Subcontractors by the Contractor. There are two ways that this can happen. The first is where the Contract itself requires the Contractor to employ a particular named Subcontractor, in other words it states that a particular supplier is to be used, *and* states that the supplier shall have 'nominated' status under Clause 10.1. The second is where Clause 10.2 applies.

The opening lines of Clause 10.2 are the key to the whole of the Clause. They state that a Subcontractor may only have nominated status where the Contract specifically states that certain items will be provided by a Subcontractor to be nominated by the Project Manager *after the Contract has come into being*.

Clauses 10.3–4 provide a procedure for the Contractor to object to a nomination if he feels that there are substantial grounds for believing that the actual company nominated will cause him commercial or technical problems in carrying out the Contract. Clause 10.3 lays down the procedure to be followed by the Contractor. The Contractor must notify the Project Manager of his objection within four weeks after nomination, and must give reasons for objecting. Clause 10.4 then requires the Project Manager to respond to a valid objection in appropriate fashion.

Clause 10.5 closes the door to further claims by the Contractor once he has accepted any nominated Subcontractor. Of course in a reimbursable contract the risks posed to the Contractor by a nominated Subcontractor are much reduced.

Clause 10.7 requires the Purchaser to accept the responsibility, or risk, and Target Cost implications for any extra cost incurred by the Contractor because of a failure by a nominated Subcontractor to perform properly. This is in fact justifiable in the context of the process plant where there may be potential process implications affecting the selection of almost every equipment item.

Clause10.6 emphasises the special status of the nominated Subcontractor by, in effect, giving the Subcontractor a possible right of appeal to the Project Manager in the event of any dispute between himself and the Contractor.

It has to be said that the nominated Subcontractor is a difficult beast to manage at the best of times for both Contractor and Purchaser, however reasonable the theoretical position. Clause 10.7 could leave the Purchaser responsible for cost overruns caused by a Subcontractor with whom he had comparatively little real bargaining power. Therefore there are two precautions that the Purchaser who intends to nominate should always consider taking:

- To ensure that the potential nominated Subcontractor is not informed of his position in case he should allow his 'monopoly' status to influence his bargaining position vis-a-vis the Contractor, or
- To set up a separate contract between the Purchaser and the potential Subcontractor in advance of or at the time of nomination. This would require the Subcontractor to accept the appropriate Subcontract terms and also create direct responsibility from the Subcontractor to the Purchaser, in case Clause 10.7 should ever be activated.

Subcontract terms

Finally we come to a small group of Clauses that deal with some standard situations.

Clauses 9.10–11 provide that wherever confidential information is passed between the Purchaser and a Subcontractor, in whichever direction, then the recipient will be directly responsible to the other party for any breach of confidentiality, under the terms of the Contract (Rights of Third Parties) Act. The practical arrangements for this of course are the responsibility of the Contractor, through the terms of the Subcontracts and his communications with the Project Manager.

Then Clause 9.7 requires the Contractor to obtain guarantees in the names of both the Contractor and Purchaser from all Subcontractors in respect of the items that they supply. The supplier of structural steelwork or ready-mixed concrete might, in practice, be asked for very different guarantees to those of a pump or vessel manufacturer. The period of those guarantees is to be as close to those of the Contract as possible. (Bear in mind that Materials might be delivered by the Subcontractor long before the Plant is taken over). These guarantees are enforceable by the Purchaser directly under the terms of the Contract (Rights of Third Parties) Act.

Finally Clause 9.9 bars 'pay-when-paid' Subcontracts.

4.3.6 Vesting

CLAUSE 25 and CLAUSES 34.3–5

In one sense it is illogical to deal with these Clauses at this point, because they are more concerned with the problem of the possible liquidation of the Contractor than the delivery of equipment to Site. They provide a standard 'vesting'/'devesting' procedure. Its purpose is, so far as possible, to try to minimise the disruption to the project in the event of the financial collapse of the Contractor. They are dealt with here only because they have to be taken into account during procurement.

Essentially a vesting procedure seeks to minimise the problems that might be caused by a seller's financial disaster. It can do no more than that. If a company goes into liquidation, control of all the assets of the company will pass to a liquidator who has a duty to convert the company's assets into money for distribution to creditors. He will therefore sell those assets, including any work in progress, to the highest bidder. The purpose of a vesting clause is to transfer ownership of equipment from a seller to a buyer, while it is still work in progress. If then the seller then gets into financial difficulties and is put into liquidation (or receivership) the buyer would have the right to take possession of the equipment, as it is his property, and remove it from the seller's premises. Then any necessary work can be carried out by another manufacturer and the equipment put into use. Of course the liquidator would have the right to recover reasonable payment from the buyer for any work done by the seller, but would not have any other legal power to delay the project.

Clause 25.1 provides that where the Purchaser is due to make phased payments for equipment under the Contract, and does actually make such a payment, then the ownership of the equipment will transfer to the Purchaser.

The Clause applies to all equipment, both manufactured by the Contractor and by Subcontractors, therefore this Clause needs to be taken into account in Subcontracts by the Contractor. (By 'phased payments' we mean any advance, stage, or progress payments.) Clause 25.3 is self-explanatory.

If the Contract does not include for phased payment then ownership will transfer on delivery to the Site (not on installation/erection).

Clause 25.2 deals with the marking/storage considerations. If a vesting clause is to work properly it must allow the Purchaser to be able to identify precisely which items have become his property, otherwise a liquidator would, quite properly, refuse to release them.

Clauses 34.3–4 then deal with the situation that arises when items are no longer needed for the project or need to be removed so that they can be replaced or reworked. They are reasonably self-explanatory. Finally Clause 34.5 deals with the question of surplus Materials that are to be left on Site.

4.3.7 Project/site meetings

The aim of Clause 29 is to outline an arrangement to ensure monthly (at least) progress meetings to monitor progress on the Contract. The Clause states that meetings are only at the option of the Contractor or Project Manager, but in practice regular meetings, probably held a few days after the submission by the Contractor of his monthly progress reports under Clause 3.7, are very worthwhile.

CLAUSE 3.7
The last paragraph is a straightforward procedural clause requiring monthly (at least) progress reports, supported by whatever backup Documentation is necessary in the circumstances, to be submitted by the Contractor. Usually the Contract would allow the Project Manager or the parties to fix or agree precise timing for reports. Usually too the aim would be for progress reports to be submitted a few days in advance of project meetings.

CLAUSE 29
Clause 29.1 is needs no comment. Note that the meetings will, or may, be attended by four different groups of people—the representatives of both project management teams, Subcontractors and then any others who need to be there on an ad-hoc basis.

Clause 29.2 provides for the meetings to be minuted by the Project Manager, and for minutes to be signed by both parties. The Clause is very cumbersome in the way it deals with the minutes of progress meetings—but it is very difficult to think of an alternative that would not be equally cumbersome.

Note that, under Clause 29.3, the agreed minutes of progress meetings are automatically contractually binding where they record any notice or instruction, once they have been signed in accordance with Clause 5.3.

4.3.8 Pre-delivery inspection

Repairing or replacing defective equipment is always far more expensive in time and money once that equipment has left the factory. Therefore Clause 22 assumes that the Contract will include, in Schedule 13, specific descriptions of the pre-delivery tests and pre-installation tests which will be carried out on any critical items of equipment, plus probably a general provision that all equipment will be subject to normal pre-delivery tests before being accepted for delivery to the Site. Clause 22 is a standard procedural clause, similar to the pre-delivery inspection clauses found in other sets of model conditions.

The Clause also allows the Project Manager to nominate inspectors who will exercise his functions under the Clause, if he wishes.

Principles

Clause 22.1 gives the Project Manager, and any inspector nominated by the Project Manager under Clause 22.8, access to the premises of the Contractor and also those of his Subcontractors. (The Contractor must take Clause 22 into account when preparing his Subcontracts.) The Clause gives the Project Manager the right both to observe tests, and also to inspect equipment in the course of manufacture and other work such as calibration. The Clause does not make any specific provision for the right to reject any equipment found to be defective by the Project Manager during any inspection, leaving the Project Manager and Contract Manager to settle the matter by discussion. It would, of course, be extremely unusual for the Contract Manager to refuse to take note of any reasonable objections raised by the Project Manager during any inspection. Indeed the Contractor could well be in breach of Clauses 2.4 and 3.2 (and 3.8) of the Conditions in doing so.

Clause 22.2 sets out the basic obligation of the Contractor to arrange and carry out tests.

Procedure

Clauses 22.3 and 22.5–6 set out the procedure for giving notification of readiness for test and the testing of equipment. The Clauses are reasonably self-explanatory. Note that the Clause does not deal with the costs of carrying out or witnessing any repeat tests. The Conditions assume that each party would bear its own costs.

Additional tests

A process contract will cover many different types and items of equipment, many of which may not have been identified at the time of Contract. It is impossible for the Contract to set out in detail what pre-delivery tests are to be carried out on every single item. Therefore Clause 22.4 allows the Project Manager to require any item of equipment to be given any pre-delivery tests that the Project Manager wishes, in addition to the tests specified in the Contract.

The Project Manager must notify the Contractor of any additional tests in adequate time to allow the Contractor to arrange for the tests. With respect to the equipment manufactured by the Contractor himself this could mean at almost any time up to delivery itself; if however a test would involve the use of scarce test-bed facilities, notice would in practice need to be given much earlier. With respect to equipment manufactured by a Subcontractor the problem is much more difficult because the Contractor would almost certainly be charged extra for *any* test not written into the purchase order. This would then lead to a claim by the Contractor for a Variation to the Contract. Therefore the Project Manager should, as far as possible, be prepared to indicate any tests that he might require at the time of procurement by the Contractor, so that the Contractor can make adequate provision when ordering.

As regards the cost of additional tests, Clause 22.4 provides that tests that are normal practice should not be charged for. Other tests may be charged for, as stated in the Clause. Of course the question will always arise of exactly what is 'normal practice', but few serious problems arise. Clause 22.7 repeats the basic cost principle.

4.3.9 Site activities

Any engineer looking at the Conditions for the first time will wonder why they have so little to say about the construction of the Plant, especially compared, for example, to the ICE or RIBA model conditions. All that the Conditions do is to specify in outline the facilities that the Contractor is to provide and then to lay down general rules about the way that he is to organise the Site and his workforce. In fact the Site activities clauses occupy only two to three pages in the Conditions, compared with two pages on insurance/responsibility for Site damage, three pages on Variations, or over four pages on Site tests.

The reasons are simple:

- the Contractor must, to some extent at least, be left to run the project his way, and can be manipulated if necessary;
- the terms of the Contract relating to administrative detail and work quality and supervision can be safely left to the Schedules and Specification;
- as the Conditions are for use by professionals they concentrate upon the essentials—the testing procedures to demonstrate that the Plant will produce what the Contract requires it to produce—rather than the control of the construction process.

Since all the Clauses that deal with Site activities are concerned with setting out general rules, they are reasonably straightforward.

Availability and access
CLAUSE 23
In general terms this Clause speaks for itself.

Clause 23.1 deals with the date for access to the Site. It lists the possible options open to the parties for fixing the date in order of precedence. The Conditions do not make any specific provision for the consequences of delay by the Purchaser in making the Site available to the Contractor. Simple failure to provide access would of course be breach of the Purchaser's obligations, allowing the Contractor to claim costs, plus time. The Purchaser does have other options such as suspending the Contract under Clause 42, and/or allowing the Contractor to deal with delay under Clause 14.2(d), or, if justified, claiming force majeure.

Clause 23.2 then provides for the access route to the Site, stating that it is the responsibility of the Purchaser to provide an adequate access route to the Site boundary from a convenient point on a public road. Clauses 23.2 and 23.3 then make the Contractor responsible for the suitability of the route up to that convenient point. There are two problems with the suitability of any route—the weight of traffic, or individual loads that it must carry, and its ability to take unusually wide, long and high loads. Should any Plant require the bringing to Site of 'extraordinary traffic' this would obviously need special consideration, and probably a Special Condition.

Clauses 23.4 and 23.7 are straightforward and need no comment.

Control and access

Clauses 23.5–6 are self-explanatory. The Contractor has possession of the Site under Clause 23.1 and therefore control of it. Under Clause 23.6 he can and must exclude from it any third party who does not have specific authorisation from the Purchaser and anyone who has no need to to be there, and under Clause 23.5 he can *and must* also refuse access to other contractors where their work would unreasonably impede his own. Of course this will often be of great importance to the Contractor. He has a large and complex construction/ erection job to do, and the presence of others on the Site will almost inevitably impede his work at some time or another. Apart from that he must allow reasonable access to the Site to the Purchaser and other contractors. The consequences of Clauses 23.5–6 are that the Contractor will need to set up facilities for controlling access to the Site.

CLAUSE 24
Clauses 24.1, 24.2 and 24.4 need no comment.

One comment upon Clause 24.3 is necessary. It provides that the Contractor may not move anything on to the Site in advance of the Approved Programme without the consent of the Project Manager. This is because the Purchaser may need to prepare the Site or access route and arrange for permission for the Contractor's traffic to use the route from the owner of the land. The Purchaser will almost certainly use the Approved Programme as guidance as to when the Site and access route must be ready for the Contractor.

Construction
CLAUSE 3.3
The Clause is straightforward and needs no comment.

CLAUSE 26
This Clause is of major importance, but needs very little comment. The principles are straightforward and will be well known to all Contractors and Purchasers. Also note Clause 7.2.

CLAUSES 26.1–4
These Clauses combine with Schedules 4 and 5 to set up a Site regime in line with best practice. It will be obvious from the wording of Clause 26.1 that the

Clauses are drafted to comply with UK law—but there are no significant differences between UK law and law throughout the rest of the European Union, and probably very few between European law and law in the rest of the world. Therefore the Clauses would need modification in any Contract where the Plant was to be constructed on a Site outside the UK, but they provide a good framework to begin from. In particular the references to UK legislation in Clause 26.1 would need amending. Note especially the requirements of Clauses 26.3 and 26.4(c).

CLAUSE 26.5

This Clause requires the Contractor to accept responsibility for pollution and hazardous material, and all consequential costs, arising from the Works, subject however to a number of limits, as follows:

- where pollution occurs as the inevitable result of the Works;
- where pollution occurs as the inevitable result of instructions by the Project Manager or Purchaser;
- where the pollution was already in existence at the Site but could not have been foreseen; or,
- where the sheer extent of the pollution was more than could reasonably have been foreseen.

The effect of the Clause is to underline the need for both parties to plan for the risks of pollution and hazardous materials that might arise during the Contract, and to carry appropriate insurance cover.

CLAUSE 27

This Clause deals with the subject of the resources needed to construct, erect and test the Plant, apart from the Site management team called for by Clause 12. The principle is very simply that the Contractor is to provide everything required to carry out the Work on the Site unless it is specifically stated in the Contract that a particular item is to be provided by the Purchaser. There is no mention of any right for the Contractor to use any power supplies or lifting gear or other facilities of the Purchaser on the Site.

Clause 27.1 is simply a clear statement of the general principle. The Contractor will provide all the Materials at the Site as stated in the Contract, together with all resources such as labour, construction equipment and services necessary to carry out the Works, other than those which the Purchaser is to provide.

Clauses 27.2 and 27.3 are a straightforward list of the main support services that the Contractor is expected to provide for the construction operation. In effect the Contractor is being asked by these Clauses to ensure that the Site can operate as a complete, safe, self-contained unit without needing any support from the Purchaser.

Clause 27.4 needs no comment.

Clause 27.5 requires the Contractor to be able to produce certification for his construction equipment, such as safety inspection certificates for cranes and slings, whenever requested.

Clause 27.6 requires the Contractor to make the necessary arrangements to ensure that no construction equipment will be removed from Site until no longer needed. In particular this may require special arrangements to be made with the suppliers of equipment under hire, so that the hiring agreements can be transferred from the Contractor to the Purchaser in case of the Contractor's receivership or liquidation.

Employment conditions

Clause 28 is really not so much a clause as an outline statement of a number of agreements in principle that may need to be covered at greater length in Special Conditions.

CLAUSE 28

Clause 28.1 requires the Contractor to provide, and to require his Subcontractors to provide, reasonable pay and conditions for personnel working on the Site. Clause 28.3 then adds to this by stating that where the Site on which the Contractor is working is covered by a general agreement on working conditions the Contractor will conform to that agreement. (On very large construction sites, or sites where a number of different contractors are working, general agreements are sometimes used to minimise disputes over problems such as differential pay rates, poaching of labour, job demarcation, etc. A general agreement will provide for common or co-ordinated recruitment of labour, generally similar pay structures for all contractors, co-ordinated safety procedures, common policies for personnel matters, etc.)

Then Clause 28.2 requires the Contractor to keep the Project Manager/ Purchaser advised of any potential or actual industrial relations problems on the Site.

Clause 28.4 allows the removal of *any other person* from the Site (compare Clause 12.5) for unsafe conduct, incompetence or serious misconduct of any other kind, at the cost of the Contractor.

Clause 28.5 is self-explanatory.

Site clearance

CLAUSES 34.1–2

These Clauses are standard and need no comment.

4.4 Completion and testing

The Clauses to be covered in this section are those listed under the heading 'Tests' in Figure 3 (see page 171).

4.4.1 General approach

The completion and testing phase is the most critical part of any process contract for both parties.

For the Contractor it is the crunch, the culmination of everything that he has been trying to achieve, and it happens so late in the Contract that there is very little time to put things right if they go wrong.

For the Purchaser the position is much the same. If the Plant passes its tests then he has to accept it, even if it is not really what he wants, and if it fails then his project is potentially a disaster.

Consequently there is a change of emphasis as the test period approaches. In the design and manufacturing periods the question is always 'does the Plant (or Works or Materials) meet the Specification?' At the testing stage that question changes to 'will it pass the tests?' The tests become the definitive requirement of the Contract in place of the Specification.

The Conditions assume that the Contract will contain or result in an agreed test or tests which will be a fair examination of whether or not the Plant does comply with the Contract. It is critical to both Contractor and Purchaser to ensure that this is so. If the tests are too stringent or lax the result will be unfair to one or the other. The issue is of particular importance, because of the scope of testing provided by the Conditions.

4.4.2 Defining the tests

Every Contract Specification has to deal with three separate aspects of the equipment or Plant that it describes. These are *physical* dimensions and characteristics, *quality* of finish or manufacture, and *performance*.

When a Specification deals with something very simple, such as a knife or fork, the Specification will be very simple. It concentrates on the physical nature and quality of the item being described. It will not mention performance at all. When the buyer wishes to check whether the item meets the Specification, the test that he will carry out will be equally simple. He will merely inspect the item to check that it is made from the proper materials to the proper dimensions, the quality of finish, and that there are no obvious defects.

When a Specification deals with something slightly more complex, such as a bicycle, the Specification/tests will cover more ground. In addition to physical characteristics and quality, the Specification will now also deal with performance required, and the buyer's checks will now include a running test to ensure that the wheels go round and the brakes work.

Go to something more complicated such as a machine tool and the Specification will change again. It will concentrate less on detailed physical description, though it will still deal with the physical characteristics that are required. Instead it will deal more with reliability, quality and performance. Also the running test will now concentrate on the ability of the machine to produce the product. (If a performance test is a test to demonstrate whether anything performs in accordance with the requirements of the Contract, then a running test is a performance test for a machine.)

Once the Specification has to deal with a Plant, it will include only the minimal amount of physical description. It will put far more emphasis upon the general characteristics, quality and performance required. Also the running tests on the Plant will change. Because a Plant comprises a large number of separate items of equipment which must operate as a single integrated unit there will now need to be tests to show that each item of equipment works and then tests to show that integration has been achieved. This is difficult to do properly without putting the Plant into operation, and a series of tests now need to be carried out.

4.4.3 The tests in context

The testing Clauses are part of a series of design/approval/testing stages that accompany or are allowed for by the Conditions.

The very first stages take place pre-contract. There may be a formal pre-qualification stage. Negotiations for the Contract will certainly include discussions on the Contractor's ability to design and construct the Plant, together with the design of Plant that he will supply. The Purchaser will wish to be sure that the Contractor can do the job. He will check that the Contractor understands what it is that is required, and that he can and will construct a Plant that is at least approximately what the Purchaser wants it to be.

These negotiations will also need to settle a number of specific contractual questions. These are:

- the wording of the Specification;
- the description of the Works (Schedule 1);
- the description of the various items and services to be provided by the Purchaser in accordance with Clause 4 and Schedules 2 and 3, both to assist the Contractor in the design/construction of the Plant, and also during the test stages;
- detailed descriptions, so far as can be achieved at this early stage of the project of the various inspection and testing procedures to be carried out before delivery and at each test stage, comprising:
  - pre-delivery tests under Clause 22.2 (Schedule 13);
  - construction completion tests (Schedule 14);
  - taking-over procedures and take-over tests (Schedule 15);
  - performance tests (Schedule 16).

The next two stages are then those of Documentation approval and pre-delivery inspection under Clauses 21 and 22, when the Project Manager is given the opportunity to query the Contractor's detailed designs, and when the Materials are inspected and tested.

Then come three test stages following construction of the Plant—construction completion, take-over tests and performance tests. (The Conditions state that performance tests are optional, but this is an option that the Purchaser will almost always use unless his process is secret.) The purpose of these stages is to demonstrate progressively the fitness of the Plant to meet the requirements of the Contract.

The construction completion procedures demonstrate that the construction of the Plant has been completed and that it is in good and safe condition for commissioning.

The take-over test demonstrates that the Plant is in operating condition and can be run on a production basis. As the Plant can now run the Purchaser is getting benefit from it, therefore the risk in the Plant will transfer from the Contractor to him and the Defects Liability Period will commence.

The performance test demonstrates that the Plant is capable of meeting the output/quality guarantees given by the Contractor in the Contract, once the Plant has been run up to full operating condition and any final adjustments or modifications have been made by the Contractor.

4.4.4 Test specifications

It is always entirely a question for the parties to agree upon what the tests are to be, though of course in practice one party will tend to impose its own ideas upon the other. There is no such thing as a standard test. Therefore it is impossible to set out any precise rules for defining any test under the Conditions.

Tests will also vary depending on precisely when they are carried out. This is a question to be decided by the Purchaser. Practice varies considerably. In some industries, such as the water or food industry, it is normal practice for the Contractor to carry out the take-over test on a Plant that is in full normal production. In other industries, such as the pharmaceutical industry, the Purchaser might not put the Plant into production until after the Contractor has withdrawn from the Site. Nevertheless there are a number of general suggestions that can be made.

4.4.5 Construction completion tests

The purpose of the Construction Completion Certificate procedure is to demonstrate that the Plant is complete and in good condition. It also needs to show that the Plant is in a *safe* condition because no process material can be allowed into the Plant if there is danger of leakage or accident.

Therefore following the issue of any draft Construction Completion Certificate by the Contractor the Project Manager should conduct a complete inspection of the relevant parts of the Plant to check, so far as he has not done so already, that:

- those parts have been completely constructed;
- nothing is in poor or damaged condition;
- the parts have been correctly constructed (for instance non-return valves operate in the correct direction);
- there is no internal obstruction or dirt left inside them;
- all work is of the correct quality.

Next the Project Manager will wish the Contractor to demonstrate that the various items of equipment are in working order, that valves open and close, for example. Finally the Contractor may be required to carry out appropriate tests to demonstrate mechanical integrity, perhaps pressure tests or leak tests using water or air rather than the process fluids, and perhaps tests to demonstrate that the control and safety systems and equipment are in operational order.

The specific requirements for this programme of inspections, demonstrations and tests should be included in Schedule 14.

4.4.6 Take-over tests

The take-over tests are important for both sides. The Purchaser will usually want to get the Plant into operation as soon as it is in working order, because delay in bringing the Plant on stream can have a serious effect on the economics of the project by delaying and then extending the pay-back period for the Plant. However he will not want to take over a Plant which is not capable of being put into production, and the Project Manager will not want to release the Contractor from his obligations until the Plant is in operating condition.

The Contractor will obviously want the Plant to be taken over as soon as he has put it into operating order. The Take-Over Certificate will almost certainly trigger a payment and also transfers responsibility for the Plant to the Purchaser, starts the guarantee period running, and gets the Contractor off a major Contract hook. However once the Plant has been taken over, the Contractor will lose control over it and will still be responsible if it fails the performance test. Therefore the Contractor will not want to carry out a take-over test until the Plant is generally fit for the performance test.

The take-over procedures in Schedule 15 will normally do two things. First the Contractor will be required to demonstrate that all the various parts of the Plant, electrical and mechanical equipment, control systems, etc, are in proper order. Then the Contractor will be required to carry out a running test on the Plant, either using process materials or using a non-process material such as water, to demonstrate that the Plant is capable of normal operation.

4.4.7 Performance tests

The performance test is a test to prove that the Plant is capable of manufacturing the products for which it is designed under all normal operating conditions foreseen by the Contract.

That is the theory. In practice of course no Purchaser can expect this. The Plant is still at the teething stage, in need of fine tuning and being run by operators who are not yet used to its little ways, and perhaps not yet fully experienced in the process or the equipment. Most companies would expect the production from any Plant to be measurably higher after a year or two of normal operation than at the time when the Plant is first put into production.

Also no test can really reproduce all normal operating conditions.

Therefore every performance test (and take-over test) has to be something of a compromise. It has to be for a comparatively short operating period, and probably the Plant will only make a limited selection of the possible product range, or operate under a part of the full range of operating conditions. But it has to be a test from which the parties can make deductions about the capability of the Plant to make the full range of products over its normal operating life.

Again there are a number of general principles:

- The test should not be unreasonably long. Obviously it needs to be for long enough to enable proper measurement of performance and to give some indication of equipment and process reliability. However a test that goes on for too long proves very little and risks being interrupted by something that has nothing to do with the Plant at all, when the whole thing has to start all over again at the Purchaser's cost.

- The test must be selective. The Purchaser can never expect any test to cover the whole of the Plant's product range.
- There has to be a limit to the number of parameters that the parties seek to measure during the test.
- The test should be run using the Plant's own controls and instrumentation. It is seldom practicable to try to install supplementary instrumentation to measure additional parameters during the test.
- Finally, the most important. Unless you can design a test that will measure something accurately there is no point in asking for it to be guaranteed.

4.4.8 Performance guarantees and liquidated damages

The main reason why any performance test must be selective is that the test is used to do two entirely distinct things. First it is used to determine whether the Plant operates in accordance with the Contract. Secondly it is used to measure the degree of any shortfall in the performance of the Plant.

Should there be a major shortfall, the Plant will fail the test and must be modified or adjusted before being re-submitted.

Should there be only a minor shortfall in performance however the Plant may be accepted by the Purchaser, subject to the payment by the Contractor of liquidated ('agreed' in legal jargon) damages. Liquidated damages may be fixed for a number of different parameters, such as production quantity, degree of impurities, wastage of raw materials, usage of power or chemicals, etc. The problem for the Purchaser is that the more complex the test he uses, or the more parameters he tries to measure for liquidated damages, the more tempting it becomes for the Contractor to set the Plant up to minimise his exposure to damages rather than to make the product.

There is no standard way of setting up a liquidated damages structure, but again there are some general principles:

- unless a parameter can be measured accurately it should not carry liquidated damages;
- unless a parameter has *real* significance in process *and* economic terms it should not carry liquidated damages;
- always allow a measuring tolerance—no instrument outside a laboratory ever measures with complete accuracy;
- one, or perhaps two, parameters may be treated as mandatory, with no shortfall allowed (except for a measurement tolerance);
- one, two, or perhaps three at the most, other parameters may then be subject to liquidated damages;

If it is the intention of the Purchaser to include provision for liquidated damages in the Contract then Schedules 16 and Schedule 17 should be completed. In other words the performance test and liquidated damages should be defined in the Contract and not left to be agreed later.

The Conditions set out a practicable testing scheme. Clearly no two projects and no two Plants will ever be the same and therefore the Clauses will often be modified or supplemented by the parties.

The scheme is as follows. The Contractor issues a draft Construction Completion Certificate under Clause 32 when the Plant, or any part of the Plant, is fully erected. That work is then inspected. Once the Plant has been fully constructed, take-over procedures are carried out under Clause 33 including any take-over tests specified in the Contract. On successful completion of the take-over procedures, a Take-Over Certificate is issued by the Project Manager and the Plant then passes over to the Purchaser and the guarantee period commences. When the Purchaser (or perhaps in practice both parties) is ready, performance tests are then carried out during the early part of the guarantee period under Clause 35, and an Acceptance Certificate is issued once those performance tests have been properly completed.

4.4.9 The testing procedure

Construction
CLAUSE 32

This Clause requires few comments. Clauses 32.1–4 set out a procedure for the approval by the Project Manager of a series of Construction Completion Certificates as the work of constructing the different parts of the Plant is carried out. Clause 32.5 deals with the cost of repeat tests. Clause 32.6 deals with the certification procedure for tying back the completion of construction to the Contract dates set out in Schedule 11, if appropriate. Finally Clause 32.7 suggests that any dispute concerning certification should be decided by an Expert.

Clause 32.1 establishes that the Plant may be treated as a single construction exercise, or as a number of separate exercises. This allows for two possibilities that can often happen in practice, that the various sections of the Works might be carried out at different times, or that they might be treated as entirely separate exercises. For instance, preliminary civil engineering work to prepare the Site might be carried out by a different workforce well before the erection of the Plant begins. The erection of a tank farm might be carried out over the same time-scale as the main Plant, but by a separate workforce.

Clause 32.2 then sets out a further basic principle, that approval of construction can, and probably will, be carried out on a piecemeal basis, rather than as a single all-embracing exercise.

The procedure is initiated by the Contractor who may issue a Construction Completion Certificate for all the Plant (or a section of the Plant if Clause 32.1 applies), or any 'appropriate part' of the Plant, when he considers that it is 'substantially' complete. An appropriate part of the Plant will be any area or part that can reasonably be inspected and tested as a unit. Something is 'substantially' complete when it is sufficiently complete to be capable of use for its intended purpose, though not necessarily absolutely complete.

In the Certificate the Contractor will define the part of the Plant being offered for inspection and tests and will set out his programme for the tests. The

Project Manager is allowed a week's grace to make whatever preparations are necessary before the inspection/test period begins, unless he is prepared to respond more quickly.

Clause 32.4 then provides that if the part fails on inspection and test the Project Manager must identify the shortcomings that he has found so that the Contractor knows precisely what to correct before re-submitting the part.

Clause 32.3 then deals with the proper form to be used by the Project Manager when accepting that construction of any part of the Plant is complete and also reminds him of the whole purpose of the construction completion exercise. He is to endorse the Construction Completion Certificate with the statement that the part is complete and *safe for the take-over work to commence*, and then return the Certificate to the Contractor. When returning the Certificate he may also attach a snagging list—a list of minor items, that do not affect the safety of the Plant or taking-over procedures, that need correction.

Certification of Completion of Construction

Under Clause 32.6, if completion of construction is of contractual significance— that is if it is referred to in Schedule 11 to the Contract—the Project Manager is required to issue a Certificate when construction of the entire Plant or a section is complete.

Taking over
CLAUSE 33

Clause 33.1 allows for the Plant to be taken over in sections where stated in the Contract. Sectional take-over is, to some extent at least, always an advantage to the Contractor, because it enables him to concentrate his resources on each part of the Plant in turn, rather than having to bring the entire project up to taking over simultaneously. It gives the Contractor the added benefits perhaps of obtaining some payments earlier than might otherwise be the case, and also getting part of the Plant through its Defects Liability Period earlier.

Of course sectional take-over also benefits the Purchaser, simply because the sooner he can put some part of the Plant into production the sooner he can obtain a return on his investment. This consideration is the key to the approach any Purchaser should take towards sectional take-over. Ideally, though in practice it may not always be the case, where a Contract allows sectional take-over, each section should produce something that the Purchaser can *use*.

The basic procedure

The basic procedure for taking over is set out in Clauses 33.2–4, and 33.6–7.

Following the completion of construction, the Plant is prepared by the Contractor for take-over. When he is satisfied that the Plant is ready, he gives notice to the Project Manager under Clause 33.2 and the procedures specified in Schedule 15 are carried out, including any take-over tests (that is, running tests) specified.

If the Contract does not include a Schedule 15 then the Project Manager can still introduce take-over tests and procedures by using the Variation procedure. It is, however, questionable whether it is advisable to use this route.

When successful procedures (and tests) have been carried out a Take-Over Certificate is issued by the Project Manager under Clause 33.7. The Plant is now taken over by the Purchaser and the Defects Liability Period commences. From this point the Contractor is no longer responsible for the care, maintenance or operation of the Plant, but will be responsible for correcting any defects or damage under Clause 37.

Although the Clauses are logical and clear in what they say, they need to be operated carefully by the parties.

Clause 33.4 sets out the basic principle that the Contractor provides everything necessary for the take-over tests except where the Purchaser has agreed to supply it.

Clause 33.2 simply permits the Contractor to give the Project Manager reasonable notice of when the Contractor intends to commence the take-over procedures, provided that the Contractor cannot do so until after the approval by the Project Manager under Clause 32.2 that construction has been completed. Clause 33.3 then entitles the Project Manager to observe the procedure, and obliges the Contractor to ensure that it is possible for him to do so. In the somewhat unlikely event that the Project Manager fails to attend the procedures, Clause 33.6 allows the Contractor to proceed without him.

If the Plant passes the take-over procedures and tests then under Clause 33.7 the Project Manager must issue a Take-Over Certificate to the Contractor, although the Project Manager does not have to issue the Certificate until after the Contractor has dealt with the construction completion snagging list. The Project Manager cannot however withhold the Take-Over Certificate for minor defects that emerge during taking over. These are to be dealt with by another snagging list, which must then be dealt with promptly by the Contractor under Clause 33.8.

The Plant then passes from the Contractor to the Purchaser.

Failure of a test
Clause 33.5 provides the usual procedure to require the Contractor to repeat whatever take-over tests the Project Manager considers reasonable, if the Plant fails the tests.

Issue of a Take-Over Certificate in other circumstances
Clause 33 then provides, in Clauses 33.9 and 33.10, two possible ways in which the take-over tests may be postponed or shelved, one by agreement and the other by default.

Under Clause 33.9 the Project Manager may, with the Contractor's consent, issue a Take-Over Certificate without the Plant having completed the take-over procedures. The Certificate may be issued even if the Plant has actually failed procedures. This allows the Purchaser a route to bring the Plant into operation if he is in serious need of it, without waiting for taking over to run its course. The only condition is that this can only be done with the Contractor's consent, which cannot of course be unreasonably refused. The Contractor's consent is required because the Contractor must be satisfied that the Plant is in proper condition for future taking over procedures and tests, and probably also for performance tests, and that the Purchaser is able to run it *safely* before he allows it to be put into operation. The Contractor will then remain liable to carry out the remaining take-over procedures during the Defects Liability Period, if requested to do so, but any extra costs will be borne by the Purchaser (Clause 33.11).

Clause 33.10 provides the usual protection for a Contractor who is prevented from carrying out any take-over procedure, by allowing him to bypass that procedure and claim his Take-Over Certificate. However the Clause contains two safeguards for the Purchaser. Firstly, the Contractor is only permitted to bypass those procedures that he is actually prevented from carrying out, and where the Contractor is acting reasonably in claiming the Certificate. (It might be unreasonable to claim the Take-Over Certificate if the Purchaser had delayed the commencement of the test by one day—it might be very reasonable if the start of the test was delayed for several days or weeks.) Any other procedures must be completed. Secondly, the Purchaser can require the Contractor to carry out the remaining procedures during the Defects Liability Period as under Clause 33.9. In other words delay by the Purchaser in providing facilities for the tests does not mean that the Contractor can avoid the need to carry out the tests altogether, only that they may be postponed.

The final safeguard is added by Clause 33.12, which permits the revocation of any Take-Over Certificate which has Acceptance Certificate status (see below) in the event that any deferred take-over test fails.

Finally Clause 33.11 deals with the question of the extra costs of any testing procedures which have been deferred under Clauses 33.9 and 33.10.

Performance tests

The performance test/Acceptance Certificate stage is covered by Clauses 35 and 36. Clause 35 deals with the tests themselves and Clause 36 deals with the issue of the Acceptance Certificate, confirming that the Plant is accepted by the Purchaser as complying with the requirements of the Contract.

CLAUSE 35

Under Clause 35.1 performance tests are, in theory anyway, optional, in that this Clause only applies if the Contract calls for performance tests. In practice the performance test is one of the main benefits of these Conditions for the Purchaser.

Clause 35.2 allows performance tests to be specified in Schedule 16, or to be agreed during the Contract. In theory both methods offer equal advantage to both sides. (Before Contract the Purchaser has more negotiating power to demand whatever tests he thinks appropriate. After Contract he learns more about the Plant and the process, so that he can negotiate with greater knowledge.) In practice most Purchasers prefer to include details of the performance tests in Schedule 16.

Procedure

The basic procedure is set out in Clauses 35.3–6 and Clause 35.8–9. The procedure is intended to ensure that the performance tests are carried out as quickly as possible after the Plant has been taken over, so that the Plant can then be put into normal operation.

Under Clause 33.7 the Purchaser is required, when the Plant is taken over to *start up* the Plant and *prepare* it for performance tests, and then *carry out* the performance tests. (Clause 35.9 follows on from this by requiring the Purchaser not to cause unreasonable delay to performance tests.) Clause 35.4 then requires the Purchaser to carry out the performance tests as soon as practicable after the Plant or section has been taken over. (Possible sectional performance tests are covered by Clause 35.2, and the same considerations apply as for sectional take-over tests.)

In practice the Purchaser will obviously exercise some control over the timing of the performance tests. This is important because the Purchaser has to provide all the resources necessary for the test. The actual procedure for initiating a test is that the Purchaser must give notice under Clause 35.5, which must then be acknowledged and accepted by the Contractor.

Strictly speaking the Contractor will not be entitled to make any further adjustments to the Plant between take-over and the commencement of the performance test. In practice his Site personnel will almost inevitably advise either the Project Manager or the Purchaser of anything that they consider needs doing before the performance tests begin.

The reasoning behind these Clauses is straightforward. The Contractor has demonstrated that he has constructed the Plant and put it through its preliminary tests, (construction completion and take-over). It is now the responsibility of the Purchaser to complete the testing sequence and to do so with reasonable speed so that an Acceptance Certificate may be issued and the Contractor may be paid whatever sum is due to him.

The test will then be run in accordance with Clause 35.4. Note the words in the last sentence of Clause 35.4 that the test will be run 'as far as practicable' in accordance with the Contract. This is reality—no Plant is ever run precisely in accordance with the Contract or Specification.

During the test the performance of the Plant will be monitored and recorded by both sides acting together. Then, once the test is complete, the results will be jointly evaluated by both sides. The reasons for joint evaluation are so that:

- The parties can reach an agreed interpretation of what the results of the test actually show. In some processes the simple output figures will not tell the whole story.
- The parties can agree measurement tolerances and allowances.
- The parties can agree any necessary adjustments to the test results. No test ever runs totally smoothly, and minor hitches in operation seldom justify the trouble, time and expense of repeating the whole test.

Problems

Clause 35.6 deals with the question of whether or not a test that is failing to achieve its required parameters may be terminated. Of course it may be terminated if the Contractor and Project Manager agree that it should. Unless they agree then the test may not be terminated unless there is risk of damage or injury, or it is unacceptable to either party, for good reason, to allow it to continue. The reason for this is that the results of even a complete failure are of importance, because they enable the Contractor to analyse what is wrong and to plan corrective action.

Clause 35.9 allows the Contractor only a limited period after taking over within which to achieve a successful performance test. Obviously there is a conflict here. The Purchaser has overall control of the tests, since he has to provide resources and trained operators, and give notice of any test. However if a test fails and has to be repeated, especially if it needs to be repeated more than once, it will be the Contractor who will be eager to move as quickly as possible. The answer to this conflict lies in Clause 35.4, that tests must always be carried out as quickly as possible.

The problem is also covered by Clauses 35.10–11. Clause 35.10 allows the Project Manager to defer the work of carrying out modifications to the Plant if the Purchaser is not willing to take the Plant out of production during the test period allowed by the Contract. Any extra costs caused to the Contractor by the deferment will of course be met by the Purchaser. Any deferment beyond the end of the Defects Liability Period brings the Contractor's obligations to an end.

Where the results of any test falls short of the requirements of the Contract, but are within the limits of the performance liquidated damages specified in Schedule 17, the Contractor has a choice, (Clause 35.9). He can either pay the appropriate liquidated damages, or seek to modify or adjust the Plant to improve performance and then repeat the test, provided that this can be done within the Contract period. If he decides to pay liquidated damages then under Clause 35.9 the Plant has to be accepted by the Project Manager and an Acceptance Certificate issued.

If the results of the tests are outside the limits of Schedule 17, or the Contractor chooses to carry out further work on the Plant, then Clause 35.7 will apply. The Contractor has to decide what further work to carry out and must, if the Project Manager requests, inform the Project Manager of what he intends to do and get his approval before doing it. The Contractor must then be allowed reasonable opportunity to carry out the adjustments or modifications, before the Plant is put back into operation and the test repeated. In the meantime the Purchaser is entitled to operate the Plant.

If the Plant fails the performance tests then Clause 35.9 allows the Purchaser to reject the Plant, or to accept it on whatever terms are agreed between the parties or fixed by an Expert.

Clauses 35.11–13 then deal with the question of what happens if the Purchaser, or events outside the Contractor's control, prevent the Contractor from successfully completing a performance test within the Contract period.

Essentially if that happens the Project Manager must issue an Acceptance Certificate so that the Contractor can be paid, but the Contractor will remain liable to carry out the tests when possible during the Defects Liability Period. The extra costs to the Contractor of delayed tests will be met by the Purchaser and added to the Target Cost (under Clause 4.7). The Project Manager can require the Contractor to provide security for any payments or liquidated damages that might be involved before issuing the Acceptance Certificate, so that, if the Plant fails when the test is finally carried out, the Purchaser can recover the payment from the Contractor.

4.4.10 Acceptance Certificate

CLAUSE 36

The Acceptance Certificate is the last stage of the approval/testing process. In one sense it is purely a formality, because it follows and is governed directly by the performance test. But it is a very important formality because it will virtually always be a payment document. It also acts as conclusive evidence that the Plant is accepted by the Purchaser as complying with the requirements of the Contract.

If there are no performance tests required by the Contract then the Take-Over Certificate will double as the Acceptance Certificate.

The Acceptance Certificate must be issued by the Project Manager as soon as the Contractor has complied with the terms of Clause 35. Like all other Certificates up to this point, it may contain a snagging list of items to be corrected by the Contractor in the usual way.

4.5 Variations, changes and claims

The Clauses to be covered in this section are those listed under the heading 'Claims & Variations' in Figure 3 (see page 171).

4.5.1 General approach

These Clauses cover two areas, firstly the procedure for dealing with Variations to the Contract, and secondly the procedure for dealing with claims under the Contract. Remember that the Conditions use the Variation Order procedure to do two different things. It is used to order a change to the Works by the Project Manager. It is also used to record and formalise *other changes* to the Contract, see for example Clause 14.1 or 18.4.

Change is the most likely area for project management problems. At least one in three project managers will say that change management is the most difficult problem they face. Change in the Target Cost contract presents a number of problems, in particular:

- the need for a different approach before and after the Target Cost has been agreed;

- when the cost of change may be added to Actual Cost;
- when the cost of change may be added to Target Cost.

Change is generally a function of complexity and duration of the project. A simple contract (however large) that takes merely a few days or weeks to carry out is unlikely to be subject to any changes. A complex contract that takes years to carry out, especially if there is a degree of uncertainty about the objectives, is likely to be subject to a whole range of different types of change. Some changes may be outside the parties' control, such as a change in legislation, or the loss of a particular feedstock for the Plant. Others will be partly or wholly within control, such as a change to the product range to meet market requirements, or a modification to the Plant to improve its performance.

The Conditions assume that some change is virtually inevitable. They give the Project Manager a range of options to use in initiating Variations. They also assume that the Project Manager is sufficiently process-skilled to be able to manage the Contractor and negotiate Contract amendments. In case problems arise which cannot be solved quickly by the parties they allow for the use of an Expert as the preferred option to resolve the matter.

For ease of reference, the Clauses covered in this section can be divided into the following groups:

- changes in Target Cost (Clause 18.6);
- legislation (Clauses 4.5 and 7.3–4);
- breach by the Purchaser (Clause 4.7);
- Site problems (Clause 6);
- Variations:
  - definition and limits to the Project Manager's powers (Clauses 16.1 and 16.7);
  - initiation by the Project Manager (Clauses 16.1–3, 16.5–6 and 37.3–4);
  - feasibility studies (Clause 16.4);
  - Contractor's proposals (Clauses 3.5 and 17);
- claims for extensions of time.

4.5.2 Changes in Target Cost

CLAUSE 18.6

This Clause establishes two principles. Where appropriate a Variation may adjust the Target Cost. In any other circumstances justifying a change to Target Cost, the Contractor must give appropriate notice and keep proper records.

4.5.3 Changes in legislation

CLAUSE 4.5

This Clause needs no comment.

CLAUSES 7.3–4

Clause 7.3 allows the Contractor to claim what is in effect a Variation, to cover any increases in cost plus any consequent extension to the programme as a result of legislation which is passed or comes into force during the period of the

216

Contract. No special procedure is required for the Contractor's claim. Where the legislation is passed or comes into force after the Target Cost is agreed, then the cost will also be added to the Target Cost.

The Clause is not limited to legislation in one particular country. Therefore the Clause could apply if legislation in Japan, which made the export of a key item of equipment more costly, affected a UK contract.

The effect of Clause 7.4 is to exclude all tax and related charges from Clause 7.3. They remain with the Contractor. If therefore the Contract was likely to be affected by any exceptional tax it would need to be dealt with by a Special Condition.

4.5.4 Breach by the Purchaser as a variation

CLAUSE 4.7

Breach by the Purchaser, unless very serious, does not entitle the Contractor to terminate the Contract. Performance must continue. But breach will almost always increase the Contractor's costs. This Clause spells out the consequences—both Actual Cost and Target Cost are to be increased.

4.5.5 Site problems

Unforeseen ground conditions will always be a problem in Contracts involving site construction work. The higher the ratio of civil/building work to structural/process/electrical/mechanical work, the worse the potential problem. Within the chemical or oil industries the problem is small because the ratio is often low. In other process industries the position may well be different.

CLAUSE 6

Clause 6.1 requires the Contractor to behave professionally with respect to the Site. He is expected to inspect the Site properly. This means that he must take account of:

- the information actually in his possession concerning the Site;
- information available from a visual inspection of the Site;
- information resulting from reasonable enquiries prompted by that visual inspection;
- information in the public domain, such as geological maps of the area.

The phrase 'visual inspection of the Site' means precisely what it says. All that the Contractor is required to do is to look at what is visible on the Site at and above ground level and then draw reasonable conclusions and ask whatever reasonable questions are prompted by that inspection.

If then at any time during the Works, usually but not necessarily during the Site construction period, the Contractor comes up against problems on the Site that were unforeseeable at the time the Target Cost was agreed, other than weather (though the *results* of weather, such as flooding, could qualify), which cause extra cost then the Contractor will be entitled to claim additional costs as an increase to both Actual Cost and Target Cost. Of course unforeseeable conditions would usually be ground-related, though the Clause will also cover other Site problems, such as a pollution problem caused by other premises in the vicinity.

The Clause lays down a precise procedure that the Contractor must follow in making his claim, and also lays down a strict time limit for any claim.

Project Manager's instructions

Clause 11.2 permits the Contractor to trigger the Variation procedure in the event that manipulation by the Project Manager affects his ability to meet any time or other requirements of the Contract. Again the Clause sets out a time-scale and procedure that the Contractor must follow in making his claim.

4.5.6 Variations

Definition of a Variation and the limits to the Project Manager's powers
CLAUSE 16.1

The first principle laid down by Clause 16.1 is that only the Project Manager, or a Project Manager's Representative specifically authorised by the Project Manager under Clause 11.5, can initiate a Variation.

Secondly Clause 16.1 defines a Variation. Clarifications will not constitute a Variation, nor will an instruction to carry out work already covered by the Contract. However any change, even minor, to the Specification or work to be carried out by the Contractor will constitute a Variation. Also any changes to methods of working, which are not simply to rectify unsafe methods being used or proposed by the Contractor, will be Variations.

Therefore *any* order or instruction by the Project Manager to the Contractor to make any material change, whether an amendment, increase or omission, will constitute a Variation Order. In particular any instruction that is in conflict with the Contract, and especially in conflict with Schedule 1 or the Specification must be deemed to be a material change and therefore to be a Variation.

Under Clause 5.1 a Variation can only be ordered in writing. Therefore Clause 16.1 allows the Contractor to insist that the Project Manager issues formal written Variation Orders to cover any material changes instructed by him.

CLAUSE 16.7

This Clause deals with the limits to the Project Manager's power to order Variations by allowing the Contractor to object to Variations in certain circumstances. It is unacceptable for the Project Manager to have the right to use Variations to change a Contract by more than is reasonable, since this could place excessive strain on the Contractor's organisation and his ability to plan the Contract properly. Therefore Clause 16.7 allows the Contractor to object to any Variation once the cumulative effect of Variations is to increase or reduce the cost of the project by more than 25% of the Initial Target Cost, or 5% in the case of Variations issued after take-over. In effect once this percentage change in Initial Target Cost is reached the Contractor is able to pick and choose which Variations he wishes to carry out. (Of course if the Contractor is happy to carry out Variations above the 25% limit then there is nothing to prevent him doing so.)

In addition Clause 16.7 allows the Contractor to refuse to comply with any Variation when it would have the effect of requiring the Contractor to infringe the terms of any agreement with a third party, such as a process licence, or any third-party patent or other intellectual property right.

Finally Clause 16.7 allows the Contractor to refuse to comply with any Variation which would have the effect of pushing the Contractor into areas where he lacks the appropriate capacity, technology or expertise, unless the Project Manager agrees that a suitable nominated Subcontractor may be brought in (when Clause 10.7 would protect the Contractor against claims).

The Clause then sets out the proper procedure for objections to Variations by the Contractor. Essentially the Clause requires the Contractor to set out his objections in writing by at the latest two weeks after any order and even before the order if possible.

Initiation of Variations by the Project Manager

Normally the Purchaser should consult the Contractor in advance about the way in which the Contract may need to be amended to take account of a Variation (Clause 16.5).

The principles followed by the Conditions are then straightforward. They are that Variations to a complex process plant may well be complex in themselves. Therefore the Purchaser may need assistance from the Contractor in deciding whether a particular Variation is feasible (Clause 16.4) and the Contractor may notify the Project Manager of any problems likely to be caused by a Variation (Clause 16.6).

Even more important, perhaps, is the principle set out in Clause 16.2 that the Project Manager must decide clearly what changes to the Plant he wants before the Contractor can be expected to begin work.

CLAUSES 16.2–3

These Clauses state the basic principles. Firstly that the Variation Order, whatever form it may take, must define clearly what Variation is required by the Project Manager. Any purported Variation Order issued by the Project Manager that did not clearly define the 'Variation' would be invalid and must not be acted upon by the Contractor. Secondly that the Contractor must proceed to carry out any Variation properly ordered, subject of course to Clauses 16.6–9. Thirdly that the Contractor is entitled to receive payment for carrying out the Variation in accordance with the terms of Clause 18 and the Target Cost is to be adjusted appropriately. Finally the Contractor is entitled to an appropriate adjustment of Programme (and other Contract requirements).

CLAUSE 16.5

In the normal course the Project Manager would discuss any proposed Variation with the Contractor in some detail and agree the necessary Contract amendments and perhaps even a cost for the extra work before issuing a Variation Order.

However the Clause gives the Project Manager another option. If he decides that the Variation is sufficiently urgent he may order it, provided that it can be fully defined, without agreeing anything or giving the Contractor any opportunity even to comment/quote in advance.

CLAUSE 16.6

Clause 16.6 provides the machinery by which the Contractor can raise any contractual/process/ technical problems caused by a Variation with the Project Manager. In effect it is the Clause that allows the Contractor to bring any or all 'knock-on' consequences of the Variation to the Project Manager's attention, so that the problems can be dealt with *immediately*. Therefore the Clause only allows the Contractor *seven days* to notify the Project Manager of any problems, plus a further seven days to define them. If the Contractor does invoke the Clause then the Variation is put into abeyance until any confirmation by the Project Manager that the Contractor is to proceed with the Variation. In that case the Contract must be suitably modified to take reasonable account of the problem raised by the Contractor, either by agreement or in accordance with Clause 16.8.

CLAUSE 37.4

This Clause deals with a further power of the Project Manager to require the Contractor to repair defects in equipment supplied by the Purchaser or damage caused by the Purchaser in the Plant or equipment as a part of the defects repair service by the Contractor, but paid for as a Variation, as a part of both Actual Cost and Target Cost. It covers defects that arise both during the construction period and during the guarantee period.

Feasibility studies

Any process plant is best known to its designer, and the designer of the Plant is the Contractor. Therefore the Conditions give the Project Manager the right to call upon the Contractor's expertise to investigate potential Variations.

CLAUSE 16.4

If required by the Project Manager, the Contractor will draft or collaborate with the Project Manager in drafting the technical content for a possible Variation Order. The Contractor will also provide a statement on the Contract implications in line with Clause 16.5–6.

Contractor's proposals for Variations
CLAUSE 3.5

Clause 3.5 is very much a 'teamwork' clause. It requires the Contractor to make the Project Manager aware of any possible improvements/modifications to the Plant, Works or methods of operation, which would either eliminate defects or hazards, or which could benefit the Purchaser. If appropriate the Contractor will then take action under Clause 17.

CLAUSES 17.1–4

Clause 17.1 recognises a situation that may often arise in a process context—that the Contractor may find himself in a position to recommend an improvement in equipment or process to the Purchaser. (Of course this Clause partly overlaps Clause 3.5.) If this should be the case the Contractor must put forward a brief proposal for the improvement to the Project Manager. If the Project Manager then wishes to take the idea further he can use Clause 17.2 to develop further details, as a part of Actual and Target Cost. The choice of whether the improvement is to be incorporated in the Plant is then for the Purchaser/Project Manager to make within the time-scale(s) provided in the Clause.

If any improvement proposed by the Contractor has the effect of increasing the cost of the Works, the cost of the Variation will be added to Actual Cost and Target Cost. If, however, any improvement proposed by the Contractor has the effect of *reducing the cost* of the Works, the Target Cost will not reduce. In other words any cost-saving ideas put forward by the Contractor will increase his chance of earning a gainshare bonus.

The Clause would also be used by the Contractor to put forward a proposal for any Variation to correct any error in the Plant which was the responsibility of the Contractor.

Clause 17.4 would then permit the Contractor to insist upon the right to carry out a Variation which he has proposed under Clause 17.1 where there were safety or operating implications, and if necessary to appeal the point to an Expert.

CLAUSE 17.5
This Clause then deals with another problem, where the Contractor has detected an error in the Contract. (This could of course be due either to an error by the Purchaser or the Contractor, but would be more likely to be used by the Contractor in the case of an error by the Purchaser.) It is straightforward and needs no comment.

Valuation of Variations
Variations will normally be priced on the basis of the rates set out in Schedule 18 or agreed between the parties. Of course, many Variations will in practice be carried out largely on the basis of fixed prices quoted by Subcontractors and agreed in advance between the parties. The Conditions do not therefore include any price claim procedure. Clause 16.10 simply requires the Contractor to compile and keep costing records for each separate Variation—not always as easy as it sounds in a large and complex project.

4.5.7 Claims and disputes
Even in the collaborative relationship, disputes can still arise about the effects of a Variation, cost, delay, Specification, etc.

What often happens is that the parties leave resolution of the problem until the end of the Contract, often because the project management teams on either side are just too busy to handle the extra work involved while the Contract is still live. This always causes difficulties for both sides. Claim/Variation problems are best settled at the time they occur. The Conditions therefore suggest (Clause 16.9) that any disputes should be settled quickly by reference to an Expert.

Extensions of time

In this section we have only mentioned in passing the question of the Contractor's rights to claim an extension to the Contract programme or period. Claims for an extension of time for a Variation will be discussed in more detail in the next section.

At this point it is only necessary to point out that the Contractor must always remember that if he wishes to claim an extension of time for any Variation, and in most cases this will be the case, then he must notify the Project Manager of his claim in accordance with Clause 14.2 *as soon as reasonably possible*.

4.6 Delays and lateness

4.6.1 Lateness law

See section 1.5.

4.6.2 The Conditions

The Clauses to be covered in this section are those listed under the heading 'Delay' in Figure 3 (see page 171).

For ease of reference the Clauses can be divided into the following groups:

- suspension (Clause 41);
- extensions of time (Clause 14);
- liquidated damages (Clause 15 (and Schedule 12)).

4.6.3 Suspension

In one sense Clause 41 is closely allied to the Variation procedures discussed in section 4.5. There is always the risk in a Contract with a long time-scale that some unexpected but serious (either actually serious or potentially serious) problem will be found. Perhaps the Contractor may be found to have committed a serious error that has put the success of the Contract into question. Perhaps a change in market conditions means that the Purchaser needs time to consider whether the Plant should be modified to manufacture a different product. Perhaps a serious problem has arisen on Site. Perhaps the Plant may need modification to handle different raw materials. When that happens it may sometimes be advantageous to the Purchaser to, so to speak, stop the clock for a short time while he considers how best to tackle the problem. The suspension clause allows him to do just that.

Of course one can never stop the clock, or more accurately one can stop the clock only to some extent, in the sense of asking the Contractor to suspend work, but one cannot stop the Contractor's costs increasing. Therefore the Clause should only be used when *really* necessary, because there will always be a cost to the Purchaser, unless the suspension is because of a serious error by the Contractor.

From the Contractor's point of view also the Clause is a difficult one. He must keep his Contract team and his Subcontractors idle but ready to recommence work if and when requested to do so, and probably in a situation of considerable uncertainty. He may be able to employ *some* resources on other contracts, but will not be able to transfer major resources to other contracts in case they need to be transferred back again.

Neither party can therefore allow a suspension of the Contract to last indefinitely.

CLAUSE 41

Clause 41.1 needs no comment. It is a simple enabling clause allowing the Project Manager to suspend the Works, subject to any safety implications.

Clause 41.2 deals with the consequences of a Suspension Order. Where the Suspension Order is due to breach/error by the Contractor, the Contractor must bear the consequences. Otherwise the Contractor is entitled to extra time, which should be claimed in writing as soon as practicable in accordance with Clause 14.1, and also to his extra costs resulting from the suspension, both as Actual Cost and as an addition to Target Cost.

Clause 42.3 then allows the Contractor to require the Project Manager to decide whether or not the Contract is to be resumed if suspension continues for three months, so avoiding indefinite suspension, and Clause 41.4 deals with the programme implications of a suspension/resumption.

Disputes on cost and time should go to the Expert.

4.6.4 Extension of time

There are two groups of reasons which allow an extension of the Contract dates or periods. There is 'force majeure', which permits both the Contractor and the Purchaser to claim an extension of time if they are delayed by causes beyond their reasonable control. Then there are other delays that entitle the Contractor to a reasonable extension of time.

CLAUSE 14.2

The term 'force majeure' is regularly used commercially as meaning events generally beyond a party's control. The Conditions define the term as events which are beyond a party's control and which affect that party's ability to perform the Contract to time. The Clause then lists a number of circumstances that are within the definition and some others that are not.

There will always be some difficulty in defining, in the abstract, all the possible circumstances that could be considered to come within this definition of force majeure. In purely contractual terms the problem is one of exactly how the Clause should be interpreted. Would it, for instance, include terrorist activity—near the Site or near a route to the Site—which was making people reluctant to stay on the Site?

The answer is, of course, that nobody does know what the abstract answer is, but that the abstract answer is unimportant. Like all 'force majeure' clauses, Clause 14.2 is not intended to define the parties' rights with legal precision. All it does is to lay down the basic principle, which is that if some fairly serious event or chain of events causes delay to either party then that party should have a defence against claims by the other party arising out of the delay. It is up to the parties to the Contract, or an arbitrator, to reach a common-sense and fair decision between them about any actual circumstances that may arise.

CLAUSES 14.1 and 14.3–6

Clause 14.1 sets out the *procedure* for claiming an extension of time and deals with the *rights* of the Contractor to claim an extension to the Contract in a range of situations, including force majeure, but mainly situations which arise out of the natural interplay between the parties in a complex long-term Contract.

The Clause lists the different circumstances that allow an extension of time:

- Clause 14.2(a)—Clause 6.1 deals with the consequences of problems on the Site;
- Clause 14.2(b)—the parties would need to use Clause 16 to amend the Contract;
- Clause 14.2(c)—straightforward;
- Clause 14.2(d)—breach of the Contract by the Purchaser covers a range of Clauses, such as a failure to do work or provide information (Clause 4), or lateness in providing access to the Site (Clause 23). See also Clauses 4.7 and 14.4;
- Clause 14.2(e)—see Clause 10.7. The Contractor would also receive an indemnity against extra costs, but must be able to demonstrate proper management by him of the nominated Subcontractor.

The procedure is that the party (Contractor or Purchaser as the case may be) claiming extra time should give notice of the delay to the Project Manager, under Clause 14.1 'forthwith' (as soon as is practicably possible) after delay has actually occurred. The Contractor should then follow this with a further notice of the extension of time caused and therefore claimed. The Project Manager must then investigate the impact of the delay upon the Contract, and grant a reasonable extension by means of a Variation Order. (In other words the extension granted by the Project Manager may be for a shorter or longer period than the actual duration of the situation causing the claim.)

Clauses 14.3–4 are reasonably self-explanatory and need no comment, but note the reference to Actual and Target Cost in Clause 14.4.

Finally Clause 14.5 allows either party to bring the Contract to an end if force majeure circumstances, claimed or not, cause the Works to be completely or substantially stopped for a *continuous* four-month period. In that case the Purchaser would be required to pay the Contractor his costs/profit up to termination. (Note that there is a difference between Clause 14.5 and Clause 41.3. Under Clause 14.5 *either* party can terminate after 120 days stoppage. Under Clause 41.3, after 90 days stoppage, the Contractor can ask the Project Manager to make a decision in a further 28 days whether or not to terminate or recommence work.)

4.6.5 Liquidated damages

Clause 15 then deals with the question of delay by the Contractor in carrying out the Contract. In commercial terms the Clause is of enormous importance because it provides that delay by the Contractor is to be recompensed by liquidated damages. Little comment is necessary here, however. Clause 15.1 simply allows the parties to decide and negotiate their liquidated damages, as Schedule 12 to the Contract.

Clause 15.2 sets out a procedure to deal with one difficult point, where an excusable delay occurs after liquidated damages have become payable. It simply suspends damages until the excusable delay has ceased.

Clause 15.3 suggests the Expert as the proper route to settle disputes on time problems.

4.7 Defects, Site accidents, insurance and exclusions

4.7.1 The law

See section 1.5.

4.7.2 The Conditions

The Clauses to be covered in this section are those listed under the headings 'Defects/Final Certificate', 'Insurance etc' and 'Liability' in Figure 3 (see page 171).

For ease of reference the Clauses can be divided into the following groups:

- guarantees:
  - guarantee period (37.1–2 and 37.12–3);
  - normal defects procedure (Clauses 37.2);
  - Contractor's responsibility (Clause 37.3–4);
  - extension of guarantee period (Clause 37.6 and 37.10);
  - repetition of tests (Clause 37.5);
  - repair by the Purchaser (Clauses 37.7–9);
  - access to Site (37.11);
  - access to Plant and records (Clause 33.13);
- Final Certificate:
  - procedure (Clause 38.1);
  - purpose/effect (Clause 38.4);
  - time of issue (Clauses 38.1–3);
  - disputes (Clause 38.5);
- insurance:
  - responsibility for cover (Clauses 31.1–4);
  - administration (Clauses 31.2 and 31.5);
- Site work—accidents and responsibilities:
  - Contractor (Clauses 4.6 and 30.1–4);

- Purchaser (Clauses 30.3–4 and 30.9);
- limits of Contractor's liability (Clauses 30.3–4 and 30.7–9);
- employee risk (Clauses 30.5–6);
- overall exclusions of liability (Clauses 15, 43 and 44).

4.7.3 Guarantees

Guarantee period

CLAUSES 37.1–2 and 37.12–3

Clause 37.1 allows for sectional defects liability periods. The basic Defects Liability Period is then set by Clause 37.2. It starts when work commences or Materials arrive at the Site and continues until one year after take-over. If a different period or periods is agreed, a Special Condition will be necessary to modify the Clause.

Then there are two clauses that allow for limits to the extent of the Contractor's liability. Clause 37.12 and Schedule 10 deal with items that have a limited life, such as filters. Clause 37.13 limits the Contractor's liability if he is unable to obtain full back-to-back guarantees from Subcontractors.

Normal defects procedure

The Clause enables the Purchaser to ensure that the Contractor repairs or replaces equipment that is found to be defective as a result of some error in design or manufacture, for which the Contractor is responsible, during the guarantee period. Clauses 37.2 and 37.4 do this, and they also cover two other situations as well, firstly that of a defect which comes to light before the guarantee period commences, and secondly that of a defect which is not due to the fault of the Contractor. There is a cross-relationship between these Clauses and the testing and Variation Clauses.

CLAUSE 37.2

The Project Manager may notify the Contractor in writing of a defect in work/Materials or failure of the Plant/section to conform to the requirements of the Contract. Therefore 'defect' has a very wide meaning. It includes a deterioration in the performance of the Plant as well as equipment breakdown or failure. Clause 37.4 then extends the meaning of 'defect' further by including defects which have been caused by the Purchaser or others, for instance by incorrect operation of the Plant.

The notice by the Project Manager must describe the defect and must be given quickly. The Project Manager is not entitled to delay notification because it might be more convenient to delay repair, since this could increase the cost of repair to the Contractor. If the Purchaser does delay then the Contractor is entitled to charge him with the increase in his repair costs.

The Contractor must then be given all necessary access to the Plant and must carry out whatever work is necessary to correct the defect. The Contractor has the right to decide what corrective action to take—whether to repair or replace a defective item for example—but must inform the Project Manager of what action he intends to take if the Project Manager asks him to do so and obtain his approval.

Contractor's responsibility

The allocation of responsibility for the cost of correcting a defect is dealt with in a totally different manner under the Green Book Conditions to that of the Red Book Conditions. Under the fixed-price contract the Contractor bears the risk of defects, and will meet the cost. He will be expected to have allowed for this in his price and to protect himself by suitable terms in his Subcontracts. Under the reimbursable contract the Purchaser bears the cost of remedying defects, where not picked up by a Subcontractor, unless the Contractor has failed to exercise a professional standard of work.

The Burgundy Book adopts a position half-way between the two. The Target Cost should include an allowance/contingency to cover the costs of repairs. Subcontracts should include, where possible, proper defects repair undertakings from the Subcontractors, and if they cannot do so Clause 37.13 protects the Contractor. The Contractor is expected to exercise a proper professional standard of work and is not entitled to charge his defects repair costs if he has not done so. Provided that he *has* shown a professional standard, his defects repair costs can be charged to the Contract as Actual Cost. Where the defect is the fault/responsibility of the Purchaser *all defects repair costs* will be added to the Target Cost and charged as Actual Cost.

CLAUSE 37.3

Clause 37.3 states that any cost to the Contractor of making good defects will be paid by the Purchaser as Actual Cost, except in two situations:

- Firstly, and most importantly, where an item of equipment is defective and equipment defects will make up the vast majority of defect claims, the Subcontractor is to be required to comply with the terms of the guarantees included in his Subcontract (Clause 9.7 etc.).
- Secondly, where the Contractor has failed to exercise proper skill and care. The process plant is a large and complex thing. The job of designing and constructing it is also large and defects are bound to occur. The cost of those 'inevitable' or 'normal' defects is to be met by the Purchaser. If, however, the Contractor makes mistakes of the type that a contractor should never make, or makes far too many mistakes ('mistakes' meaning 'mistakes which result in defects') then the Purchaser may wish to hold the Contractor liable for the cost of their repair.

CLAUSE 37.4

Clause 37.4 then deals with defects that are not the Contractor's fault, but due to actions by others. The Contractor will take the necessary corrective action but the work must be dealt with as a Variation, so that Target Cost will be adjusted.

Extension of guarantee period

Clearly if the Plant becomes defective the Purchaser suffers in two ways. He may lose part of his original guarantee protection because an item of equipment

227

will have been changed or replaced. Also he may lose part of his guarantee period because the Plant will have been put out of action for a time. The Conditions deal with both of these problems.

CLAUSE 37.6

This Clause gives the Purchaser a new Defects Liability Period of one year upon any repair, as opposed to re-adjustment, and on any item of equipment or work which is replaced under Clauses 37.2–3. The Clause is fair—since repair/replacement implies a greater degree of failure than re-adjustment—but it will obviously influence the Contractor's thinking when faced with the decision of how to make good any particular defect.

CLAUSE 37.10

This Clause then provides that any Defects Liability Period will be extended by the time that the Plant or relevant section has been put out of use due to a defect.

To a certain extent this remedies the possible shortcoming of Clause 37.6, in that it applies to delay due to re-adjustment, but it does raise one problem of its own. It only applies where the defect is sufficient to put the Plant/section out of use. In other words where the defect or corrective work by the Contractor does not actually stop the Plant from operating or producing, but only *limits* or *restricts* its use then the Purchaser is not entitled to any extension, even though the restriction in output may be relatively serious.

Repetition of tests

It is normal to provide for the possible repetition of Contract tests on the Plant, in case serious defects show themselves during the guarantee period, to demonstrate that the corrective action taken by the Contractor is adequate to ensure that the Plant has been put back into proper order.

CLAUSE 37.5

The Project Manager may require the Contractor to repeat take-over tests to establish that defects have been properly corrected. The Clause refers only to take-over *tests*, however, not to take-over *procedures* or *performance tests*, and also allows the Project Manager only to require *appropriate* take-over tests. In other words, Clause 37.5 will apply only where the defect is of such a type that a take-over test is suitable to decide whether the defect has been properly corrected and the defect will normally have to be fairly serious to justify a repetition of a complete test. Clause 37.10 then allows an appropriate extension to the Defects Liability Period to allow for these tests.

Repair by the Purchaser

Clauses 37.7 and 37.9 provide the Purchaser with the usual remedy against the Contractor who fails to honour his defects obligations. He can carry out repairs for himself and then back-charge the costs to the Contractor. The Purchaser will often wish to retain some form of security against this possibility, usually in the form of a bond/bank guarantee or a cash retention. Clause 37.8 deals in the same way with urgent repairs.

CLAUSES 37.7–9

Where a repair is urgent, the Purchaser can carry out repairs himself (Clause 37.8) without invalidating the guarantee, if the Contractor cannot or will not do so. Furthermore if the Contractor fails to correct *any* defect with reasonable speed, even a defect which has been caused by the Purchaser, Clause 37.7 permits the Purchaser to carry out the repair, provided that he must first give the Contractor fourteen days notice that he will do so. In both cases the Purchaser is then entitled to recover his costs of corrective action from the Contractor under Clause 37.9.

The Clauses pose two practical problems for the Purchaser. The first is how to assess whether the Contractor is moving with reasonable speed in carrying out corrective work. The second is that the Purchaser's ability to use the powers given to him by the Clauses may be limited by a lack of knowledge of the process or technology involved.

Access to Site

CLAUSE 37.11

If the Purchaser, for whatever reason, does not give access to the Contractor to carry out the necessary work to correct a defect, then the Contractor does not have to carry out that work. If the Purchaser simply *postpones* the correction work then the Contractor will carry out the work at the end of the postponement and will be entitled to the extra costs of the delay (added to Actual Cost and Target Cost).

There are three problems. The first is the difference between refusing or not allowing access, and deferring access. This is all a matter of degree in one sense, but one test of refusal/deferment is whether or not, when access is denied, a date is set when access will be given (and is then given). The second is that delay in repairing a defect may simply mean that the defect becomes more serious and difficult to repair. The third is that repairing defects often involves equipment manufactured by Subcontractors, who are considerably less than enthusiastic about extending the guarantees on their equipment (under Clause 37.6) in these circumstances.

Access to plant records

A process plant is a highly complex unit. This means that it may not always be easy to diagnose the root cause of a process problem or defect. Therefore the Contractor must have access to the Plant and to all operating data. It may also be necessary to investigate the way in which equipment is performing to assist in diagnosis.

CLAUSE 33.13

Clause 33.13 lays down the general principles of the Contractor's right of access to the Plant and its associated operating records, and also sets out the procedure to be followed. The right is primarily there for use in case of defects problems, but is a general right of the Contractor and could be used at any time during the Defects Liability Period.

229

4.7.4 Final Certificate

Procedure

The procedure for issuing a Final Certificate is essentially the same as for any other certificate. It is to be issued by the Project Manager to both the Contractor and Purchaser. It should be issued when it is due without any need for application by the Contractor, unless a payment is also due, though the Contractor will normally apply for it anyway.

CLAUSE 38.1

The Clause states the procedure in simple terms, and needs no comment. The Clause does not require any application from the Contractor for the Certificate per se. Where take-over is by sections then a separate Certificate should be issued for each section.

Purpose and effect

The Conditions operate on the principle that the Contractor's obligations end once the Defects Liability Period or Periods have been completed. The purpose of the Final Certificate is therefore to confirm formally that the Contractor has carried out all his obligations, *and therefore* to bar the Purchaser from any actions against the Contractor for breach of the Contract once it has been issued. As a result the Project Manager must take great care in issuing the Final Certificate.

CLAUSE 38.4

The Final Certificate performs a number of functions:

- it brings to an end the Contractor's obligation to do any further work on the Plant or relevant section under the Contract, except for any 'insurance' repair work;
- it confirms that the Plant or section as constructed complies with the Contract;
- it confirms that the Contractor has properly performed his obligations during the Defects Liability Period;
- the Certificate (or, where take-over has been by sections, the *last* Certificate) will act as a formal legal document which the Contractor can use to prevent any litigation/arbitration by the Purchaser for breach of Contract ('conclusive evidence . . . in any proceedings that the Contractor has completed the Works').

This last function actually raises a problem in the Clause. The Clause *requires* the Project Manager to issue the Certificate once the Defects Liability Period is complete. However, the Clause does not formally permit the Project Manager to qualify a Certificate. Therefore there could be a problem where the Project Manager is required to issue a Final Certificate under a Contract which is the subject of a dispute. Effectively the Project Manager would have to issue a qualified Certificate.

Time of issue

The Clause provides that in principle a Final Certificate is to be issued by the Project Manager when the relevant guarantee period has been completed, but this is subject to a number of qualifications that are listed in the Clause.

CLAUSE 38.1

This Clause provides for the basic time of issue of the Certificate—when the defects liability has expired. It then allows the first qualification, that the Certificate may be delayed until all corrective action in respect of any defects being carried out by the Contractor under Clause 37 has been completed.

CLAUSE 38.2

This Clause then provides a further qualification. Where any equipment or work has been replaced or renewed under Clause 37.6 it is to be treated separately from the rest of the Plant or section, and separate Certificates issued as the different guarantee periods terminate.

CLAUSE 38.3

Clause 38.3 deals with the question of delayed performance tests, by simply allowing the Project Manager to delay any Certificate until any matters relating to delayed tests have been resolved.

Disputes

Clause 38.5 states that any disputes about whether or not the Plant qualifies for the issue of a Final Certificate or not—that is about issues of technical fact—should go to the Expert rather than to arbitration.

4.7.5 Insurance

Responsibility for cover

The discussions in sections 1.4 and 1.5 have already emphasised the importance of avoiding legal disputes, or at least minimising their impact upon the project as a whole. One of the most serious areas of risk is that of accidents and damage occurring during the construction of the Plant on the Site and while the Contractor is repairing defects.

There are a number of reasons why the risk is substantial in Contracts for process plants. Firstly, there is the sheer number of different companies that may be involved in Site work at any one time, the Contractor, the Purchaser, and any number of Subcontractors. Secondly there is the fact that all these different parties may be working in close physical proximity to each other. Thirdly there are the linked problems of double insurance, under-insurance and non-insurance.

The intention of Clause 31 is therefore to provide a framework within which the parties can organise a coherent insurance scheme for the project. The aim is to achieve adequate cover for the work and to avoid, wherever possible, the risk of cross-claims—disputes between different insurance companies as to which of them has to meet the costs of making good any damage. The problem is that when insurance companies argue, their clients become sucked into the dispute whether they want to or not.

CLAUSES 31.1–2

The Clauses set out the scheme as follows:

- the Purchaser is to be responsible for arranging the principal project insurance package for the Works through insurers acceptable to both parties;
- the package is in the joint names of all parties involved, Purchaser, Project Manager, Contractor and Subcontractors, simply to eliminate cross-claims and consequent delay in settling a claim;
- the insurance cover is to be against all normal insurable risks;
- the period covered by the package will be primarily that of Site construction, but the package will also cover defects in the Plant and any work done by the Contractor or any Subcontractor during the Defects Liability Period;
- the package will include the main areas of construction risk, the Documentation, the Materials and Plant;
- the insurance will be for full replacement cost, *unless* the Contract states differently (in which case the parties will need to make other arrangements for any risk in excess of the agreed amount).

Note that if under the terms of the Contract the Contractor has to remove any items of equipment belonging to the Purchaser from the Site, for example because they require refurbishment, then special insurance might need to be arranged.

CLAUSE 31.3
The second main area of cover is that of the Site, other than the Works and other property of the Purchaser adjacent to the Site. This is to be kept covered against all normal risk by the Purchaser, subject to the Contractor being liable for the first £5million of any damage caused by him in any single accident. It is therefore very much the responsibility of the Purchaser to make certain that he has an adequate level of insurance cover for his other property on or in close proximity to the Site, particularly because of the indemnity given by him to the Contractor under Clause 30.9.

CLAUSE 31.4
The Contractor is responsible for providing adequate insurance cover against the risk of accidental damage etc, both to the Purchaser and also to third parties. He will need adequate cover against the risk of damage to third-party property, especially if the Site is adjacent to high-value plant or equipment not owned by the Purchaser or its affiliated companies. (This is often the case. Major process sites regularly house plants belonging to different groups of companies, quite apart from the possibility of damage to property on adjacent premises.)

The only major areas omitted from this package are that of the Contractor's construction equipment, tools, site facilities, etc, which the Contractor and his Subcontractors will be expected to hold covered anyway, and the risk of injury to the employees of the various parties (which is covered, within the UK at any rate, by compulsory Employer's Liability insurance).

Administration
The administration of the insurance package is straightforward. The Purchaser, who has set up the package, is responsible for paying the necessary premiums.

Clause 31.1 then provides for the management of claims by the Purchaser on behalf of all parties. But the decision on settlement of any claim must be with the agreement of the Contractor. Any payments made by the insurers will be to the Purchaser, who will then use the money to fund the work by the Contractor under Clause 30.2–3.

CLAUSE 31.5
This Clause needs no comment.

4.7.6 Site work–accidents and responsibilities

Contractor
The Contractor has full responsibility for managing the Site during construction, and must repair any damage that may occur to the Works for any reason during that time. He is therefore responsible for meeting the costs of repair, subject to the limits stated in Clause 30.7, but will be assisted by payments received from the insurers under the Clause 31 insurance package.

CLAUSE 4.6
This Clause is straightforward and needs no comment.

CLAUSE 30.1
This is the basic 'responsibility/control' clause. It needs no comment.

CLAUSE 30.2
This Clause sets out the Contractor's obligations to repair or make good any accidental (and also deliberate—for example, vandalism, theft or sabotage) loss or damage to the Plant and to Materials. Up to take-over the Contractor must repair and make good *all* loss and damage (Clause 31.2). After take-over the Contractor must repair/make good where Clause 37.2 is applied by the Project Manager.

CLAUSES 30.3–4
These Clauses confirm the principle laid down in Clause 30.1, that the Contractor is in control of the Site and therefore responsible for carrying out repairs to all accidents and damage. They then list certain categories of loss or damage that the Contractor will repair, but at the cost of the Purchaser, if the Purchaser invokes Clause 37.2:

- political instability, sonic and nuclear risks (which are in any event uninsurable commercially) are best dealt with by the Site owner;
- problems arising from the use of the Site by the Purchaser need no comment;
- damage caused by the fault/negligence of the Purchaser, or designs/ information provided by the Purchaser, which would be breach of the terms of the Contract and need no comment (although it is worth pointing out that the Clause 31.1 insurance policy would probably indemnify/protect the Purchaser).

Limits of the Contractor's liability

The Conditions put a number of limits to the Contractor's liability for loss or damage on Site. These are all straightforward.

CLAUSE 30.7

(The Purchaser's property and premises)

This Clause is easy to deal with. In the insurance policy required to be maintained by the Contractor under Clause 31.4, the Contractor is required to insure against damage to the property of the Purchaser for an amount to be agreed between the parties. Clause 30.7 then limits the Contractor's liability for this damage to £5million, unless otherwise agreed. Effectively therefore what Clause 30.7 does is to limit the Contractor's liability for damage to the property of the Purchaser to the amount of insurance cover agreed between the parties pursuant to Clause 31.4.

However Clause 30.8 makes the Contractor liable for all *third-party* claims, even when made against the Purchaser, because third parties suffering damage will usually find it easier to claim against client than contractor.

Employee risk

CLAUSES 30.5–6

These Clauses deal with the risk of injury to the employees of the different parties involved during work on the Site. They provide simply that each party will accept responsibility for its own employees. This is normal practice in view of statutory Employer's Liability Insurance, and avoids cross-claims.

4.7.7 Overall exclusions

Liability

Liability of one party to the other under a Contract, and the liability of either of the parties to any third party, is always a highly emotive and contentious area, but it is an area with which all model forms have to deal.

Clauses 15 and 43 of the Conditions have already been discussed.

CLAUSE 44

The intention of Clause 44 is to put certain clear limits to the Contractor's liability.

Clause 44.1 excludes the Contractor's liability for various types of what may be called 'consequential' damage, together with damage caused because the Purchaser has imposed direct requirements upon the Contractor (subject to recovery under insurance).

Clause 44.2 then puts a general limit to the Contractor's liability. He is only to be liable for those damages allowed by the Conditions.

Perhaps, therefore, it is desirable to summarise the liability of both parties as set out by the Form:

• Performance of the Plant—if the Plant fails to pass its performance tests by a small amount, the Contractor will be liable to the Purchaser for breach of the Contract and his liability will be as agreed by the parties in Schedule 17 to the Contract. If the Plant fails to pass its performance tests by a significant amount, or fails to pass its take-over tests, the Contractor will be in breach of the Contract. (In each case the Contractor will certainly be liable for damages, and perhaps also to termination or cancellation of the Contract.)

- Third-party intellectual property—each party is liable to the other if it causes any infringement of any patent or other right owned by a third party, essentially to indemnify the other party against any claim.
- Delay—if the Purchaser delays the Contractor (other than by reason of force majeure), the Purchaser is liable for the Contractor's extra costs. If the Contractor is late other than by force majeure or various other acceptable reasons, then the Contractor will be liable to the Purchaser and his precise degree of liability will be set out in Schedule 12 to the Contract.
- Disruption—if the Purchaser disrupts the Contractor's work on Site by failing to supply work or information then the Purchaser will be liable to meet the Contractor's extra costs.
- Damage to property—damage to the Plant by either party during construction should be covered by joint insurance arranged under the Contract. The Contractor would then be expected to insure his own Site facilities and construction equipment. Damage to the Plant during the guarantee period by the Contractor would be covered by the joint insurance package. Damage by the Purchaser would be insured separately by the Purchaser. Damage to third-party owned property would be insured separately by the parties. If this insurance were inadequate then the parties would be liable for the excess.

4.8 Payments and money

The Clauses to be covered in this section are those listed under the heading 'Money' in Figure 3 (see page 171).

4.8.1 General approach

In a Target Cost contract the principle is that the Contractor is to be reimbursed for his work on the basis of Actual Cost calculated in accordance with Schedule 18 (and that reimbursement should be on a 'transparent' basis), but that the amounts paid to the Contractor should be adjusted, at or near the end of the Contract, in line with the final Target Cost and the gainshare/painshare formula set out in Schedule 19. This means that payment is dealt with in a completely different way to a price-based contract or a reimbursable contract. The following questions are to be dealt with by the Contract:

- How the Contractor's work is to be priced. Essentially this can be done in two ways, on the basis of *cost* (actual or presumed) plus a profit, or on the basis of *rate/charge/fee* per unit of work. The Conditions do not deal with this as such, because there is no need to do so. They refer to the Contractor's right to be paid his cost/expenditure, and leave the parties to define the way in which cost/expenditure is to be calculated in Schedule 18.

- When and how much money is to be paid by the Purchaser to the Contractor. Here the Contract works on a 'reimbursable' basis. The aim is to ensure that money is transferred to the Contractor as necessary to fund the Works, to ensure a neutral cash flow. This problem is dealt with by the Conditions, in Clause 39, for reimbursable payment, and also in Schedules 18 and 19, for any lump sum or milestone payments.
- Next is the need to maintain an open system of cost control. This is dealt with primarily in Clause 3.7 and Clause 19, supported by Schedule 20 to contain the detail.
- Then there is the terms of payment that will apply to Subcontractors. In a process contract, probably well over fifty percent of the total cost of the Works will be payments to Subcontractors, rather than for work done by the Contractor. This is not dealt with by the Conditions. What should happen is that the Project Manager and the Contractor will decide between them upon the payments policy to be adopted by the Contractor when letting Subcontracts. Terms of payment will then be agreed by the Contractor with each Subcontractor.
- Finally there is the calculation of the Contract Price—the amount that results from the application of the gainshare/painshare formula to the total Actual Cost when compared with the Final Target Cost, and the procedure for adjustment of the money position. The Conditions leave the calculation to be done in accordance with Schedule 19, while Clause 39 deals with the payment procedure.

The Conditions are written on the basis that payments will be made to the Contractor on a monthly basis, with enough money being transferred each month to enable the Contractor to finance his own operations and then meet Subcontractors' invoices when they become due.

4.8.2 The 'Contract Price'

CLAUSES 18 and 40

Clause 18.1 states the basic principle, that the Contract Price will only be known when all work under the Contract has been completed and paid for, and the gainshare/painshare calculation has been carried out. It is to be calculated in accordance with Schedules 18–20, especially Schedule 19.

Clause 18.2 simply states that any further items required but not covered by the Schedules will be priced either on the basis of the Schedules or by agreement between the Contractor and Project Manager. Finally Clause 18.3 deals with dispute.

Clause 40 allows for any prime cost and provisional sums required by the Purchaser to be included in Schedule 18 of the Contract. The Clause is straightforward and needs little comment.

A provisional sum is a sum, stated in the Contract, that is available for use if the Project Manager decides that he wishes the Contractor to carry out certain additional work. Provisional sums are often allowed for in contracts when the Purchaser or Project Manager realise at the start that additional or ancillary work may be needed, but when it is impossible to decide precisely what may need to be done until the Contract is well advanced. Typical examples are optional items of equipment or 'site improvement' work, such as landscaping, fencing or paths. A provisional sum might also be used to cover more important items of work, which are known to be necessary but which cannot be accurately priced at the date of the Contract, such as building or foundation work.

A prime cost sum is an amount included in the Contract Price to be used for a specific purpose as instructed by the Project Manager. Prime cost sums are regularly used where the Purchaser/Project Manager may wish to nominate a Subcontractor.

4.8.3 The payment procedure

CLAUSE 39

Clause 39 is the main payment clause. It does three things. Firstly, it lays down the procedure for monthly transfers of money to the Contractor. Secondly, it sets out the rights of the Contractor in the event of non-payment. Thirdly, it deals with final settlement.

Clause 39.1 and 39.2 need no comment.

Perhaps the best way to comment upon Clauses 39.3–5 is to describe the payment procedure, *remembering Clause 39.11* (see below).

Firstly, the time-scale. Near the end of each month during the Contract, say about the 20–24th of the month (if the parties are adopting calendar months as their payment periods) the Contractor will submit a request for the transfer of the funds needed by him during the following month. The request will take the form probably of a draft invoice or statement setting out the Contractor's estimate of the funds that he will require during that month supported by the appropriate back-up information called for in Clause 39.3. The Project Manager is allowed two weeks to check the Contractor's request/invoice/estimate and must then certify to the parties the amount that he accepts as being payable. The Purchaser then has two weeks to pay the amount certified to the Contractor. The result is that the Contractor will receive payment of the amount on or around the 20th of the month. He will then use that money during the last ten days of the month to pay any Subcontractors whatever is due to them, and also to meet his own costs and salaries.

Secondly, the request. The request for payment will be in two parts, and will refer to two quite different months. Assuming that a Contract is signed on the 1st February, the Contractor will immediately submit an invoice for that month's estimated costs, which will be paid without certification. Then at the end of *February* he will submit a request setting out his estimated expenditure (his own costs and any invoices from Subcontractors due for payment) during *March* (Clause 39.3(a)). A request submitted in *March* will then set out the Contractor's estimated expenditure during *April* (Clause 39.3(a)), *together with* details of actual charges and payments during *February* (Clause 39.3(b)). The request submitted in *April* will set out the Contractor's estimate for *May* (Clause 39.3(a)) and actual charges and payments for *March* (Clause 39.3(b)) *together with* the amounts certified by the Project Manager for that month (Clause 39.3(c)). The request submitted in *May* will set the Contractor's estimate for *June* (Clause 39.3(a)), actual charges and payments for *April* (Clause 39.3(b)), together with the amounts certified by the Project Manager for that month (Clause 39.3(c)), and so on.

Given that the Project Manager will have detailed knowledge of Subcontracts under Clause 9, and monthly reports of the Contractor's progress under Clause 3.7, as well as access to the Contractor and his records and forecasts, the request for payment procedure will quickly enable the Project Manager to build up a comprehensive Actual Cost / Target Cost / cash flow picture of the Contract.

Thirdly, the supporting 'relevant documentary evidence'. For actual expenditure this might comprise receipted copies of Subcontractors' invoices or payment documents, together with the Contractor's timesheets, etc.

For estimated expenditure this might comprise predicted manning levels and charges, plus Subcontractors' invoices awaiting payment.

Fourthly, the organisation. It will be clear that all the parties involved will need to have adequate organisation. The Contractor has to be able to submit regular monthly invoices with a mass of supporting detail. The Project Manager then has only a few days to assimilate that detail before certifying payment. The Purchaser then has to arrange transfer quickly.

Finally Clause 39.11 makes one very important exception to the above. Should it become clear that the Contractor's Actual Cost will exceed the Target Cost, so triggering a painshare calculation, the Project Manager must reduce the amount(s) certified by him under Clause 39.4 to recover the sums potentially due from the Contractor to the Purchaser.

4.8.4 Non-payment

Clause 39.13 and 39.8–9 deal with the Contractor's (and Purchaser's) rights in the event of delay in payment. Under Clause 39.13 interest is payable on any amounts overdue at rapidly-increasing rates. In addition, under Clauses 39.8–9, the Contractor has the right to suspend performance and ultimately terminate the Contract if *either* the Project Manager delays certification *or* the Purchaser delays payment.

4.8.5 Set-off

Clause 39.7 allows the Purchaser a right of set-off, plus procedure, in respect of sums due to him from the Contractor *under the Contract*. This of course is provided that the Purchaser can justify his claim—see Clause 4.3.

4.8.6 VAT

Clause 39.10 is straightforward and needs no comment.

4.8.7 Audit

CLAUSES 3.7, 19 and 39.12

Clause 19 needs little comment in one sense. Most complex contracts that include a reimbursable element include a clause allowing the Purchaser to exercise a degree of financial oversight of the way in which the Contractor controls and spends the funds that he provides.

Clause 19.1 combines with Clause 3.7 and Schedule 20 to require the Contractor to keep records of the Contract which are both complete and detailed and satisfactory to the Purchaser, that will enable the Purchaser to check progress under the Contract and its financial position. Note that the Contractor's records do not have to be in any specific form. They can be of any form or kind that the Contractor chooses, subject to Schedule 20, so long as they provide the Purchaser with the reasonable ability to ascertain progress.

Clause 19.2 then allows the Purchaser to check on progress should he wish to do so, and Clause 39.12 provides the procedure to rectify any errors that are discovered.

4.8.8 Target Cost

Clauses 18.4–8 lay down the basic rules for the Target Cost, and Clause 39.11 then deals with final settlement (see above).

Clauses 18.4–5 set out the position in relation to the establishment of the Target Cost. The first possibility is that the Initial Target Cost will be agreed before Contract and stated in Schedule 19. If this is not the case, either because Schedule 19 contains only an initial estimate or no Target Cost at all, then the Project Manager and Contractor will agree an Initial Target Cost within the period stated in Schedule 11, complete with a detailed breakdown of that Initial Target Cost, all in accordance with Schedule 19 and Schedule 18. The Target Cost is to be a comprehensive cost, covering all Materials and activities required to be carried out by the Contractor under the Contract, unless otherwise agreed.

Clause 18.6—see section 4.5.

Clause 18.7 simply establishes the basic rule for ascertaining the Contract Price.

Clause 18.8 is straightforward and needs no comment.

The Yellow and Brown Books

5

5.1 Subcontracting

5.1.1 General

Subcontracting is easy. Subcontracting well is difficult. The problems arise from four sources. There are a number of reasons for this:

- the complexity of the Main Contract;
- the variety of equipment and services that the Contractor will need to purchase;
- the different commercial attitudes of the Contractor and the various Subcontractors;
- the different levels of skill and knowledge of the Contractor and his Subcontractors.

These produce a series of conflicts that the Contractor has to deal with. These conflicts may be:

- Between the Contractor's wish to pass his contractual obligations and risks down the line to his Subcontractors and the Subcontractors' reluctance to accept contract terms which are not appropriate to their own work.

  The Contractor will often want to pass on contractual obligations to his Subcontractors—for example, design risk. But, while the Contractor might want to pass on the risk that the *Plant* will operate properly, the Subcontractors will only want to accept a limited risk, that their *work* will be to a reasonable standard or that the *equipment* which they supply will operate properly.
- Between the Contractor's wish to pass his contractual obligations down the line and his desire to buy in equipment and work at the lowest price.

  Under the Red Book Conditions in particular the Contractor will wish to keep the cost of bought-in work and materials to the minimum, consistent with the need to comply with the requirements of the Contract. But the more complex the contractual terms that the Contractor asks the Subcontractor to accept, the higher the price that the Subcontractor will ask.

There may be two reasons for this. Firstly, the Subcontractor will ask a higher price for the extra risk. Secondly, the Subcontractor will ask a higher price simply because he is afraid that he may be being asked to accept unreasonable risk.

- Between the types of risk and terms of contract that Subcontractors in different industries accept as 'normal'.

  Two examples of this. Civil engineering and building companies are not accustomed to quoting a fixed price or to accepting 'design/fitness for purpose' risk on their work. These risks are normal for suppliers within the equipment/process industries. Computer software of enormous importance to the overall success of the project will often have to be written by Subcontractors who will only accept very limited liability for any failure by their software.

- Between the different commercial interests of the Contractor and Subcontractors.

  The Contractor is concerned with the success of his Main Contract. Subcontractors generally have little interest in the success of the Main Contract. Of course they want it to be successful because a successful Main Contract reduces argument over payment—but what really matters to the Subcontractor is the success of his Subcontract.

- Between the different technical skills of the Contractor and Subcontractors.

  Often the Subcontractor will have far more expertise than the Contractor in the design and manufacture of his own equipment but will have little understanding of how it interfaces with the rest of the Plant. Equally the Contractor will often have to purchase work or Materials from a whole range of Subcontractors with far less expertise even in their own field than his.

- Between the different commercial or technical sizes or sophistication of the Contractor and Subcontractors.

  This needs no explanation, but there are a number of variables such as size, manufacturing expertise, technical expertise, commercial sophistication and specialist market or customer knowledge.

- Between the relative importance of the Main Contract or Subcontract to the Contractor and Subcontractor.

  Again this is obvious. To the process Contractor every Contract will be significant simply because of its size and time-scale. As a result any critical Subcontract will be of considerable importance to him. Not every Subcontract will be of similar importance to the Subcontractor.

- Between the levels of knowledge of the project of the Contractor and a Subcontractor.

  The Contractor will usually know the project and its commercial, technical and Site problems quite well. He will also know the Purchaser. Most Subcontractors will know only a little about these matters. Some, however, may have considerable knowledge, perhaps even greater knowledge than the Contractor.

Once the Contractor has decided how he wishes to resolve the various conflicts facing his project he then has the problem of deciding which strategy to use in achieving a reasonable balance in his Subcontracts. This will depend upon a number of factors including:

- the requirements of the Main Contract;
- market conditions;
- the type of work or Materials to be purchased;
- the range of probable Subcontract size and importance;
- the previous trading relationships between the Contractor and potential Subcontractors;
- the time-scale for the procurement operation;
- the procurement skills and resources that the Contractor has available for the project.

This last factor is often of crucial importance. Placing and managing a large number of varied types of Subcontract, probably within a limited time-scale, demands considerable resources—technical, commercial and contractual. This is an essential part of the process Contractor's repertoire.

Under a Red Book Main Contract the Contractor is of course free to decide his policy for himself (except where a nominated Subcontractor is involved). Under a Green Book or Burgundy Book Main Contract the Contractor has less freedom since Clause 9 imposes a requirement to employ procurement procedures, and implicitly strategy, which are acceptable to the Project Manager. Nevertheless the same principle still applies.

Usually he will have a large number of comparative straightforward Subcontracts to place, and usually he will have to do so within a comparatively short space of time. This will mean that the Contractor will need to adopt a standard procedure for dealing with those Subcontracts, possibly utilising a standardised 'small-print-on-the-reverse' enquiry/purchase order format, but one which takes the principal requirements of the Main Contract into account. The aim is to use a format that enables the Contractor to buy work and Materials on a fixed-price competitive bid basis, consistent with the needs of the Main Contract but with a minimum amount of effort required for each individual purchase.

The Contractor must always be prepared to use other purchasing methods as well when he considers it appropriate to do so to obtain a reasonable level of support from the project from the Subcontractor. This ability to adopt different purchasing strategies and methods, depending upon the circumstances, is one of the essential skills of the Contractor—as is the ability to adapt his own work to the different results of different procurement strategies.

There are a number of methods that may be appropriate. Specialist skills may be bought in through consultancy agreements or through day-rate contracts. Computer software may be bought in for fixed or variable fee. Process information may be obtained through patent or know-how licences. Some items may be purchased through call-off arrangements. Construction equipment may be hired. Civil engineering or construction and erection work may be purchased under measurement types of contract. Finally major Subcontracts, either for major items of equipment or work or for process packages may be placed through one-off negotiated contracts, probably more or less on a 'back-to-back' basis with the Main Contract.

In each case however the Contractor will balance the risk that he seeks to pass down to the Subcontractor against the prices or fees that the Subcontractor asks in return.

5.1.2 'Back-to-back' Subcontracts

The term 'back-to-back' Subcontract is widely and inaccurately used in industry to mean a Subcontract which gives the Subcontractor the same obligations, in terms of work and liability, towards the Contractor that the Contractor has in his turn towards the Purchaser.

This gives the Contractor a high degree of certainty that his Subcontractors will carry out their obligations in a way that will help him to carry out his own obligations under the Main Contract. Firstly, the Subcontractors' obligations will be the same as those of the Contractor. Secondly, their liability to the Contractor will be the same as his liability to the Purchaser. If then the Subcontractor causes the Contractor to be in breach of his Main Contract and therefore liable to the Purchaser, the Subcontractor will also be in breach of the terms of his Subcontract and liable to the Contractor as well.

Therefore the Contractor is secure. His Subcontractors will carry out work that contributes to the Main Contract instead of being motivated only to carry out whatever work is necessary to ensure payment under their Subcontracts. In addition he is insulated against claims from the Purchaser because they can be passed on directly to the Subcontractors. The simplicity of the logic is attractive, and the idea of the back-to-back Subcontract (in particular the Subcontract carrying back-to-back *liability*) is widely used in the building and civil engineering industries. Since these industries focus on work-related, rather than result-related, contracts, the principle works with reasonable success.

It is impossible, however, except in unusual circumstances for a Subcontractor in the process and equipment industries to be given the same obligations that the Contractor will have under the Main Contract.

Firstly, the normal Subcontractor can never be given the same breadth of *design* obligations as the Contractor. Even in an extreme case where Subcontractors each have to design and supply a complete section of the Plant, they could not be expected to accept design liability for the whole Plant. Interface risk will still be the responsibility of the Contractor.

Secondly, it is rare for a Subcontractor to have the same practical obligations towards the Contractor as the Contractor will have towards the Purchaser. The Contractor has the obligation to supply and construct a complete process Plant within a defined time-scale. The Subcontractor has the obligation to supply services or Materials that will be used by the Contractor in carrying out that obligation within a different time-scale.

Often several Subcontractors will contribute to each area of the Contractor's activities and their work will usually be interdependent, so that it becomes almost impossible in practice to hold any Subcontractor to liability identical to that of the Contractor.

Nevertheless as a rough definition of a class of subcontracts, the term is adequate. It defines Subcontracts that try to pass down to the Subcontractor

Conditions of Contract which are as similar as possible to those of the Main Contract.

However 'back-to-back' subcontract should never be used as a precise term, because it has no precise meaning. It is used to mean different and mutually exclusive things. As soon as one begins to look in detail at the way in which the back-to-back subcontract may be drafted, it becomes obvious that there are different ways of doing so which produce different results, depending upon the strategy that is being followed.

5.1.3 Example 1

The Main Contract requires documentation to be delivered to the Purchaser by a date. Some of the documentation originates from a Subcontractor. Requiring the Subcontractor to deliver his documentation on the same date would not allow the Contractor time to incorporate it into the Contractor's own documentation and then deliver on time. Therefore the Contractor must either require the Subcontractor to deliver documentation direct to the Purchaser (when he will have to devise a method to ensure that the Subcontractor's documentation will be consistent with his own), or impose a shorter delivery date on the Subcontractor.

5.1.4 Example 2

The Contractor will be responsible for giving a performance guarantee to the Purchaser in respect of the Plant—an undertaking that the Plant will produce a specified amount of product during a performance test. When he turns to his Subcontractors he will ask for different levels of guarantee. The supplier of a complete process package might be asked for an equal or more stringent guarantee. The supplier of an item of equipment might be asked for a less comprehensive guarantee. The supplier of items such as structural steelwork might not be asked for any performance guarantee at all.

5.1.5 Example 3

The Contractor may accept liability for lateness in completing the take-over test on the basis of liquidated damages. The liquidated damages will probably be stated in the Main Contract as a percentage of the Contract Price per week or month of delay. This percentage will equate to a sum of money per week or month. The Contractor will pass this liability down to Subcontractors but he must decide whether to ask the Subcontractors for the same *percentage* liability (in which case their *cash* exposure will be much lower than his own), or for the same *cash* liability (in which case their *percentage* exposure will be much higher than his own), or something in between.

These are just a few examples of the different approaches that the Contractor may take when deciding how to pass on his obligations to Subcontractors on a 'back-to-back' basis. They each require a decision by the Contractor as to what degree of liability he will try to impose on the Subcontractor. Each depends entirely upon the procurement strategy that the Contractor decides to use, and each gives a different practical result, yet all these results are 'back-to-back' with the Main Contract in the generally accepted meaning of the term.

IChemE has set out to produce two Forms of Subcontract which will enable the Contractor to pass down to a Subcontractor Conditions of Contract which are identical (so far as this is achievable in practice) to those of the Main Contract Conditions. One set, the Yellow Book, is designed for the procurement of a complete process package (perhaps a section of the Plant) with the Subcontractor carrying out the design, manufacture, supply, installation and testing of his package. The other, the Brown Book, is designed for large packages of civil engineering building and construction work.

Each contains the appropriate changes to adapt the Main Contract scenario to the Subcontract scenario and each contains the necessary changes to adapt Main Contract Conditions to Subcontract Conditions. Both Forms of Subcontract are intended for use under all IChemE Forms—fixed price, target cost and reimbursable.

Both Forms provide a series of Schedules to allow the Contractor to transfer the necessary technical and other information from the Main Contract to the Subcontract. This of course allows the Contractor freedom to decide just what information to pass on to the Subcontractor, and also gives him the freedom to adopt whatever procurement strategy he wishes.

Obviously considerable care and effort is necessary when drawing up Subcontracts in accordance with these forms. The forms are intended for use in one-off major negotiated Subcontracts where this amount of effort is fully justified. They are not intended for use in the bread and butter procurement of minor items of work or equipment.

5.2 The Yellow Book Form of Subcontract

5.2.1 General

The wording of the Form of Subcontract is almost entirely derived from the wording of the Red Book conditions. Therefore all the broad principles enshrined in the Subcontract have already been discussed in the earlier chapter on the Red Book Conditions and therefore this chapter should be read in conjunction with Chapter 2. The aim of this section is simply to go through the Subcontract Agreement and General Conditions to discuss how they have been adapted from the wording of the Red Book—'Main Contract'—conditions.

5.2.2 The Yellow Book scenario

The scenario of the Conditions is very straightforward. It is that the Subcontractor will design, manufacture or purchase, and supply materials and equipment to the Site, and then carry out any construction or erection work necessary to install that equipment. The equipment will comprise a complete process package, perhaps a separate section of the Plant. The section will then be subject to take-over tests, and probably also performance tests, as a part of the Plant.

The supply of the plant and materials, etc., will normally be on the basis of a firm price. Erection and construction work may be paid for on the basis of a schedule of rates or on the basis of a fixed price/fee. The Conditions provide for a substantial Site presence by the Subcontractor, with a Site Manager and construction/erection resources being provided over a significant period.

Strictly speaking the Conditions are not intended for 'supply-only' or 'supply-with–supervision' contracts, although they can obviously be modified for use in that way.

General note

What we are discussing here is a set of Conditions of Contract that have been taken from Main Contract conditions and re-drafted for use in a Subcontract. As a result there have been hundreds of minor changes in wording. Every time the word 'Contractor' appears in the Main Contract versions, the word 'Subcontractor' has to appear in the Subcontract. 'Plant' changes to 'Subcontract Plant'—and so on. It is pointless to comment upon such changes, and therefore I have not done so. Finally almost all the notice and response periods in the Conditions are changed from those in the Main Contract to allow for the communication chain between Purchaser, Contractor and Subcontractor. My comments on the individual clauses make no mention of changes of this kind. They are taken for granted. Even then many of my comments are only about small changes in wording.

5.2.3 The Subcontract Agreement

The Yellow Book operates upon the same basis as the Main Contract conditions. It presumes that there will be a separate Subcontract Agreement signed between the two parties. Again this Agreement will set out the various points that need to be dealt with in addition to the Subcontract Conditions.

The Agreement is particularly important. It contains a series of Schedules that include information that needs to be transferred from the Main Contract into the Subcontract, and gives the parties a framework to use when doing so. Essentially the 'quality' of any back-to-back Subcontract will largely depend upon the skill with which the relevant requirements of the Main Contract are transposed into the Subcontract. The layout of the Schedules in the Agreement is intended to assist the parties in getting this right.

Of course, the other part of the Subcontract that the parties must get right is the Specification. This may be an extremely complex exercise and, in another book, would be worth a full section on its own. All I can say here is that the Subcontract Specification needs to link back to the Main Contract Specification, to describe exactly what it is that the Subcontractor is to provide, exactly what will be provided by others, and how the Subcontractor's equipment/work will interface with everything else.

The Agreement is similar to the Agreements in the Main Contract forms. It begins with a statement of the parties to the Agreement and a standard introductory preamble.

Clause 1 lists the constituent parts of the Agreement. These are:

- the Agreement itself, together with the General Conditions;
- Special Conditions—almost inevitable;
- the Subcontract Specification;
- a series of Schedules.

The General and Special Conditions together with Schedule 20 are the principal parts of the Subcontract that set out 'back-to-back' contractual requirements incorporated from the Main Contract. Schedule 20 will include a description of the Main Contract or at least those parts of the Main Contract that apply directly to the Subcontract. Particular technical requirements may be included in Schedule 20 or the Specification. Special Conditions from the Main Contract that are to apply may be included in Schedule 20 (and see Clause 3.10) or the Special Conditions.

The other Schedules mirror the Main Contract and need no particular comment.

Clauses 2 to 5 underline the need for both parties to ensure that the Subcontract is correct. They combine to exclude anything not specifically written into the Subcontract from consideration, and set the level of the Subcontractor's overall liability/responsibility, in respect of repair and insurance liability. Lateness and performance responsibility are dealt with in the Schedules.

Clauses 9 and 10 name the main project managers for the Subcontract. These are the Contract Manager for the Contractor, who will of course usually be the same person as the 'Contract Manager' for the purposes of the Main Contract and the Subcontract Manager for the Subcontractor. This is an example of the continuity of nomenclature between Main Contract and Subcontract Conditions—where at Main Contract level we have 'Contract', in Subcontracts we have 'Subcontract'.)

Clauses 7 and 8 establish necessary dates for the purpose of the Subcontract.

Clause 12 sets the agreed profit level on claims, etc. This will relate back to the Main Contract.

Clause 14 is a simple procedural clause, but in practical terms there will probably be quite complex requirements for the numbering/identification of documentation arising out of the Subcontract. Project and safety procedures very often require that each individual document is easily identifiable.

The other terms of the Agreement require no particular comment.

5.2.4 The General Conditions

CLAUSE 1 *Definitions*
In principle the definitions of standard terms such as 'Cost' or 'Defect' remain the same as in the Main Contract conditions. Then other definitions such as 'Works' or 'Equipment', have been changed to fit a Subcontract. Finally some additional definitions, such as 'Free-Issue Materials' and 'Purchaser/Project Manager', have been added to recognise the existence of the Main Contract.

The actual definitions themselves are straightforward and need little comment. They have deliberately been written to retain the management relationships of

247

the Main Contract conditions. So the definitions of 'Purchaser', 'Project Manager', 'Contractor', 'Contract Manager', 'Subcontractor', 'Subcontract Manager' and 'Subcontract Site Manager' are consistent between the Main Contract conditions and the Subcontract. The same hierarchy of terms is maintained in respect of Specifications, 'Works', 'Equipment', 'Materials' and 'Plant'. Definitions that have been added include the 'Contract Manager's Representative' in place of a 'Project Manager's Representative', but again this is consistent with those management relationships.

Note the definition of 'Subcontract Price'. This is the only definition based upon the Green/Burgundy Book conditions, and it is there to allow for the possibility that the Subcontract might be based upon a schedule of rates or on a reimbursable basis.

CLAUSE 2 *Interpretation*
The wording of this Clause is very close to that of the Red Book conditions, except in one particular. No additional comments are necessary.

CLAUSE 3 *Subcontractor's responsibilities*
Clauses 3.1 and 3.2–4 set out the Subcontractor's responsibilities, and especially his design responsibilities, in fairly stringent terms. His responsibility is to complete the Subcontract Works and Plant:

- in accordance with the Subcontract Specification/Description of Works;
- with sound workmanship and materials;
- safely;
- in accordance with good engineering practice;
- to the reasonable satisfaction of the Contractor;
- so that the completed Subcontract Plant shall be suitable for its purpose.

Given the fact that most Subcontracts under these Conditions will be placed on the basis of a fixed/firm price, this is a high level of design/completion responsibility. (In fact it matches that of a reimbursable Contractor.) Therefore the Subcontractor must satisfy himself before accepting the Subcontract that he can comply with the terms of the Specification. If he cannot do so then he must raise the matter so that it can be discussed and a solution found. No Contractor will thank a Subcontractor who fails to carry out his Subcontract.

Clause 3.5 follows the theme of the Main Contract conditions in promoting collaboration where it can avoid problems or give benefits to the project. Note the reference in the Clause to the Purchaser as well as the Contractor.

Clause 3.8 requires the Subcontractor to keep in place a quality assurance system, and also to ensure that at least his own first-tier subcontractors do so as well.

Clause 3.9 again refers to both Contractor and Purchaser.

Clause 3.10 is very important because it defines the 'back-to-back' nature of the Subcontractor's obligation. It says four things:

- the Subcontract Plant must be fit for its purpose *as defined in the Subcontract;*
- if any Subcontractor working with reasonable care/skill could avoid causing the Contractor to incur liability to the Purchaser then the Subcontractor must do the same;

- the Subcontract Plant must perform to Contract, or if it cannot do so then well enough to avoid causing the Contractor to be in breach;
- the Subcontractor must comply with any Main Contract provisions set out in Schedule 20.

The overall result is that the Subcontractor carries a high level of obligation.

CLAUSE 4 *Contractor's responsibilities*
This Clause largely follows the text of the equivalent Main Contract clause, but with two additional clauses dealing with the Contractor's input. Note the reference to the Purchaser in Clause 4.4.

Clause 4.5 (and Clause 4.2) refers to Schedule 3, and is self-explanatory.

Clause 4.6 simply refers to 'assistance in ascertaining' laws that impact on the Works. Compliance is the responsibility of the Subcontractor.

CLAUSE 5 *Decisions*
This Clause is identical to the equivalent Main Contract clause and needs no comment.

CLAUSE 6 *Sufficiency of Subcontract rates and prices*
Clause 6.1 states that the Subcontractor takes pricing risk in respect of any 'lump-sum' prices included in Schedule 18 to the Subcontract. It then allows for the possibility that the Subcontractor might charge for all or part of his work on a 'rate payment' basis.

Apart from this the Clause follows the Main Contract clause.

CLAUSE 7 *Statutory and other obligations*
Clause 7 is identical to the equivalent Main Contract clause. No additional comment is necessary.

CLAUSE 8 *Patent and other protected rights*
Clause 8 is again virtually identical to the equivalent Main Contract clause. There are only two changes that need any comment.

Clauses 8.1–2 split responsibility for payment of licence fees into two.

Clause 8.7 permits the use of the Subcontractor's Documentation to improve or enlarge the Subcontract Plant, but subject to a 25% increase in the capacity *not of the Subcontract Plant, but the Main Contract Plant.*

CLAUSE 9 *Assignment and Subcontracting*
Clause 9 is very close to the Main Contract clause and needs no further comment.

CLAUSE 10 *Nominated Subcontractors*
Clause 10 is very close to the Main Contract clause and needs no further comment.

CLAUSE 11 *The Contract Manager*
Clause 11 is identical to the equivalent Main Contract clause, except that the Red Book Clause 11.3 is omitted. The reason for this is that, while under a Main Contract a Purchaser might possibly wish to use an independent consultant as project manager, it would be unlikely for the Contractor to do so.

CLAUSE 12 *Subcontract Manager and Subcontractor's staff*
Clause 12 is very close to the Main Contract clause and needs no further comment.

CLAUSE 13 *Times of completion and Approved Programme*
Clause 13 is very close to the Main Contract clause and needs no further comment.

CLAUSE 14 *Delays*
Clause 14 is very close to the Main Contract clause and needs only one comment. The period of fourteen days stated in Clause 14.1 *is the same* as that stated in the Main Contract clause. This is perhaps a mistake, and should have been twenty-one days.

CLAUSE 15 *Damages for delay*
Again this Clause is identical to the equivalent clause in the Main Contract conditions and needs no comment.

CLAUSE 16 *Variations*
This Clause is close to the Main Contract clause, but one comment is necessary.
In the Main Contract Clause 16.7 permits the Contractor to object to any proposed Variations that would have the effect of increasing or decreasing the Contract Price by more than 25%, or 5% after take-over. These limits are omitted from the Subcontract Conditions. The reason is that a small Main Contract change might need to become a very major change within the context of the Subcontract.

CLAUSE 17 *Subcontractor's Variations*
Clause 17 is very close to the Main Contract clause and needs no further comment.

CLAUSE 18 *Subcontractor's claims*
Clause 18 is identical to the equivalent clause in the Main Contract conditions and needs no comment here.

CLAUSE 19 *Valuation of Variations and claims*
Clause 19 is very close to the Main Contract clause and needs no further comment.

CLAUSE 20 *Confidentiality*
Clause 20 is very close to the Main Contract clause but with a few changes that need to be noted. Clause 20.4 extends the Subcontractor's obligations of confidentiality beyond his own Site to the whole of the Main Contract Site and the premises of the Purchaser. Then there are references to the Purchaser that should also be noted.

CLAUSE 21 *Documentation*
Clause 21 is very close to the Main Contract clause and needs no further comment.

CLAUSE 22 *Inspection and pre-installation tests*
This Clause follows exactly the wording of the equivalent Main Contract clause, with the single exception that reference is made to the rights of the Project

Manager to witness inspections and tests. This in fact recognises and passes on the Project Manager's rights in the Main Contract conditions.

CLAUSE 23 *The Site*
This Clause follows the wording of the equivalent clause in the Main Contract conditions, with one change.

Clause 23.1 states that the Contractor will only give the Subcontractor non-exclusive possession/access to Site. This is different to the conditions of the Main Contracts, which state that the Contractor will be given 'possession' of the whole Site. This is not possible in the case of a Subcontractor. The Contractor must, however, give the Subcontractor adequate access to all parts of the Site which he needs to carry out his work. Any failure to do so by the Contractor would be a breach of this Clause and would entitle the Subcontractor to a claim for extra time and cost.

CLAUSE 24 *Delivery to Site*
This Clause follows the wording of the equivalent clause in the Main Contract conditions. It needs no comment.

CLAUSE 25 *Ownership of Subcontract and Free-Issue Materials*
This Clause again follows the wording of the equivalent clause in the Main Contract conditions. The only change is that a Clause, 25.4, has been added reserving the ownership of Free-Issue Materials to the Contractor at all times, and that they are to be duly marked and stored separately.

CLAUSE 26 *Health, safety and environment*
This Clause follows the wording of the equivalent clause in the Main Contract conditions. It needs no further comment.

CLAUSE 27 *Site services*
In general terms this Clause deals with all the points covered in the equivalent clause in the Main Contract conditions. However Clauses 27.1–3 have been changed. In the Main Contract the Contractor is required to provide full facilities, although allowance is made for the possibility that the Purchaser might provide some facilities. The Subcontract automatically expects a split supply, with the Contractor supplying some facilities to the Subcontractor free of charge, and the Subcontractor supplying the rest.

CLAUSE 28 *Site working conditions*
Clause 28 follows very closely the wording of the equivalent clause in the Main Contract conditions. No further comment is necessary.

CLAUSE 29 *Meetings*
Again Clause 29 follows very closely the wording of the equivalent clause in the Main Contract conditions. No further comment is necessary.

CLAUSE 30 *Care of the Subcontract Works*
This Clause follows the wording of the equivalent clause in the Main Contract conditions, except for the deletion of a reference in Clause 30.1 to the control of access to the Site.

CLAUSE 31 *Insurance*
Clause 31.1 simply repeats the Main Contract clause, but with some additional provisions:

- that the Main Contract insurance may be provided by either the Contractor or the Purchaser, as appropriate;
- that the Subcontractor shall be a named insured party under the policy;
- with a reference to the fact that the Subcontractor will be liable for any losses that are his responsibility up to the deductible; and
- that the Subcontractor will comply with the requirements of the policy.

The rest of the Clause follows the Main Contract clause.

CLAUSE 32 *Completion of construction*
This Clause follows the wording of the equivalent clause in the Main Contract conditions, with the addition of a sentence at the end of Clause 32.2 covering the provision of inspection facilities to the Contract Manager and Project Manager.

CLAUSE 33 *Taking over*
This Clause follows the wording of the equivalent clause in the Main Contract conditions, except that it omits Main Contract Clause 33.13, covering work after take-over. It needs no other comment.

CLAUSE 34 *Site clearance*
The wording of this Clause is almost identical to that of the equivalent clause in the Main Contract conditions. It needs no further comment.

CLAUSE 35 *Performance tests*
The wording of Clause 35 has remained identical to that of the equivalent clause in the Main Contract conditions, except that the necessary changes have been made to allow for the inevitable involvement of the Purchaser in performance tests and for the changes in time periods necessary to allow for this. Therefore as with Clause 34 the overall balance of the Clause remains precisely the same.

CLAUSE 36 *Acceptance*
The wording of Clause 36 is identical to that of the equivalent clauses in the Main Contract conditions. No further comment is necessary.

CLAUSE 37 *Liability for Defects*
There are two minor changes to the wording of this Clause and, apart from these, the wording is identical to that of the equivalent clauses in the Main Contract conditions. Clause 37.13 has been slightly improved. Clause 37.14 has been added, covering the enforcement rights of the Purchaser.

CLAUSE 38 *Final Certificate*
The wording of Clause 38 is identical to that of the equivalent clause in the Main Contract conditions.

CLAUSE 39 *Payment*
Clause 39.1 is a Green/Burgundy clause rather than the Red Book clause. Apart from that no comment is necessary. The Clause simply allows for

monthly invoicing of the Contract Price on whatever basis is provided by the Subcontract.

CLAUSE 40 *Provisional and prime cost sums*
The wording of the Clauses is identical to that of the equivalent clause in the Main Contract conditions, except for a minor deletion at the end of Clause 40.3.

CLAUSE 41 *Suspension of the Subcontract Works*
The wording of Clause 41 is identical to that of the equivalent clause in the Main Contract conditions.

CLAUSE 42 *Termination by the Contractor for convenience*
The wording of Clause 42 is, again, identical to that of the equivalent clause in the Main Contract conditions.

CLAUSE 43 *Termination for Subcontractor's default*
The wording of Clause 43 is virtually identical to that of the equivalent clause in the Main Contract conditions, except that Clause 43.4(b) has been modified as a result of recent decisions in the UK courts. As a result, it is now inconsistent with the Red and Green Books although consistent with the Burgundy Book.

CLAUSE 44 *Limitation of liability*
The wording of this Clause is virtually identical to that of the equivalent clause in the Main Contract conditions. No further comment is necessary.

CLAUSE 45 *Disputes*
The wording of this Clause is virtually identical to that of the equivalent clause in the Main Contract conditions. No further comment is necessary.

CLAUSE 46 *Adjudication*
The wording of this Clause is virtually identical to that of the equivalent clause in the Main Contract conditions. No further comment is necessary.

CLAUSE 47 *Reference to an Expert*
The wording of this Clause is virtually identical to that of the equivalent clause in the Main Contract conditions. No further comment is necessary.

CLAUSE 48 *Arbitration*
The wording of this Clause is virtually identical to that of the equivalent clause in the Main Contract conditions. No further comment is necessary.

CLAUSE 49 *Related issues under the Main Contract*
This Clause is like Clause 3.10—a necessary part of a 'back-to-back' Subcontract. Clause 49.1 lays down the principle that the Subcontractor will support the Contractor, free of charge, in claims under the Main Contract that reflect his own Subcontract claims.

Clauses 49.2–3 then cover two aspects of Main Contract disputes—that the Subcontractor will agree to his claims being joined in any claims between the Contractor and Purchaser and will support the Contractor in those claims.

5.3 The Brown Book Form of Subcontract

5.3.1 Introduction

Like the Yellow Book, the Brown Book civil engineering subcontract is very largely based upon the Red Book conditions, modified to allow for whatever pricing/payment scheme the parties have agreed, and for the obligations of the Subcontractor, apart from defects repair, to end at the completion of construction. Its scope is therefore smaller than the Yellow Book, and it is several clauses (and Schedules) shorter.

5.3.2 General

Again all the broad principles enshrined in the Subcontract have already been discussed, in Chapter 2 on the Red Book conditions, and in the previous section and therefore this section should be read in conjunction with these. The aim of this section is simply to go through the conditions to discuss how they have been adapted from the wording of the Red and Yellow Books.

5.3.3 The Brown Book scenario

The scenario of the Conditions is very straightforward. It is that the Subcontractor will design, where necessary, supply materials and equipment to the Site, and then carry out building/civil engineering or construction work to prepare the Site for the erection of the Plant. The Subcontractor will therefore be the first on the Site, but his work will be largely complete by the time that equipment erection is able to take place.

The work may be priced and paid for on almost any basis, probably on a combination of a schedule of rates and fixed prices/fees. The Conditions provide for a substantial Site presence by the Subcontractor, with a Site Manager and construction/erection resources being provided over a significant period.

General Note

When considering Chapter 2, remember the comment that I made in the last section. The Conditions contain hundreds of minor changes in wording from the Main Contracts. Every time the word 'Contractor' appears in the Main Contract versions, the word 'Subcontractor' has to appear in the Subcontract. 'Works' changes to 'Subcontract Works'—and so on. It is pointless to comment upon such changes, and therefore I have not done so. Finally almost all the notice and response periods in the Conditions are changed from those in the Main Contract to allow for the communication chain between Purchaser, Contractor and Subcontractor. My comments on the individual clauses make no mention of changes of this kind. They are taken for granted.

5.3.4 The Subcontract Agreement

The Brown Book operates upon the same basis as the Main Contract conditions. It presumes that there will be a separate Subcontract Agreement signed between the two parties. Again this Agreement will set out the various points that need to be dealt with in addition to the Subcontract Conditions.

The Agreement is important. It refers to a Specification and a series of Schedules that include information transferred from the Main Contract into the Subcontract, and gives the parties a framework to use when doing so. Essentially the 'quality' of any back-to-back Subcontract will largely depend upon the skill with which the relevant requirements of the Main Contract are transposed into the Subcontract. The layout of the Schedules in the Agreement is intended to assist the parties in getting this right.

Of course, the other part of the Subcontract that the parties must get right is the Specification. This may be an extremely complex exercise and, in another book, would be worth a full section on its own. All I can say here is that the Subcontract Specification needs to link back to the Main Contract Specification, to describe exactly what it is that the Subcontractor is to provide, exactly what will be provided by others, and how the Subcontractor's work will interface with everything else.

The Agreement is similar to the Agreements in the Main Contract forms. It begins with a statement of the parties to the Agreement and a standard introductory preamble.

Clause 1 lists the constituent parts of the Agreement. These are:

- the Agreement itself, together with the General Conditions;
- Special Conditions—almost inevitable;
- the Subcontract Specification;
- a series of Schedules.

The General and Special Conditions together with Schedule 15 are the principal parts of the Subcontract that set out 'back-to-back' contractual requirements incorporated from the Main Contract. Schedule 15 will include a description of the Main Contract or at least those parts of the Main Contract that apply directly to the Subcontract. Particular technical requirements may be included in Schedule 15 or the Specification. Special Conditions from the Main Contract that are to apply may be included in Schedule 15 (and see Clause 3.10) or the Special Conditions.

The other Schedules mirror the Main Contract but omit the Schedules dealing with training, take-over procedures, performance tests and performance liquidated damages, and parts with limited operating life.

Clauses 2 to 5 underline the need for both parties to ensure that the Subcontract is correct. They combine to exclude anything not specifically written into the Subcontract from consideration, and set the level of the Subcontractor's overall liability/responsibility. Lateness responsibility/liability is dealt with in the Schedules.

Clauses 9 and 10 name the main project managers for the Subcontract. These are the Contract Manager for the Contractor, who will of course usually be the same person as the 'Contract Manager' for the purposes of the Main Contract and the Subcontract Manager for the Subcontractor. This is an example of the continuity of nomenclature between Main Contract and Subcontract Conditions— where at Main Contract level we have 'Contract', in Subcontracts we have 'Subcontract'.)

Clauses 7 and 8 establish necessary dates for the purpose of the Subcontract. Clause 12 sets the agreed profit level on claims, etc. This will relate back to the Main Contract.

Clause 14 is a simple procedural clause, but in practical terms there will probably be quite complex requirements for the numbering/identification of documentation arising out of the Subcontract. Project and safety procedures very often require that each individual document is easily identifiable.

The other terms of the Agreement require no particular comment.

5.3.5 The General Conditions

CLAUSE 1 *Definitions*
In principle the definitions of standard terms such as 'Cost' or 'Defect' remain the same as in the Main Contract conditions. Other definitions such as 'Works' or 'Equipment', have been changed to fit a Subcontract. Some additional definitions, such as 'Free-Issue Materials' and 'Purchaser/Project Manager', have been added to recognise the existence of the Main Contract. A definition of 'Permanent Works' has been added, and the definitions of 'Subcontract Materials' and 'Subcontract Works' have been modified. *However the principal change is that a number of definitions are now omitted.* The reason for this is, of course, that they are unnecessary. They are the definitions of the different categories of 'Software'; 'Acceptance'; 'Subcontract Plant'.

The actual definitions themselves are straightforward and need little comment. They have deliberately been written to retain the management relationships of the Main Contract conditions. So the definitions of 'Purchaser', 'Project Manager', 'Contractor', 'Contract Manager', 'Subcontractor', 'Subcontract Manager' and 'Subcontract Site Manager' are consistent between the Main Contract conditions and the Subcontract. The same hierarchy of terms is maintained in respect of Specifications and Works. A definition has been added of the 'Contract Manager's Representative' in place of a 'Project Manager's Representative', but again this is consistent with those management relationships.

Note the definition of 'Subcontract Price'. This is based upon the Green/ Burgundy Book conditions, and it is there to allow for the possibility that the Subcontract will probably be based upon a schedule of rates or on a reimbursable basis.

CLAUSE 2 *Interpretation*
No additional comments are necessary.

CLAUSE 3 *Subcontractor's responsibilities*
Clauses 3.1 and 3.2–4 set out the Subcontractor's responsibilities, including any design responsibilities, in fairly stringent terms. His responsibility is to complete the Subcontract Works and the Permanent Works:

- in accordance with the Subcontract Specification/Description of Works;
- with sound workmanship and materials;
- safely;
- in accordance with good engineering practice;
- to the reasonable satisfaction of the Contractor.

This is a reasonably high level of design/completion responsibility. Therefore the Subcontractor must satisfy himself before accepting the Subcontract that he can comply with the terms of the Specification. If he cannot do so then he must raise the matter so that it can be discussed and a solution found. No Contractor will thank a Subcontractor who fails to carry out his Subcontract. Note however my comments on Clause 3.10 below.

Clause 3.5 follows the theme of the Main Contract conditions in promoting collaboration where it can avoid problems or give benefits to the project. Note the reference in the Clause to the Purchaser as well as the Contractor.

Clause 3.8 requires the Subcontractor to keep in place a quality assurance system, and also to ensure that at least his own first-tier subcontractors do so as well.

Clause 3.9 is changed. It is a small Clause with large implications. It combines with Clause 6.3 but, in effect, requires the Subcontractor to make a detailed Site inspection before contract.

Clause 3.10 is very important, because it limits the extent of the Subcontractor's obligation. It says three things:

- if any Subcontractor working with reasonable care/skill could avoid causing the Contractor to incur liability to the Purchaser then the Subcontractor must do the same;
- the Permanent Works must meet the requirements of the Subcontract, or if they do not do so completely then well enough to avoid causing the Contractor to be in breach;
- the Subcontractor must comply with any Main Contract provisions set out in Schedule 15.

The overall result is that the Subcontractor has a significantly lower level of obligation than the Contractor. This is because the Contractor, along with equipment suppliers and any Yellow Book Subcontractor, will carry *fitness for purpose* responsibility for their equipment or the Plant, whereas the civil engineering Subcontractor merely carries an obligation to use 'reasonable care and skill'. Reasonable care and skill is, of course, the standard usually expected of contractors within the civil engineering and building industries. It should be adequate where the civil engineering subcontractor is simply employed to carry out standard civil engineering/building work in accordance with designs and information supplied by the Contractor. *If, however the Subcontractor is to be responsible for any design work, or the supply or installation of any equipment which is to form part of the Plant*, then it would be advisable for the Contractor to impose fitness-for-purpose liability on the Subcontractor by means of a Special Condition in the Agreement.

CLAUSE 4 *Contractor's responsibilities*
This Clause largely follows the text of the equivalent Main Contract clause (except for Clause 4.4, requiring the provision of adequate operating, etc personnel, which has been omitted), but with two additional clauses dealing with the Contractor's input.

Clause 4.4 (and Clause 4.2) refers to Schedule 3, and is self-explanatory.

Clause 4.5 simply refers to 'assistance in ascertaining' laws that impact on the Works. Compliance is the responsibility of the Subcontractor.

CLAUSE 5 *Decisions*
This Clause is identical to the equivalent Main Contract clause and needs no comment.

CLAUSE 6 *Sufficiency of Subcontract rates and prices*
Clause 6.1 states that the Subcontractor takes pricing risk in respect of any 'lump-sum' prices included in Schedule 13 to the Subcontract. It then allows for the possibility that the Subcontractor might charge for all or part of his work on a 'rate payment' basis.

Apart from this the Clause follows the Main Contract clause.

CLAUSE 7 *Statutory and other obligations*
Clause 7 is identical to the equivalent Main Contract clause. No additional comment is necessary.

CLAUSE 8 *Patent and other protected rights*
Clause 8 is again virtually identical to the equivalent Main Contract clause—so far as it goes. There are some changes that need comment.

Clause 8.2 which deals with the payment of operating/production royalties, has been omitted, as have Clauses 8.8–9, dealing with rights, etc in Software.

Finally the provisions in Clause 8.7, now Clause 8.6, permitting the use of the Subcontractor's Documentation to improve or enlarge the Plant, have also been omitted.

CLAUSE 9 *Assignment and Subcontracting*
Clause 9 is very close to the Main Contract clause, except that it does not include a fitness-for-purpose obligation in Clause 9.4 (see my comment on Clause 3.10 above) and needs only one other comment. Clause 9.4 now contains a requirement to obtain guarantees from Sub-subcontractors only in respect of those Subcontract Materials specifically identified in Schedule 7.

CLAUSE 10 *Nominated Subcontractors*
Clause 10 is very close to the Main Contract clause and needs no further comment.

CLAUSE 11 *The Contract Manager*
Clause 11 is identical to the equivalent Main Contract clause, except that the Red Book Clause 11.3 is omitted. The reason for this is that, while under a Main Contract a Purchaser might possibly wish to use an independent consultant as project manager, it would be unlikely for the Contractor to do so.

CLAUSE 12 *Subcontract Manager and Subcontractor's staff*
Clause 12 is very close to the Main Contract clause and needs no further comment. Note the reference in Clause 12.3 merely to 'the use of the Permanent Works'.

CLAUSE 13 *Times of completion and Approved Programme*
Clause 13 is very close to the Main Contract clause and, in one sense, needs no further comment. Note, however, the completion date is the date when construction of the Permanent Works is complete.

CLAUSE 14 *Delays*
Clause 14 is very close to the Main Contract clause and needs only one comment. The period of fourteen days stated in Clause 14.1 *is the same* as that stated in the Main Contract clause. This is perhaps a mistake, and should have been twenty-one days.

CLAUSE 15 *Damages for delay*
Again this Clause is identical to the equivalent clause in the Main Contract conditions and needs no comment.

CLAUSE 16 *Variations*
This Clause is close to the Main Contract clause, but one comment is necessary.
    In the Main Contract Clause 16.7 permits the Contractor to object to any proposed Variations that would have the effect of increasing or decreasing the Contract Price by more than 25%, or 5% after take-over. These limits are omitted from the Subcontract Conditions. The reason is that a small Main Contract change might need to become a very major change within the context of the Subcontract.

CLAUSE 17 *Subcontractor's Variations*
Clause 17 is very close to the Main Contract clause and needs no further comment.

CLAUSE 18 *Subcontractor's claims*
Clause 18 is identical to the equivalent clause in the Main Contract conditions and needs no comment here.

CLAUSE 19 *Valuation of Variations and claims*
Clause 19 is very close to the Main Contract clause and needs no further comment.

CLAUSE 20 *Confidentiality*
Clause 20 is very close to the Main Contract clause but with a few changes that need to be noted. Clause 20.4 extends the Subcontractor's obligations of confidentiality beyond his own Site to the whole of the Main Contract Site and the premises of the Purchaser. Then there are references to the Purchaser that should also be noted.

CLAUSE 21 *Documentation*
Clause 21 is very close to the Main Contract clause and needs no further comment.

CLAUSE 22 *Inspection and pre-installation tests*
This Clause follows exactly the wording of the equivalent Main Contract clause, with the single exception that reference is made to the rights of the Project Manager to witness inspections and tests. This in fact recognises and passes on the Project Manager's rights in the Main Contract conditions.

CLAUSE 23 *The Site*
This Clause follows the wording of the equivalent clause in the Main Contract conditions, with one change.

Clause 23.1 states that the Contractor will only give the Subcontractor non-exclusive possession/access to Site. This is different to the conditions of the Main Contracts, which state that the Contractor will be given 'possession' of the whole Site. This is not possible in the case of a Subcontractor. The Contractor must, however, give the Subcontractor adequate access to all parts of the Site which he needs to carry out his work. Any failure to do so by the Contractor would be a breach of this Clause and would entitle the Subcontractor to a claim for extra time and cost.

CLAUSE 24 *Delivery to Site*
This Clause follows the wording of the equivalent clause in the Main Contract conditions. It needs no comment.

CLAUSE 25 *Ownership of Subcontract and Free-Issue Materials*
This Clause again follows the wording of the equivalent clause in the Main Contract conditions. The only change is that a Clause, 25.4, has been added reserving the ownership of Free-Issue Materials to the Contractor at all times, and that they are to be duly marked and stored separately.

CLAUSE 26 *Health, safety and environment*
This Clause follows the wording of the equivalent clause in the Main Contract conditions. It needs no further comment.

CLAUSE 27 *Site services*
In general terms this Clause deals with all the points covered in the equivalent clause in the Main Contract conditions. However Clauses 27.1–3 have been changed. In the Main Contract the Contractor is required to provide full facilities, although allowance is made for the possibility that the Purchaser might provide some facilities. The Subcontract automatically expects a split supply, with the Contractor supplying some facilities to the Subcontractor free of charge, and the Subcontractor supplying the rest.

CLAUSE 28 *Site working conditions*
Clause 28 follows very closely the wording of the equivalent clause in the Main Contract conditions. No further comment is necessary.

CLAUSE 29 *Meetings*
Again Clause 29 follows very closely the wording of the equivalent clause in the Main Contract conditions. No further comment is necessary.

CLAUSE 30 *Care of the Subcontract Works*
This Clause follows the wording of the equivalent clause in the Main Contract conditions, except for the deletion of a reference in Clause 30.1 to the control of access to the Site.

CLAUSE 31 *Insurance*
Clause 31.1 simply repeats the Main Contract clause, but with some additional provisions:

- that the Main Contract insurance may be provided by either the Contractor or the Purchaser, as appropriate;
- that the Subcontractor shall be a named insured party under the policy;
- with a reference to the fact that the Subcontractor will be liable for any losses that are his responsibility up to the deductible; and
- that the Subcontractor will comply with the requirements of the policy.

The rest of the Clause follows the Main Contract clause.

CLAUSE 32 *Completion of construction*
This Clause amalgamates Clauses 32 and 33 of the Main Contract and Yellow Book conditions. Clauses 32.1–4 follow Clauses 32.1–4 and provide the normal procedure for construction completion. However Clause 32.5 and 32.7 then follow Clause 33.7 and requires the issue of a Take-Over Certificate. Finally Clause 32.6 follows Clause 33.8.

The result is a simplified Clause giving the Subcontractor a Take-Over Certificate after completion of construction and tests on construction. The advantage of using the 'Take-Over Certificate' terminology is of course that it dovetails neatly into the wording of the later conditions.

CLAUSE 33 *Site clearance*
The wording of this Clause is almost identical to that of Clause 34 in the Main Contract conditions. It needs no comment.

Note that Clauses 35 (Performance tests) and 36 (Acceptance) in the Main Contract conditions are both omitted.

CLAUSE 34 *Liability for Defects*
This Clause generally follows Clause 37 in the Main Contract conditions, but with some changes. The reference to 'operation and maintenance' in Clause 34.4 has been omitted.

Then Main Contract clause 37.12 limiting the Contractor's liability for repairing Defects to any sum referred to in the Agreement has been deleted, and so has Clause 37.13.

CLAUSE 35 *Final Certificate*
The wording of Clause 35 is identical to that of Clause 38 in the Main Contract conditions, except that Clauses 38.3–4 have been omitted.

The net result of these changes to Clauses 34 and 35 is to leave the Subcontractor in the same position in relation to defects in his work as he would be under a typical civil engineering contract.

CLAUSE 36 *Payment*
Clause 36.1 is a Green/Burgundy clause rather than the Red Book clause. Apart from that no comment is necessary. The Clause simply follows Clause 39 in the Main Contract conditions and allows for monthly invoicing of the Contract Price on whatever basis is provided by the Subcontract.

CLAUSE 37 *Provisional and prime cost sums*
The wording of the Clauses is identical to that of Clause 40 in the Main Contract conditions, except for a minor deletion at the end of Clause 37.3.

CLAUSE 38 *Suspension of the Subcontract Works*
The wording of Clause 38 is identical to that of Clause 41 in the Main Contract conditions.

CLAUSE 39 *Termination by the Contractor for convenience*
The wording of Clause 39 is, again, identical to that of the equivalent clause in the Main Contract conditions.

CLAUSE 40 *Termination for Subcontractor's default*
The wording of Clause 40 is virtually identical to that of the equivalent clause in the Main Contract conditions, except that Clause 43.4(b) has had to be modified as a result of recent decisions in the UK courts. As a result, it is now inconsistent with the Red and Green Books although consistent with the Burgundy Book.

CLAUSE 41 *Limitation of liability*
The wording of this Clause is virtually identical to that of the equivalent clause in the Main Contract conditions. In Clause 41.1 the reference to 'performance tests' has been omitted. No further comment is necessary.

CLAUSE 42 *Disputes*
The wording of this Clause is virtually identical to that of the equivalent clause in the Main Contract conditions. No further comment is necessary.

CLAUSE 43 *Adjudication*
The wording of this Clause is virtually identical to that of the equivalent clause in the Main Contract conditions. No further comment is necessary.

CLAUSE 44 *Reference to an Expert*
The wording of this Clause is virtually identical to that of the equivalent clause in the Main Contract conditions. No further comment is necessary.

CLAUSE 45 *Arbitration*
The wording of this Clause is virtually identical to that of the equivalent clause in the Main Contract conditions. No further comment is necessary.

CLAUSE 46 *Related issues under the Main Contract*
This Clause is like Clause 3.10—a necessary part of a 'back-to-back' Subcontract. Clause 49.1 lays down the principle that the Subcontractor will support the Contractor, free of charge, in claims under the Main Contract that reflect his own Subcontract claims.

Clauses 46.2–3 then cover two aspects of Main Contract disputes—that the Subcontractor will agree to his claims being joined in any claims between the Contractor and Purchaser and will support the Contractor in those claims.

The Orange Book

6

6.1 Contracts for Minor Works

6.1.1 Introduction

The Orange Book is a really useful set of conditions.

Every process plant, like every manufacturing unit of any kind, needs a whole range of different types of work to be carried out on a more or less regular basis. Quite apart from the need for planned, and unplanned, day-to-day maintenance and repair and the steady flow of minor housekeeping work, there will be a regular requirement for larger packages of work.

Equipment will need replacing as it reaches the end of its working life. The plant will need to be modified or updated. It may be adapted to accept different raw materials or to produce different products. It may be modified to incorporate different processes. It may be changed to use new control or safety procedures. Sections may be added or enlarged.

The work needed may involve:

- the supply and installation of equipment and materials;
- the supply and installation of instrumentation and control systems and software;
- the modification of equipment already installed within the plant;
- the removal or re-installation of equipment;
- civil, or electrical and mechanical construction work;
- erection, adjustment, modification, testing and commissioning of equipment; and
- the provision of services, such as training or the supply of manuals, drawings or computer software.

All these small projects have a number of features in common, despite the wide range of work involved:

- They all require design input and responsibility from the Contractor. Even when carrying out comparatively straightforward tasks, such as the installation of pipework, he would be expected to take design responsibility for various aspects of the work.

- They all require a significant amount of work on or within the plant.
- The Contractor's work within the plant will involve actual or potential interruption to the operation of the plant. As a result the Purchaser will always wish to monitor the Contractor's work and to exert some degree of day-to-day control. Also he will want to minimise the impact of the Contractor's work upon his normal operations.
- The Contractor's work will always have operating implications. The Purchaser will therefore need to carry out tests and inspections to check that the work is being carried out properly.
- Operating tests will be necessary to check that equipment or materials supplied or installed by the Contractor function properly and do not impair the overall performance of the plant.
- The Contractor will need to comply with a range of site procedures and rules—health, safety, environmental protection, security, etc.
- The Purchaser will always be concerned to monitor the Contractor's standards of site discipline and housekeeping.
- The standards of design, quality of equipment and work that applied to the initial construction of the plant will still apply.
- The value of the Contract will be comparatively low. Nevertheless, especially if carried out badly or late, it may have a considerable impact upon the plant. The Purchaser must manage the Contract firmly.
- Often the Purchaser will not, and sometimes cannot, specify the work in full at the time of contract. The requirements will change as the Contract proceeds, either because the Purchaser's needs alter for internal or market reasons, or because the works themselves throw up the need for new or modified requirements. As a result the management of variations and changes will always be a major factor.

6.1.2 The Orange Book scenario

The consequences of all this are reflected in the Contract scenario. The Contractor will carry out a defined Works package within a plant/ Facility owned by the Purchaser. The Facility will generally be an operating plant (though it could be almost anything). The Works will be of a value anything from a few thousand pounds up to two hundred and fifty, or five hundred, thousand pounds or maybe even higher. The Works may be of almost any kind and might involve several engineering disciplines. They will usually require the Contractor to make changes or modifications to the plant/Facility. The Works may be paid for on the basis of a fee/price or on the basis of a schedule of rates or charges, or any combination of the two. The time-scale may be anything from a few weeks to several months. Once the work is completed it will be inspected (and probably tested) and then taken over by the Purchaser. It will then be given a year's guarantee by the Contractor.

For ease of reference, the Clauses can be dealt with in the following groups (see Figure 4 on page 265):

- the Agreement;
- procedural and general clauses (Clauses 1, 4.2, 5.1, 19–20, 23, and 25–29);

	PREPARATION	SITE WORK/COMMISSIONING	DEFECTS REPAIR
Procedural & General Clauses	START 1 4.2 5.1	19 20 23 25 26 27 28 29 TAKING OVER	FINAL CERT.
Contract Management	2		
Work	3 4.1 4.3–7 5.2–3 6 7.1	21 22	
Delay & Lateness	7.2–3 8 9	7.2–3 8 9	
Taking Over		11	
Guarantee Period			12 13
Insurance	14 15	16 24	
Variations	10	10	
Payments	17 18	17 18	

Figure 4 The Orange Book

- Contract management and work (Clauses 2–3, 4.1, 4.3–7, 5.2–3, 6, 7.1 and 21–22);
- delay and lateness liability (Clauses 7.2–3, 8 and 9);
- taking over (Clause 11);
- guarantee period and acceptance (Clauses 12 and 13);
- insurance and general liability (Clauses 14–16 and 24);
- Variations (Clause 10);
- payments (Clauses 17–18).

In general terms the wording of the Conditions is fairly straightforward and easy to understand. Therefore not too many comments are necessary.

6.1.3 The Agreement

As with all other IChemE conditions, the intention is that the Contract should be set up using the form of Agreement given with the conditions. Of course in a minor works contract there is much more possibility that the Purchaser might want to use a different format, such as a standard purchase order. Therefore the form of Agreement might well not be used in all cases. However it is still important that, whatever form the Contract takes, whether an Agreement or purchase order, or something else entirely, the Contract still needs to cover the points that are dealt with in the form of Agreement.

The preamble and introduction to the Agreement are in standard form and need no comment.

The Agreement states that the Contract will comprise the Agreement itself, plus the General Conditions, as modified by any Special Conditions attached to the Agreement, then a series of Schedules together possibly with attachments (appendices). The Clause does not mention one important document—the Specification. This is an oversight, perhaps, but see below.

There are only six Schedules.

They begin with the description of the Works. Schedule 1 contains the technical definition of the Works, ie. a description. If a Specification is also needed to describe what the Contractor is required to carry out in more detail, then it should be included in Schedule 1 or as an Appendix to Schedule 1.

Then Schedule 2 lists the assistance, free issue items, etc., that will be provided by the Purchaser to assist the Contractor.

Schedule 4 describes the taking over procedures which will be inspection procedures of various categories, such as electrical, mechanical, safety, control/instrumentation, etc., as appropriate, plus probably a taking over test, where the Works affect the operability of any part of the Plant.

Schedule 5 then sets out any fixed or firm prices applicable to the Works, plus a schedule of rates and charges where required. Note that Clause 18 of the General Conditions requires payment on a monthly basis. If it is intended that payment will be made on any other basis, then a Special Condition needs to be included in the Agreement. (No statement in Schedule 5 would be adequate to change the General Conditions. They can only be overruled by a Special Condition—see Clause 2.)

Finally Schedule 6 sets out all health and safety codes and procedures, etc., which the Contractor must follow, together with all rules and codes of practice in operation within the Plant.

Clause 3 and Schedule 3 lay down the time-scale for the Works.

Clauses 4 and 5 name the contract managers for both parties—which implies that they need to be in place, and therefore aware of the requirements of the Contract, in advance.

Clauses 6, 8 and 9 are procedural and need no comment.

Clause 7 sets the Contractor's liability under Clause 16.1.

6.1.4 The General Conditions

Procedural and general clauses
CLAUSE 1

Most of the definitions are self-explanatory and need no comment.

Note that the definition of 'Completion' allows for different completion dates for different 'sections' of the Works. This must be done, if the parties wish it, by including definitions of the different sections and the appropriate dates in Schedules 1 and 3.

The definition of 'Contractor's Equipment' is the standard broad definition used in all IChemE's Forms of Contract.

The Contract will be managed for the parties by 'Representatives', rather than managers, though this change in terminology is only because the use of the title 'manager' is not usual in smaller contracts

The conditions use the definition 'Defects Correction Period' rather than defects liability period, as used in the other Forms, but there is no significance in this change.

Note the definition of 'Documentation'. It includes both drawings and other documents. It also includes documents stored in electronic form as well as documents on paper. The definition also states that the Documentation to be supplied by the Contractor should be stated in the Specification (see section 6.1.3 above).

Note the important definitions of the 'Facility', 'Free-Issue Materials' and the 'Site'.

Note also the definitions of 'Works' and 'Permanent Works'.

Finally note the definition of the Variation Order. The Variation Order is used not just as a part of the variation procedure but to deal with other necessary contract change as well.

Clause 1.2 is straightforward and needs little comment.

Clause 1.3 provides a starting point. If the parties wish the Contract to be subject to another system of law then they should modify the Clause by a Special Condition. Changing the conditions to comply with non-UK legal requirements should not present a competent contract draftsman with too many problems, and the essential meaning of the conditions would remain largely unchanged.

Clause 1.4 is self-explanatory and needs no comment.

Note Clause 1.5. Anything of contractual significance must be in writing. The Clause then defines writing, and note the reference to 'secure' e-mail. Secure e-mail software enables all text changes to be identified.

CLAUSE 4.2
This needs no comment.

CLAUSE 5.1
The aim of this Clause is to prevent the Contractor (and of course also the Purchaser) from passing the Contract on to another to carry out in his place, although the Contractor is allowed to employ a debt factor if he wishes.

CLAUSE 19
Little comment is necessary on Clause 19.1. It requires the Contractor to respect *all* confidential information received from the Purchaser during the Contract, *both* technical *and* commercial.

The other Forms contain clauses that provide for *mutual* confidentiality, but in this case it is felt that the Contractor must be given access to a lot of information concerning the Facility, some of which must be confidential, whereas the Purchaser may not be given or need to have access to any confidential information of the Contractor.

The Contractor is allowed to use the Purchaser's confidential information only during the period of the Contract and for the purposes of carrying out his work. Any disclosure to others—for example, a Subcontractor—must also be in confidence.

Clause 19.2 is self-explanatory and needs no comment.

Clause 19.4 bans the use of cameras by the Contractor without prior consent. This looks old-fashioned, especially since when properly used a camera is an invaluable means of recording a situation. There are two reasons for the Clause. The first is that photographs of the Purchaser's Site should not to be used for publicity without his consent. The second is that a photograph should not be taken of any secret process or equipment belonging to the Purchaser.

Finally Clause 19.3 requires the Contractor to give the Purchaser an indemnity against all intellectual property infringements except where the direct responsibility of the Purchaser. This is normal anyway, and in this type of contract the risk should be small.

CLAUSE 20
The Clause is simply a standard 'vesting' clause. Its purpose is to minimise the effect of the financial collapse of the Contractor. It is largely self-explanatory.

CLAUSE 23
Clauses 23.1–2 give the Purchaser the right to suspend the Contractor's work on twenty-four hours' notice; and even the twenty-four hours notice period can be waived in the circumstances covered in the last sentence of Clause 23.1. Essentially the Purchaser has to retain the right to stop the Contractor working, for reasons of Facility management if nothing else. If the suspension is because of the Contractor's fault then the Contractor must carry the risk of the costs of suspension. If however the suspension is not because of the Contractor's fault

then the Purchaser will compensate the Contractor for all reasonable additional cost incurred.

Clauses 23.3–4 then deal with the right of the Purchaser to terminate the work at any time for the Purchaser's own convenience. In this case the Contractor will cease performance of all or part of the Works, as instructed by the Purchaser. The Contractor will be entitled to full payment for carrying out the Works until the date of termination, at the rate or prices stated in the Contract, plus the costs of closing down the Works. (The Contractor will not however be entitled to any payment in respect of profit on the part of the Works that has been cancelled.)

Clauses 23.5–7 give the Purchaser the normal right to terminate the Contract in the event that the Contractor is in serious financial trouble or is failing to carry out the Works properly. In the event that the Contractor is in default or negligent in the performance of the Works, the Purchaser must give the Contractor notice in writing of the fault, so that the Contractor has the opportunity to correct his failure. If he fails to do so then the Purchaser can terminate. (No such notice of course is necessary in the event of the Contractor having serious financial problems.) In either case the Purchaser can claim back from the Contractor any extra costs incurred by him in completing the Works instead of the Contractor or offset them against any payments due to the Contractor.

CLAUSE 25
This Clause needs no comment.

CLAUSE 26
This Clause needs no comment.

CLAUSES 27–30
To begin with, please see the note on the Housing Grants etc. Act 1996 in section 1.4.2.

The problem with disputes in minor works contracts is always going to be that the amount of money at stake in the dispute will be comparatively small, in global terms, and small disputes can never justify the payment of large costs, whether for arbitration, adjudication or anything else.

The dispute settlement process begins with Clause 27. The aim of Clause 27.1–2 is to make sure that if there has to be a dispute, then at least the parties will have endeavoured to settle the dispute by discussion. Then, if that fails, the Clause lays down, in Clauses 27.3–4, a procedure to make sure that the basis of the dispute has been clearly defined between them.

(This is not as silly as it sounds. It is astonishing how often parties involve themselves in an expensive dispute without trying to ensure at the beginning that both sides are aware of the issues that are actually in dispute.)

Every dispute will sooner or later lead to a decision by the Purchaser's Representative that is considered unreasonable or wrong by the Contractor. The procedure therefore is for the Contractor to require formal reconsideration of this decision by the Purchaser's Representative. This will then result in a formal decision by the Purchaser's Representative that will clarify the issues because it will set out the reasoning behind that decision.

Clauses 27.5–8 need no comment, except to mention the possibility of conciliation/mediation.

Then Clauses 28 and 29 give the parties two choices. Clause 29 gives both parties the right to require any dispute to be settled through arbitration (and of course the parties could go to a judge if they both agreed to do so). Arbitration might be preferable since the nature of the dispute would probably be more technical than contractual, and a decision by an arbitrator with technical knowledge of the industry might well be quicker and of higher reliability. However it is unlikely to be very much less expensive.

Clause 28 gives the parties another alternative, that of adjudication. Clause 28.1 gives both parties the right to demand adjudication of any dispute, even if the Contract is not a construction contract within the meaning of the Housing Grants etc Act. IChemE seriously considers that disputes in minor works contracts are suited for quick, though not necessarily legally perfect, resolution.

Contract management and work
CLAUSE 2
This Clause states several basic principles in a straightforward and simple way. It needs little comment.

Clause 2.1 gives the Purchaser's Representative his authority to act to manage the Contract. He cannot, however, release the Contractor from any obligation under the Contract on his own authority.

Clause 2.2 requires all notices, decisions, approvals, instructions, etc., given by the Purchaser's Representative to be in writing. Oral approvals, etc., will only be valid if confirmed in writing by the Purchaser's Representative within five working days.

Then Clauses 2.2 and 2.3 require the Representative to be reasonable and 'impartial' in the way he manages the Contract. Of course no Representative who is employed by the Purchaser can ever be totally impartial. What is required is that in making decisions which affect the commercial interest of the Contractor the Representative must give reasonable consideration to the interests of the Contractor as well as those of the Purchaser.

CLAUSE 3
Clause 3 defines the assistance that the Purchaser is to give to the Contractor in carrying out the Works.

Clause 3.1 allows the Contractor non-exclusive access to the Site, and the Site means those parts of the Facility where he is allowed access. The Site should always be defined clearly, probably in Schedule 1. The Contractor has no control over the Site, merely continuous safe and free access to the area; his access will however be subject to any 'operational restrictions' which the Purchaser imposes. Obviously these restrictions should be stated in the Contract and should be set out in Schedule 1 or in a Special Condition.

Free-issue materials, facilities, etc., will be defined in Schedule 2 to the Contract.

Clause 3.2 state that any materials must be of a sound design and workmanship, etc. It then deals with the time at which they will be provided. The wording is standard and needs no particular comment. Then Clause 3.3 also requires the Purchaser to provide Documentation as listed in the Specification, together with all further information required by the Contractor, in a form and at times which will not prejudice the Contractor in carrying out the Works.

CLAUSE 4

Clause 4.1 and 4.3–6 lay down basic rules for the Contractor.

Clauses 4.1 and 4.3 are self-explanatory and need no comment.

Clause 4.4 lays down two principles. Firstly, the Works must be executed to a reasonable standard and in accordance with good practice, etc. This is obvious and should not cause problems. Secondly, the Works must be to the reasonable satisfaction of the Purchaser's Representative. Where the Specification defines precisely what the Works are to be then, if the Contractor supplies Works in accordance with that description, the Purchaser's Representative has no choice but to accept them as being satisfactory. Where the Specification is less precise then what is done must meet with the Purchaser's Representative's satisfaction.

Clause 4.5 requires the Contractor to comply with all national and local laws and regulations. Any breach of law will require the Contractor to accept responsibility, and indemnify the Purchaser.

Clause 4.6 is self-explanatory. If any instruction is given in accordance with the Contract that is within the authority of the Purchaser's Representative and given in the proper manner then the Contractor should comply.

Clause 4.7 is again self-explanatory. It gives the Contractor's Representative his authority. Note the words 'appropriately qualified and experienced' and the requirements regarding replacement.

CLAUSES 5.2–4

Clause 5 deals with the question of subcontracting. The view of the Conditions is that the Contract is primarily concerned with work to be carried out inside the Purchaser's Facility, while that Facility is operational. Therefore it is important to the Purchaser to be able to identify and to control at all times the organisations working within his Facility. As a result the Conditions, in Clause 5.2, give the Purchaser's Representative the right to refuse his consent, remembering the terms of Clauses 2.2–3, to any subcontractor proposed by the Contractor. Therefore the proper way for the Contractor to deal with the matter, if he does wish to subcontract any part of the Works, is to ensure that his potential subcontractors are named in the Contract. The Contractor will of course take full responsibility for any subcontractor's work.

Clause 5.3 makes provision for early termination of any subcontracts in case of termination of the Contract by the Purchaser.

Clause 5.4 is procedural and needs no comment.

CLAUSE 6

Clause 6 deals with the time-scales for the Works.

The Agreement allows a date to be specified for the commencement of the Works (Clause 3), and Schedule 3 will set out required milestone dates and any sectional completion dates.

Clause 6.1 provides simply for the start of the Works. They are to start on the commencement date stated in the Contract or within four weeks from receipt of an instruction to proceed by the Purchaser's Representative. If the Agreement does not state a commencement date it will usually provide for an approximate commencement date. Clause 6.2 then simply states that the Works are to be completed by the completion date(s) stated, subject to any allowable extensions of time.

Clause 6.3 then deals with the question of agreeing an Approved Programme for the Works. The procedure is self-explanatory, but note that, as with all IChemE Forms of Contract, the programme submitted by the Contractor must be in the format, and show the detail required by the Purchaser's Representative. Even though a Works Contract may be comparatively small, it will still involve the Contractor in carrying out work within the Purchaser's Facility. It is therefore necessary that the Purchaser should have the right to insist upon a detailed programme, so that he can prepare for the Contractor's presence on the Site.

Clause 6.4 is self-explanatory and needs no comment.

CLAUSE 7.1
Clause 7.1 simply follows on from the provisions of Clause 6. It needs no special comment.

CLAUSE 21
Clause 21 is a very important clause that needs little comment.

Clause 21.1 provides that the Contractor must comply with national and local laws relating to the protection of health, the environment and safety at the Site. The Clause then states that the Works are to be carried out in accordance with the requirements of the CDM Regulations (1994). A Special Condition will be required to identify the 'Principal Contractor', 'Planning Supervisor', etc.

Clauses 21.2–4 deal with procedural matters concerning health and safety at the Site, including the application of the Purchaser's own site rules and the authority of the Purchaser's health/safety department.

Finally Clause 21.5 deals with liability for any pollution caused by the Works. The Contractor should ensure that he has appropriate insurance cover.

CLAUSE 22
Clause 22 is another very important clause that needs little comment. It is concerned with a number of issues relating to the presence of the Contractor's personnel on the Site.

Clauses 22.1–2 deal with the question of maintaining good industrial relations on the Site. The Contractor is required to maintain reasonable rates of wages to his employees, so that internal industrial dispute should be minimised, and will also seek to minimise any friction between his employees and those of the Purchaser and other companies on the Site.

Clause 22.1 also deals with hours of work of the Contractor. No comment is necessary.

Clauses 22.3–4 require the Contractor to carry out the Works in a way that will minimise any unnecessary impact of those Works upon the Purchaser's normal operations at the Facility.

Finally Clause 22.5 deals in standard fashion with problem of misbehaviour by the employees of the Contractor.

Delay and lateness liability
The Conditions are fairly tough on delay.

They take the position that late completion by the Contractor is a very serious matter. After all, delay might disrupt the operations of a large process plant and cause enormous loss to the Purchaser. Therefore they contain a clause which requires the Contractor to take whatever measures are required to eliminate or minimise delay if the progress of the Works is significantly delayed by the Contractor. Then they impose liquidated damages for any lateness that is the responsibility of the Contractor, without any limit as to time. He will be liable for liquidated damages for the whole period from the date when the Works should have been completed until the time when he does actually complete the Works, however long that might be. (Naturally proper programming and time/resource management should keep any delays to a minimum.) Finally the Conditions allow reasonable extensions of completion dates for any force majeure, Variations, or any problems caused by the Purchaser or any conditions on site which are not the fault of the Contractor.

CLAUSES 7.2–3
Clause 7.2 imposes liquidated damages on the Contractor for any delay in achieving completion that is the responsibility of the Contractor. The actual rate or rates of liquidated damages are to be stated in Schedule 3, and the Clause states that damages may be payable for each and every week or day of the delay.

Clause 7.3 then requires the Contractor to be prepared to take, at his own cost, whatever measures are necessary and 'acceptable to the Purchaser's Representative' to eliminate or minimise any delay in the event that progress is delayed or not maintained for reasons which are the Contractor's fault. Of course in practice the Contractor would only normally take such action when notified or instructed to do so by the Purchaser's Representative (and then probably somewhat reluctantly).

CLAUSE 8
The term 'force majeure' is regularly used commercially as meaning events generally beyond a party's control, but in law it has no clear meaning. Here it is used correctly, as a defined term, meaning events which are beyond a party's control and which affect that party's ability to perform the Contract to time. Clause 8.1 lists a number of circumstances that are within the definition and some other circumstances which are not.

There will always be some difficulty in defining, in the abstract, all the possible circumstances that could be considered to come within the definition of force majeure that is used in Clause 8.1. In purely contractual terms the problem is one of exactly how the Clause should be interpreted. Would it, for instance, include terrorist activity—near the Site or near a route to the Site—which was making people reluctant to stay on the Site?

The answer is, of course, that nobody does know what the abstract answer is, but that the abstract answer is unimportant. Like all 'force majeure' clauses, Clause 8.1 is not intended to define the parties' rights with legal precision. All it is concerned to do is to lay down the basic principle, which is that if some fairly serious event or chain of events causes delay to either party that party should have a defence against claims by the other party arising out of the delay. It is up to the parties to the Contract to reach a common-sense and fair decision between them about any actual circumstances that may arise.

Clauses 8.2 and 8.3 are straightforward and need no comment.

CLAUSE 9

Clause 9 deals with the procedure for extending the contract dates for completion.

Clauses 9.1–3 lay down a simple and straightforward procedure. The Contractor will notify the Purchaser within seven days of any delay within terms of Clause 9.4. Then as soon as possible the Contractor must decide the likely extent of that delay and notify the Purchaser. Then the Purchaser's Representative will decide a reasonable extension of completion and issue a Variation Order providing for that extension. Where the cause of the delay also entitles the Contractor to claim extra cost, then that Variation Order should deal with that as well.

Clause 9.4 then lists the matters that allow the Contractor to claim an extension to the date for completion. Apart from force majeure they would all usually allow the Contractor to claim an increase in the Contract Price. However, one comment is necessary here. The matters referred to in paragraphs 9.4(c–f) are all covered specifically by Clauses in the conditions—3, 10 and 23 respectively. Clause 9.4(b) is not, and might need to be dealt with in a Special Condition (although virtually all 'above-ground' risks would be the responsibility of the Purchaser). The reason why it has not been dealt with specifically within the General Conditions is that Works contracts may cover a wide range of different activities and in some contracts the Contractor might accept this risk, whereas in others he would not. Also the Works contract is unusual in that the Contractor, especially when carrying out electrical or mechanical work, will usually have been given the opportunity to carry out a detailed inspection of the equipment or structures on which he will be working. Therefore he might well tender on the basis of an 'inclusive' price for above-ground risk. Below-ground risk would be a very different matter.

Taking over

When the Contractor considers that any section of the Works, or all of the Works, are complete, he may notify the Purchaser's Representative and the inspection procedures or tests specified in Schedule 4 will be carried out. Once those procedures have been successfully passed, the Purchaser's Representative will issue a Take-Over Certificate for the Works and the Defects Correction Period will begin. Take-Over Certificates may include a snagging list, and will not necessarily be conclusive as to whether the Works have been completed. (Should a problem later show itself the Contractor would still be expected to take corrective action. This is because many Works contracts will be for work that cannot be inspected or tested adequately at the time of taking over.)

CLAUSE 11

Clauses 11.1–3 need little comment. They are straightforward procedural clauses that define the process of inspection/testing and the issue of the Take-Over Certificate.

Clause 11.4 is again procedural and needs no comment. Its purpose is obvious. Clauses 11.5 and 11.6 also need no comment.

Clause 11.7 is unusual in that it runs contrary to the equivalent clauses in other IChemE Forms of Contract. The reason for this is that very often the Works contract will be for items of work which can only be partly inspected or tested at the time of taking over. Therefore some rights must be reserved for the Purchaser if at a later date any such work is found to be 'deficient' or inadequate (that is, not in accordance with the Specification or Schedule 1), as opposed to 'defective', during the guarantee period.

Guarantees and final acceptance

If any defect or 'deficiency' (see the comment on Clause 11.7) is found in the Permanent Works, during construction or during the Defects Correction Period, then the Purchaser's Representative may require the Contractor to remedy that defect or deficiency, at the Contractor's cost. If he fails to do so, or if the Purchaser is unable to allow him access to the Site, then the Purchaser may correct the defect or deficiency himself. In that case the Contractor will have to reimburse the Purchaser for the cost that of that repair, but only on the basis of what it would have cost the Contractor to carry out the work. If the Contractor carries out the work he must be given a safe working environment.

Once the Defects Correction Period, or all the Defects Correction Periods on the various sections, are complete and all remedial work has been carried out, the Contractor may require the issue of the Final Certificate. This will be conclusive evidence that the Works and Permanent Works have been properly completed by the Contractor.

CLAUSES 12 and 13

Clause 12.1 gives the Purchaser a guarantee period that begins when any Equipment or Materials are delivered to Site, and continues until the end of a twelve-month period after the taking over of each individual section of the Works.

Clauses 12.2–4 are straightforward procedural clauses and need no comment.

Clause 13.1 again is straightforward and needs no comment.

Clause 13.2 gives the Purchaser's Representative one final fourteen-day period to check that all work has been completed properly before he issues the Final Certificate.

Clause 13.3 states that once that Final Certificate is issued, then, unless there is any fraud, which would be very unusual, that certificate will signify that the legal/contractual liability of the Contractor is at an end.

Insurance and general liability

The Contractor is responsible for the proper care of the Works, and all equipment, etc., supplied for the Works until taking over. The Contractor will also provide insurance cover against public/third-party damage for a figure of two million pounds, but will have no further liability beyond that. The Purchaser will provide insurance cover, for full replacement value, for the Works and the Facility. Any other liability of the Contractor is excluded, except for the deductible.

As with all IChemE Forms of Contract, the aim is to set up an insurance package that will deal adequately and fairly with the risks involved. The Purchaser is obviously better placed to insure against the risk of damage to the Facility and work going on within it. Any normal Purchaser will have this risk insured anyway,

275

simply because he must insure against the risk of damage to his plant by his own personnel. Adding a Works Contractor on to that insurance cover should generally not be too much of a problem, nor should it be too expensive. The Contractor on the other hand will provide third-party/public liability insurance cover. Therefore this division of the risk ensures reasonable cover for all potential liability without too many special arrangements being necessary.

CLAUSE 14
Clause 14 is self-explanatory and needs no comment.

CLAUSE 15
Clauses 15.1 and 15.3 follow on from Clause 14 and require the Contractor to take responsibility for repairing any damage to any part of the Works, or Materials and Equipment under his control, up until taking over. He will also be responsible for damage caused by him during the guarantee period. His responsibility however will only be for the first ten thousand pounds of any damage caused plus the value of any money recovered under the Purchaser's insurance policy. He will also be responsible for correcting any loss or damage caused by the 'excepted risks' listed in Clause 15.2, but only if requested to do so by the Purchaser and at the Purchaser's cost.

The 'excepted risks' comprise, in paragraphs (a–b), damage caused to the Works by mistakes in design of the Works by the Purchaser or his advisers or caused by the fault of the Purchaser or any other party for whom the Purchaser is responsible. Paragraphs (c–e) then cover what are normally classed as uninsurable risks.

Clauses 15.4 and 15.7 require each of the parties to carry the risk of injury to their own employees, for which, in the UK anyway, they will already have insurance cover.

Finally Clauses 15.5 and 15.6 require the Contractor to have third party insurance cover up to the stated amount, and then to carry the risk of any damage caused to the property of the Purchaser, other than the Works, up to that amount. That property will include the Facility itself and also any part of the Works that has been taken over by the Purchaser and that is not defective.

In addition of course each party carries its own risks of damage to any third party property. Here there could be a real risk for the Contractor if he is carrying out the Works within a multi-occupation site.

CLAUSE 16
Clause 16 is a vitally important clause. However it is self-explanatory and needs very little comment. As with all the other Forms of Contract, the aim is to have single-source insurance cover for any loss to avoid insurance cross-claims, and to have the main risk areas and property properly insured.

Clause 16.1 covers insurance by the Purchaser of the Works, which is to include the Contractor and Subcontractors, and Clause 16.2 then requires the Purchaser to have appropriate cover for other property on or close to the Site, and to have the interest of the Contractor noted on the policies.

Clause 16.3 deals with insurance by the Contractor.

Clause 16.4 is procedural and important but needs no comment.

CLAUSE 24
Finally the effect of Clause 24 is to limit the Contractor's liability to that stated in Clauses 14 to 16. It excludes all indirect and consequential liability.

Variations
Clause 10.1 gives the Purchaser's Representative the authority to order any Variation to the Works. Note that he has the power to delete work as well as to add or alter it and that he can also change the programme and the sequence of the Works.

Clause 10.2 is purely procedural. If the Contractor considers that there will be an increase or decrease in his costs as the result of a Variation, or that it will require a change to the date(s) for completion, then the Contractor must submit a claim in writing for the necessary adjustments to the programme and to the Contract Price. Any claim must be supported by the appropriate back-up information 'in a form acceptable to the Purchaser's Representative'.

The principles by which the effects of a Variation on the Contract Price will be assessed are set out in Clause 10.3. It is straightforward and needs no comment.

Clause 10.4 then gives the Purchaser's Representative the authority to decide upon the adjustment to the Contract Price if agreement cannot be reached. Remember that he has the obligation to act professionally and impartially in doing so and that any decision he may make could be subject to the dispute procedures.

Payments
Clause 17 deals with the Contract Price. It is self-explanatory and needs no comment.

Clause 18 sets out the procedure for making payments to the Contractor. At monthly intervals the Contractor will submit a statement to the Purchaser's Representative setting out the various sums that he believes to be due to him, in accordance with Schedule 5. Within one week the Purchaser's Representative will certify the amount that he accepts. Then the Contractor will submit his invoice and the Purchaser will pay the invoice within fourteen days.

Clause 18 also deals with supplementary matters including the Contractor's rights in the event of non-payment or unreasonable delay in payment.

Clause 18.1 is self-explanatory, but note that the Contractor may submit complex statements. The interim statement must:

- provide an assessment of the value of Works carried out;
- be supported by the appropriate back-up documentation;
- cover any milestone or other scheduled payments; and
- cover any other sums that the Contractor is entitled to claim.

This means that a monthly statement could be quite complex, and the Purchaser's Representative might need support in dealing with it within the seven-day period allowed by Clause 18.2, particularly if the end of a monthly period should coincide with a holiday of some kind.

Clause 18.2 then allows the Purchaser's Representatives to question claims by the Contractor. All undisputed claims must be certified by him immediately and the Representative must deal with disputed claims as quickly as possible (see Clause 2.2).

Clauses 18.3–4 then deal with the procedure for the final statement and payment certificate.

Clause 18.5 authorises the deduction of any retention from interim payments, and then deals with the release of that retention.

Clause 18.6 sets a fourteen-day payment period for the Purchaser.

Clause 18.7 provides a procedure for any deductions or set-off of any amounts by the Purchaser. Note that this is limited to amounts due solely under the Contract.

Finally Clauses 18.8–9 deal with the Contractor's right to suspend the Works for delay in payment, and to claim interest on any unpaid invoice.